THE
ELECTROGENETICS
OF
ALBERTO PIROVANO

An historical account of a phenomenon and a philosophy — not quite forgotten.

Alberto Pirovano, 1882-

The
Electrogenetics
of
Alberto Pirovano

An historical account of a phenomenon
and a philosophy — not quite forgotten.

JOHN L. SPENCER

Vice President and Director of Research
Walker Laboratories Div. of
Richardson-Merrell Inc.
Mount Vernon, New York

Foreword by

Henry Thomas Yost, Jr.
Associate Professor of Biology
Amherst College
Amherst, Massachusetts

HAFNER PUBLISHING COMPANY INC.
New York and London
1964

First Printing 1964

Printed and Published
by
Hafner Publishing Comany
31 East 10th Street
New York 3, N.Y.

Library of Congress Catalog Card Number 64-14801

Manufactured in the United States of America
by Noble Offset Printers Inc.
New York, 10003 N. Y.

Dedicated to –

The memory of ALBERT F. BLAKESLEE

and to

EDGAR ANDERSON

and

KARL SAX

their inspiring genius and enlightening guidance
stimulate curiosity — an essence of all sciences

Contents

Introduction

THE EVENTS that have their results in the appearance of this book commenced a half century ago. Their significance is of a much more recent origin.

Some time during the second week of July, 1955, there came across my desk, as Geneticist at the Federal Experiment Station in Mayaguez, Puerto Rico, W. Ralph Singleton's article in the *Agronomy Journal* (March, 1955) on "Contribution of Radiation Genetics to Agriculture." This area of applied science was of especial interest to me. In fact, I previously had co-authored a paper with Dr. Singleton (and A. F. Blakeslee) on thermal neutron effects for the National Academy of Sciences. Continuing to read, in chronological order, the issues of this journal, I came upon a letter in the communications section of the July issue from Vincent Sauchelli. Dr. Sauchelli, a friend and fellow alumnus of the University of Massachusetts, was Research Director for the Davison Chemical Corporation, and he had written to comment on Ralph Singleton's article. In his letter he noted that he had a copy of a "very informative treatise" concerning electrically induced mutations of plant species by Alberto Pirovano, published in Milan, Italy, in 1922. Apparently, radiation genetics had its inception considerably before the researches undertaken by H. J. Muller and L. J. Stadler in 1927 and 1928. I was much intrigued by Dr. Sauchelli's statement ". . . Pirovano preceded these other scientists by many years."

The three decades from Roentgen's development of the x-ray tube in the late '90's, to the time of Muller's and Stadler's studies, appeared almost devoid of investigations on the possibility of induced mutations. The work of Professor Alberto Pirovano, might, I thought, fill this historical gap in a scientific field that has to its credit many recent and notable contributions. The variants made possible through the action of x-rays and other radiation on biological systems have given us better horticultural varieties and have contributed significantly toward man's conquest of plant diseases and insect infestations.

I wrote Dr. Sauchelli asking where I might obtain a copy of Pirovano's publication, and he very generously forwarded to me his copy of *La Mutazione Elettrica delle Specie Botaniche e la Disciplina dell'Ibridazione*. When I had read but a small portion of this report, I knew I had to find out more about the investigator and author, Pirovano. Mr. Charles M. Gottschalk, head of the Science and Technology Reference Section of the United States Library of Congress, furnished invaluable data and gave me the clue that Professor Pirovano might still be active. This reply was received from my letter to his latest known address: "I am very grateful for your interest in my work and forward to you the book *Elettrogenetica* (1957) in which are summarized the pertinent results obtained by me as a private worker and as Director of the Institute of Fruit Culture and Electrogenetics. In this book you will find on pages 145-147 references to publications which may be of interest to you. They are in the Italian and French languages, the tongues that I know best. Best regards, sincerely yours, Professor Alberto Pirovano." Now I not only had the record which might fill the scientific gap, but I also had located the very person whose initiative and curiosity created these original studies. Alberto Pirovano employed, among other things, x-ray tubes made by Roentgen.

The English translation of his *La Mutazione Elettrica delle Specie Botaniche* was sent to Pirovano for his comments and approval. Subsequently it was returned with the suggestion that certain portions be omitted in any re-publication. As Professor Pirovano wrote ". . . of course you can do as you like, but I must point out that, especially in electrology, many things have been changing since 1922 and, in my opinion, Chapter 5 should be omitted . . . I would do the same with some experiments which have proved to be unreliable. . . ."

Professor Henry Thomas Yost (Amherst College) was provided with a copy of the translated manuscript and the author's notations for the purpose of checking the copy against current concepts and terminology. We discussed Pirovano's suggestion to delete the obvious and outdated. Since this English edition was undertaken to more adequately fill an historical gap in science, we concluded that the text must be made available in its entirety. In fact, our desire for a faithful English reproduction, may cause the reader some concern. For instance, numbers 98 and 108 of the consecutively numbered figures, are missing, just as they are in the original Italian version. We have neither added to, deleted from, or altered Pirovano's descriptive style and report.

Dr. Yost, who became enamored, as I had, with Alberto Pirovano and his remarkable fundamental contribution to radiation biology, kindly consented to write a foreword for this work. I can think of no one better qualified to place Pirovano's historical contribution in the right perspective. 'Tom' Yost, too, has made a number of notable contributions to genetic research, particularly in the area of infra-red radiation. Furthermore, he keeps very well informed on current thinking and study in this dynamic field. The orientation he has provided in the foreword brings both Pirovano and his early work into focus.

JOHN L. SPENCER

July, 1963

Foreword

ALBERTO PIROVANO is a distinguished Italian horticulturalist whose interest in electricity has led him to found an entirely new field of horticultural practice. His list of accomplishments is long and includes a number of new, commercially important varieties of grapes, fruit trees and herbaceous shrubs, more than 270 publications and two major monographs on the subject of electro-genetics. His achievements have earned him membership in several academies, including the Academy of Agriculture and the Academy of the Vine and Wine, and the directorship of the Fruitgrowing and Electrogenetics Institute in Rome, a position which he held from 1926 to 1959, when he retired at the age of 75.

The publication which first established Pirovano's position in the field of electro-genetics was his monograph, *The Electrical Mutation of Vegetable Species*. Published in 1922, this work was a summary of ten years of patient and thorough investigation of the alterations in form and reproductive capacity engendered in various plants by their exposure to a number of magnetic devices, as well as to ionizing or ultraviolet radiation. His interpretations of the results he obtained are of historical interest, since he was one of the early workers who attributed the effect of these agents to alterations in the hereditary material and since he demonstrated clearly that the most sensitive stage of the life cycle was some part of meiosis. The final justification of this interpretation has been achieved only very recently for most forms. Pirovano's manuscript, therefore, stands as an important milestone in the history of radiation biology, in its broadest sense. The publication of the book in an English edition is justified on this basis alone.

Indeed, it is a remarkable fact that little of Pirovano's work is known in America. It is clear that this work represents one of the earliest sets of experiments on the mutagenic effect of ionizing radiation with plants. When one reads the description of the mechanism whereby the radiations produce their effect, one is immediately struck by the "modern" approach to the problem. The author suggests that these agents cause ionization or promote the dissociation of existing molecular-ions with a consequent rearrangement of these ions within the chromosomal elements. This rearrangement is taken as the cause of mutation. Such an interpretation clearly anticipates present thought on the mutation process, and when it is considered that Pirovano was apparently unaware of the Drosophila work (begun simultaneously with his), that his work preceded the work of Muller and Stadler by a number of years, and that he maintained the mutation concept of De Vries, it is truly remarkable that he should have adopted the approach at all. This is the work of a pioneer in the field of radiation biology, but it is also the work of a pioneer neglected outside his own country.

With the passage of time, any author is ready to retract some of his most precious words of an earlier day. Pirovano is no exception to this rule. On rereading the English manuscript, he desired to delete certain areas which in today's light seem either unnecessarily obvious or completely outdated. Such a procedure did not seem justified, since this edition is published primarily for historical interest. It has been possible to indicate the areas which Pirovano wished to have deleted or substantially changed, however, by employing a vertical line in the right margin opposite these sections. In this way, it is possible to catch a glimpse of the changes in the approach that have occurred of the author during the past forty years.

The passage of time has indeed dated much of this manuscript. The modern reader will find more amusing than instructive the attack on Darwin based on Mendelian Laws, an attack justified with regard to Darwin's acceptance of Pan-genesis but carried a bit further, by implication at least. The treatment of the effects of radiation in terms of the β emission of radium seems unusual today, when we would stress the effects of gamma rays. There are times when it seems the author has confused the two, as in his description of radioactive materials; however, it is mostly the result of an over-emphasis on the beta component of decay. For such reasons, it is necessary to read the text as a document of the origins of radiation biology and modern horticultural practice.

The major part of the manuscript is concerned with the effect of magnetic fields on the heritable characteristics of plants. This has been the area of Pirovano's continuing activity, his last monograph on this subject having been published in 1957.[1] The literature on the biological effects of magnetic and electric fields ranges from cures for arthritis to trophic responses in bacteria. However, there is practically no treatment of the effects on the genetic material, other than that coming from the group working with Dr. Pirovano. Consequently, the publication of this monograph should serve to introduce the reader to a rather large body of works which have appeared in the Italian literature, as well as to supplement his knowledge of the development of radiation biology.

Since the most novel aspects of this monograph are the findings with magnetic fields, one is forced to comment, however slightly, on this material. The first obvious difficulty is the lack of tabular data. No modern geneticist would be satisfied with a series of observations put down in such a way that the complete history of the mutant plants is obscure and the control data are difficult to extract. However, it is clear from a careful reading of the text that Pirovano is a careful worker who is meticulous in his experimental design and who has a very healthy respect for controls. The lack of F_2 data, in many cases, makes the conclusions hard to accept; on the other hand, the Institute has continued this work for over thirty years with apparent success. It would be ridiculous to say (almost forty years later) that the publication of the findings is premature. More extensive data have been obtained by Pirovano and his associates since 1922. These data, which support the interpretations stated in this original work, in the broad sense, are readily available in the literature. One other comment is certainly in order. The lack of clearly defined criteria for the assay of mutational events will be disturbing to any who have never been associated with a highly skilled horticulturalist or plant geneticist. Anyone who has seen the late Professor Blakeslee walk through an acre of Datura and pick out mutant plants will not find the reports of Pirovano hard to accept.

[1] Pirovano, *Electrogenetics. Morara, Rome,* 1957.

Certainly it was the attempt to design experiments with magnetic and electric fields and the interpretation of the results of such experiments which put Pirovano in a position to properly assess the effect of radiations on the genetic material. He was forced to think of the chromosomal elements as ions which could be reorganized by strong magnetic fields. This conception has important consequences for all of his interpretations of mutational processes. The question we would like to be able to answer concerns the validity of such assumptions. The failure of the various mitotic theories based on repulsions and attractions of molecular ions has lead us away from a consideration of the colloidal nature of the genetic material. However, it is quite clear that we are dealing with molecules having colloidal properties and subject to the same variations of charge which were originally proposed for them as part of an explanation of mitosis. This has been brought forcibly to our attention by the recent evidence that weak electric fields can orient the chromosomes during mitosis. Whether such weak fields can cause alterations in the submicroscopic organization of the genetic material must be regarded as an open question. The impressive amount of data which has been accumulated suggesting that such fields are mutagenic must cause us to consider the question seriously. Certainly the strict limitation of the effect to one particular point in the life cycle lends support to Pirovano's hypothesis.

One final question must be raised. That question concerns the suppression of the "dominance" of the treated plants, in some cases. Pirovano makes this an important part of his discussion. To a horticulturist, the suppression of certain "dominant" traits in hybridization is the difference between success and failure. Apparently this can be achieved by treatment with magnetic fields, thus insuring hybrid progeny which would otherwise be lost. It seems impossible to comment on this phenomenon without having first-hand experience with the material. However, it also seems to be an improbable event, when viewed from a distance. The instability of the effect is the most perplexing part. There are, to be sure, uncertain mutagens which produce their effects in a seemingly haphazard manner and whose effects when produced, are, at best, metastable. Infrared radiation is certainly one of these. Until further investigation of this phenomenon has been accomplished, one can say no more.

The primary reason for the publication of the English edition of this monograph is its historical interest. In a field that has expanded as rapidly as radiation biology, we are apt to forget the point from which we started not so long ago. History can be made short-ranged. On the other hand, this book is an introduction to the field which the author has named, "electrogenetics." To the extent that this edition can stimulate interest in these findings and tests of the assumptions implicit in their interpretation, the book will be useful to modern science. It is to be hoped that the reader will find its value in both of these aspects.

H. T. YOST, JR.
Amherst College
January, 1963

Preface

I HAVE ALWAYS had a great love for the science of electricity, and a true devotion for Nature. Faced early with the need to choose a profitable vocation between the former and the latter, I selected the horticultural career, already engaged in by my father and my grandfather. However, while keeping abreast of the new conquests in the field of physics and devoting my best activity to botanical genetics, I have often reflected on the mating of these two sciences so dear to me.

My first, and truth to say ingenuous, efforts began in 1899. After several years of attempts, persistently carried on, with unswerving faith in my line of reasoning, despite adverse reasons that distracted me for awhile from my undertaken task, I saw the first results of electricity usefully applied to the fertilization of plants.

Interest grew within me at that time. The process was applied to diverse species, was compared with analogous means suited to reproduce it; and on this work I lavished profusely every bit of energy, every spare moment in my daily work. The results increased from year to year, although with minor and expected divergencies, confirming my conviction that the foundation was indubitably good.

Now I have some data that serve as a demonstrational base of the theoretical concept, but as yet I do not have any system of observations that are concrete and exact.

Much of the road still remains to be covered; but by this time the road is laid out; and I flatter myself that I am proceeding along it in good company.

In no other field of science can the cooperation of many minds, of many specialized disciplines, be so valuable as in this disparate wedding of the unknown entity called Electricity with living Nature. Of both these, only the exterior is known. Electricity becomes manifest only when it is in motion and is observed only by way of the phenomena of light, heat, magnetism and chemistry as these occur; life, or vitality, and, particularly, the phenomenon of reproduction is equally little known as regards its innermost mechanism.

These considerations have prompted me to publish my experiments, although I recognize the fact that only further improvements can render them valid. As the reader will learn further on, the tolerance for the artificial application of various agents to which the genital organs are to be exposed varies tremendously from species to species and is not immune to complications.

The restriction of Nature is the one that represents greatest difficulties; it is almost completely outside the dominion of man, physical forces, and artificial stimuli, is an anomaly, in the strict naturalistic sense of the word, an organism destined to disappear as soon as it is left to itself. Only individuals in Nature (wild) are physiologically perfect, biologically superlative, genetically immutable.

"Chase the natural and it will come right back." An irrefutable truth; but this thought should not worry us overmuch. The ionolysis that the Reader will learn to recognize is, like the direction of horticultural selection, an artifice engrafted on a biological phase, known only in its outer aspect—sexual reproduction; but it is not the only artifice of which useful plants avail themselves, since the environment in which we cultivate them is in turn an artificial one. Cultivated plants, unlike wild ones, are not abandoned to chance to fight for their existence. Cultivational practices, repeated working of the soil, magnificent manurings, grafts effected, where needed, on resistant subjects, all go to maintain alive even biological weaklings. Horticultural races, naturalistically speaking, are groups of weak, or defective, individuals. And yet no cultivator cares to turn to wild types.

Horticultural selection tends to produce individuals that more readily lend themselves to profitable purposes, to conversion into cash of energies used up on them. Large fruits, double or giant flowers, the best, most tender vegetables, all that which Horticulture obtains in the way of natural types, in the natural order of life, is a monstrosity; but for these very factors they are preferred. Business, fashion, demand it. *Even the most ardent admirers of Nature prefer to acquire or cultivate the most beautiful flowers, the most tasty vegetables, and never the wild varieties. Jaws, palate and stomach of modern man rebel against it.*

It does not go against evolution. In due time the human race has evolved to where man is more demanding insofar as he has exploited the gifts of his rare mind as far as civilization allows personal specialization in any given field of activity.

So it is with plants. Those preferred by Agriculture, which are best suited for business, are generally very fertile kinds, of delicate constitution; selection always tends to render them sterile.

The task of innovators, in Genetics, is to find such types as are best adapted to the environment in which they are to be cultivated. The usual means employed to achieve such a purpose, that is, to obtain genetic variations, will be presented later on; but it must be pointed out here that the limit of variability attainable is restricted. The action of electromagnetic agents on the genital plasma, which is the subject of this publication, is the latest arrival in the series of stimuli to variation, but it promises a great future, especially if applied in hybridization. It is not an exaggeration to affirm that, thanks to "ionolysis" it will be possible to obtain types with given predetermined properties. It has already been possible to subvert the immutable laws governing gametic hybridization.

The power of human intervention is not unlimited, however. It has been proven that the enhancement of one property of an individual organism serves to prejudice that normal linkage which is the primary condition for the conservation of its species.

Nature is not violated with impunity. One needs but to substitute oneself for it in order to become aware of it. What actuates the author is not, therefore, the claim to outdo her in the miraculous, harmonious order of the Creator, nor the foolish notion of emulating the works of the Lord, but the modest aim of benefitting man by use of a new artifice, adapted to producing variations in plants, variations in which Nature is quite frugal.

Having to experiment in an area that is still new, where reference data are lacking, I have had to proceed by trial-and-error. Consequently, I am still at the stage of first empirical soundings, insufficient for an exact evaluation. And it is precisely the certainty of not being able to achieve all by myself a rational and orderly piece of work with my modest private means, that prompts me to publicize my experiments, however incomplete and lacking in that organized gradualness upon which depends the ultimate development of the study.

The possibility of controlling the dominance of characteristics in hybrids is, however, such a conquest that it justifies even by itself the opportunity of making known what I have done.

Before going into my subject, I am in duty bound to single out the well-deserving individuals who have been kind and accommodating enough, with their help and advice, to contribute in concrete form to the practical development of my experiments: First of all my father, Cav. Luigi, tolerant sufferer from the intrusion of a mess of spoilable and spoiled plants, which from year to year claimed ever-increasing space on his farm. The engineer, Carlo Viscardi, of Monza, and the electro-technician, Mr. Giuseppe Rodegher, who have advised and served me so well as to the electro-magnetic apparatus; Cav. Emilio Balzarini for X-rays; the engineer, Corrado Landi of Milan, for the instruments of high frequency, and lastly the Honorable Prof. Remigio Banal of Torino, devoted and most learned adviser, in the part on Physics.

In all of them I have found so much personal courtesy, selflessness, outgoingness, and good will: to all of them a cordial "Thank you."

Vaprio d'Adda, 1922   ALBERTO PIROVANO

The present volume is divided into eight chapters. The sequence followed is one suggested to me by the subject.

In Chapter I, I review briefly the electro-physiological experiments already tried with plants by other experimenters. With the summary of brief theories of botanical Genetics in Chapter II, which most readers can perhaps omit if well acquainted with the subject, I follow up in Chapter III with the informative concept on which the experimental work is based.

The origin of botanical and electro-biological variations in connection with the anomalous structure of the molecular composition of the genital plasma constitutes the subject treated in Chapter IV, which is to be read attentively.

Chapter V offers summary descriptions of the types of apparatus conducive to effecting ionolysis[1], with special regard to electromagnets with a variable field, which have proved best suited to stimulate ionolysis in living plasma.

Chapter VI is devoted to demonstrational experiments. In it are described the genetic results of ionolysis, and there are reproduced, with pictures, the deformations induced in various botanical species and horticultural varieties.

After several informative summaries regarding hybridization and the genetic behavior of hybrid types, which comprise Chapter VII, I pass on to a new group of experiments in hybridization with ionolyzed pollen, these experiments being the most interesting ones, and covering Chapter VIII, followed by a short concluding recapitulation.

[1] Ionolysis is a new term adopted in order to differentiate the molecular breakdown of organized living matter from other forms of ionization effected, by the same means, in inert matter.

Chapter I

Electro-Physiological Experiments

1.

Introduction

THE APPLICATION of electricity to the cultivation of plants has been practiced for a long time and in various ways. The first experiments were undertaken with hardly anything being known of static electricity, except a most primitive way of producing it. Professor Bruttini, who has diligently collected various data on this subject, drawing up a detailed chronology of his findings, cites experiments going back as far as 1716,[1] and references to 817

[1] A. Bruttini, *Influence of electricity on botanical species*. Hoepli, Milan.

1

experiments which from that period to 1911 he confirms as having been carried on, for the purpose of studying the effect of electricity on agricultural and horticultural plants, the promotion of fertility in the soil through electric currents, atmospheric electricity and that static kind at high potential produced by electric machines. Recently, Baines[1] has added a new contribution, publishing various electro-physiologic experiments.

It is not necessary to expatiate, even in summary fashion, on the procedures adopted, because in no case have any appreciable results been obtained, nor results in any way linking up with the attunement essential to pointing to a reliable road likely to lead to success.

It is quite true that most of the experimenters, the first ones in particular, drawn into error by fortuitous and related causes, boast of marvelous results effected by electrical action on experimental plants; but the most conscientious and serious modern experimenters, like Becquerel, Tolomei, Lodge, Di-Muro, not to mention Bruttini himself, have found ineffectual the action of electricity on plant life, as already foreseen (although without practical control) by the great Volta.

The experiments were quite varied. It may be said that every form of application of electricity has been tried.

Inasmuch as the scope of this brief treatise is in the nature of a critical review, I consider it convenient to state in summary fashion the experiments involved, grouping them as follows:

Electrostatic flow	Natural, drawn from the atmosphere with metallic points	On to plants on to seeds at rest and in germination
	Produced by electrostatic machines with constant polarity	on to plants (electric wind) on to seeds, moist, dry, and in germination
	Produced by high-tension alternating current generators	applied on plants on a vast scale

[1] A. E. Baines, *Germination in its electrical aspect*. Routledge, London.

2

Presumed extraction of atmospheric electricity from about the plants			with wire or mesh-wire ground-posts with point-arresters on the plants in the open field in the germination medium
		passing through land under cultivation	
Electric currents	Continuous (Direct)	Used on seeds . . .	dry humid immersed in saline solution
		Used on plants	(low tension) (high tension)
	Alternating	As above	as above
Magnetic field with fixed polarity		with solenoids with magnets	on adult and germinating plants on seeds and ova of various species

To these experiments are to be added those on the indirect action of electricity, i.e., on the very rapid vibrations induced by electricity; ultraviolet and X-rays (Roentgen), as well as those explorative investigations on the electrical state and the diverse values it may have in various organs of a plant during the different phases of its development.

2.

Experiments with Static Electricity on Plants

Static electricity has been applied by many experimenters: Van Marum, Bertholon, Williamson, Marat (the famous doctor during the Reign of Terror). Naudin, Leclerc and Grandeau, Ingen-Houst, Pouillet, De-Candolle, experimented with processes known in their day, and mainly used the electric flow-off from one or more points counterposed to the experimentally used plants and duly insulated by the soil. The electromotor, viz., the source of

3

electricity, was the friction-electric machine and, originally, the rotating, hand-rubbed sulphur sphere.

As the science of electricity progressed, during the last century, the old machines were replaced by powerful ones. The concept, however, always remained the same, nor does it vary today, except as to scale, and the system of application. On the one hand there is a group of experiments undertaken by Lodge, sometimes with no success, sometimes with a modicum of success, covering increase, and yield from grains, forage, etc. Breslauer, Kapp, Koestermann find, from analogous experiments, with more or less different devices, some advantage in so-called electro-culture while Di Muro, Raps, Neumann, Munerati obtain negative or uncertain results in adopting identical media.

The various results, regrouped into a single computation, give zero, or inconclusive results, according to the opinion of Volta and of Lord Kelvin.

Why is the electrostatic flow ineffectual?

During the reading of this book, the Reader might well ask himself why I should ever have gone to such trouble in choosing means suited to effecting such minor transfers of electricity to the extremely delicate genital plasma, whereas with the application of already known types of energy and means I could have worked directly on the plants.

Electricity applied to plants, whether in full development or in a state of rest, not excluding the seed, cannot be a profitable stimulus to their development.

It is necessary, in order to obviate any doubt, to face right now the examination of this subject.

Skimming over the applications of atmospheric electricity, which several insulated points placed at scores from the ground are supposed to capture (Electro-capteur, Geomagnetifer, etc.—those are the pompous names given to that type of device), I must insist solely on the point of maximum electrical efficiency attainable by an electrified point at a short distance from a living plant. Considering the extreme case, comparisons are not far apart except in their proportion .

The following case is offered as a hypothetical one:

The plant communicates electrically with the ground unless it is already right on the ground itself; a metallic point, supported on an insulating stand, is connected up with a pole of a powerful modern induction machine (Wirmshuerst or Holtz type) while the other pole is connected with the ground and consequently with the plant to be exposed to the experiment. The distance of the point from the tip of the plant should be the very minimum compatible with the production of the slow flow, such, in other words, that it will not permit a spark to occur between the plant and the point.

In estimating this distance, we should observe how close the extremity of the short metal rod, as tall as the plant, can be brought into the vicinity of the plant when the machine is operating without causing sparks. When the sparks appear, the extremity is brought closer and one can observe whether the sparks cease when maximum velocity is induced in the apparatus.

Once the safe distance has been established, the experiment may begin, and it is quite interesting if it is watched in the darkness. Under such working conditions, one observes the formation of tiny purple-blue luminous flakes either on the metal tip, especially in the case of positive electric discharges or at the extreme edges of the leaves opposite the point itself. If the leaves are excessively acuminated or covered with ciliae, or hairlike processes, the luminous flakes are quite diffuse and give off a thin efflorescent light; if, instead, they are smooth and even, the flakes cluster on only a limited portion of their edge; their light is brighter but more restricted, and it is perceptible at the edges that are most salient and close to the point.

At the very start, one who is present at the phenomenon has the impression that the plant should really experience some effect of the electric shower, which obviously invades it, all the more so since the so-called electric flow constantly being discharged by the point is strong enough to extinguish a candle lighted in its vicinity. But such is not the case.

First of all, it must be established that the flow of the point is not a flow of electricity, but of electrized air which, being charged on contact of the metal point with the electricity of the latter, is violently repelled due to the fact that two bodies free to move repel one another when both are either positively or negatively charged.

5

The electrized air is violently repelled by the point by dint of the potential energy that there reaches its maximum intensity.

In its turn, the plant emits only in its most salient points and in those nearest to the point an opposite and equivalent quantity of electrized air oppositely charged and directed. *Between these two currents takes place, along the aerial trajectory, the reestablishment of the neutral state.* Prevailingly, the collision between the particles of electrized air respectively with the electricity drawn to the point or by the plant, takes place in the immediate vicinity of one or the other, giving rise to the purple-blue light which surrounds it, paling to a sort of halo.

The reestablishment of the electrical equilibrium occurs therefore in large measure *before* molecules of electrized air contact the surface of the plant. Should the latter have perfectly smooth and not very soft leaves, the reestablishment occurs in minor measure at the surface of the latter; "surface" is to be taken in the mathematical sense of the word, the *limited surface,* i.e., the one that separates the plant (conductor from the air [non-conductor]), a *surface absolutely devoid of depth.*

It is quite true that the molecule complex, or electrized air particles, which invade the plant, sparking their tiny electric charge, form collectively an electric current, but the latter has a negligible intensity, and develops, as does the remainder of the process, only at the extreme surface wholly on the outside, of the plant being used, completely outside of all its organs, characteristically covered with integument. The back of our hand is very sensitive. If it is placed near the plant, under the point, one merely gets the impression that it is surrounded by some air being blown past it. Nothing more.

The experiments carried on with most diverse types of plants, even though they do not agree, do offer, however, a multiple confirmation of the physiological inefficacy of the flow, particularly in the best conducted cases in which a vast network floods extensive cultivated areas.

The entire vegetation that covers the earth is pervaded by a slow, incessant flow of electricity which always courses over plants on the outer surfaces, discharges along the leaf-cusps, ridges, thorns, ciliae, etc., in the very atmosphere. The big trees, and particularly the conifers, act as dischargers of electricity, and the work they accomplish in this connection is sometimes very useful. Whenever the meteor threatens, the electrical imbalance between the clouds and the earth becomes very great; the trees then send skyward veritable torrents of electricity which collectively discharge partially the electricity of the cloud, which is negatively charged. However, they are not injured by this passage of electricity, in view of the outermost surface route pursued by the electricity.

Before leaving this subject, one fact must be pointed out. The silent discharge offered by the metallic point stimulates a secondary effect: the formation of ozone. This gas is the result of the excess atomic composition of oxygen; this stimulates, according to some, while according to others it debilitates the vegetating process of superior plants, while it hinders, by common admission, the development of micro-organisms. The quantity involved, however, is negligible in the experiments carried on in the open air. Bruttini, working the effluviation process in closed bell jars, does not find any perceptible difference with control plants that have not been treated.

Still, the process of electric flow deserves careful study in cultures of fungi and, chiefly, in the microscopic Cryptogam species, the cellular plasma of which is nearly, or totally, lacking integuments, when it does not appear on the surface, as in some mucous species.

In the case of minor fungi (molds), it has already been found that the effect of ozone is deadly. This is due to the ready assimilation effected by the Cryptogams as against the Phanerogams, the organs of which are sheathed in protective membranes.

3.

Analogous Experiments on Seeds

Some experimenters, coming close to my own concept (which will be explained later) that mutability is more easily induced into plants the younger they are, have thought they could operate more usefully by exposing seeds to electrostatic flow, discharges, and induced currents provided by induction coils.

The seeds are treated either dry or moistened, in a state of rest, or in germination. The provisions made for electrical flow on plants hold absolutely as well for seeds. I will say also that the latter are in an ever-better condition to escape electrostatic action. In fact, the vital portion, the one that could in some measure be affected, is the embryo; however, the embryo is locked in, wrapped, or coiled up about itself among cotyledons, these being protected in turn by integumental walls incomparably thicker than those that cover the aerial organs of the plants.

If one considers the fact the static electricity in conductors is distributed only on the outer surface, as the previous paragraph explained in greater detail, it requires no effort to believe that never, however potent may be the amount of energy used, can a seed feel the effect of very intense electrization via flow, nor of any powerful electrical discharge violently attacking it. In fact, in my experiments in which I tried to injure thick, dried seeds placed between the spheres of the spintherometer of a Wirmshuerst machine with a 15 cm spark, I found that the latter always crept to the surface of the dry seed, since the pathway of the seed had offered the discharge indubitably less resistance than that of the air. It is obvious that there would have been no injurious result even if the seeds had been moistened; in that case the passage area would have been diminished by the discharge, passing into the humid surface of the integument. In any case, the embryo, the vital part, is respected. No difference is observed with the use of induced currents provided by a Ruehmkorff coil, which gives off frequent discharges at alternating polarity; as regards the path that the discharge prefers, it is always the one considered just now. Nor is the result different if the seeds, previously moistened, are enclosed in a glass tube and subjected to a spark passed through it. High-potential currents provided by inductors have a convenient transmission base across the moist envelope of the seed, which in no case constitutes a danger to the vital internal parts.

In fact, the accurate experiments of Tolomei, Palmieri, Vassali, Matteucci, Manduty, Paulin, Davy, Forster, Warren, Spechnew, Loevenherz, Kinney, Heber and many other observers, who base their deductions on the speed-up or slowdown of germination of the treated seeds, are quite far from agreeing even on the universal results: no modification in the plants; no lethal case.

Recently, there has been exploited a device analogous to the one adopted in school to demonstrate the phenomenon of hail (according to the theory of Volta) for the alternately positive and negative electrization of seeds. Whenever the latter are placed between two metal plates connected up to the opposite poles of an electric machine, and they are light in weight, they are alternately attracted and repelled by one or the other plate; the dance continues as long as the machine is kept going.

The *electric dance* is caused by the repulsion of the seed at the lower plate conjoined with the attraction that the upper plate exerts on each seed that lies there and that only reverses itself as soon as the seed touches the upper plate. The seed, then falling back on the lower plate, again assumes the electric charge of the latter, so that it again rises, and so on. During the phenomenon, every seed takes on, loses, or exchanges its charge with utmost speed; but the current passes entirely along the *surface of the seed* to which, as usual in any type of conductor, it adheres in a mathematically superficial way.

The experimenters, perhaps deceived by the movement, the only new experimental feature in this field into which so much energy has been poured in vain, have believed it can contribute something new to electrical treatment by way of an efficacious device against which natural disposition and protective tissues seem to join forces. It must be admitted, however, that this device lends itself to deluding an observer not well grounded in the subject of electricity.

In order to grasp how a body that is alive and, for all we know, sensitive, is able to take a heavy electric charge without suffering harm, it suffices to think of the case of a bird that comes to rest on exposed metal wire conducting a high-tension current. Hardly has the bird settled down on the wire when it immediately assumes the potential of the line; in other words, it is charged with electricity, until in a very short time it equals the potential of the line itself. Nevertheless it does not suffer any harm, because all of the electricity that is evidently *does* "drink in," so to speak, does not invade it through the body but glides along the outer surface of its legs, skin, and feathers, not only without affecting any of its internal organs, but without affecting its tactile papillae, which are also the most superficial ramifications of the nerves.

9

If then the line current passing through that wire is an alternating one, the animal that rests on it is charged and discharges electricity of the opposite polarity a great number of times without suffering any harm. The effect would be instantaneously lethal, however, if resting on the wire, (the animal) were to touch with another part of its body the adjacent lead-off wire of opposite polarity, or were to be connected with the ground, or a large-capacity condenser, because in that case through its body there would pass *an electric current*.

From this it is easy to understand how seeds placed in a highly charged electrostatic field can dance at length between both poles, changing their own charge at every new contact, without at the same time suffering the least injury nor gaining the least benefit, except possibly the wearing out of the teguments, something which, in some species, may turn out to be useful in that it facilitates the penetration of water and by that means facilitates removal when the seeds are inserted in the soil. But the wearing out of the teguments can be effected through various mechanical means far less difficult and more economical.

However, not only seeds block electrization.

4.

Ineffectuality of the Electrostatic Discharge in Experiments on Pollens

In my experiments on pollen placed in an electric field, with an apparatus analogous to the electrostatic ball, I was able to note, as in the case also with very tiny granules of pollen, a sort of dance, which however does not last long, the pollen tending to take refuge in the "dead" corners of the glass cannula intended to contain it. It is necessary to adopt such a bowl, because the pollen would other wise be blown away the very first moment by the repulsion of the pole at which it is placed, in view of the pollen's lightness.

The pollen, placed for a few hours between two small metallic discs delimiting the glass cannula and connected up with a large model of the Wirmshuerst machine, has not lost its property of fecundity. Cyclamen and dahlia pollen, colored an orange-yellow, lost their color, at least partially (ozone effect) without their characteristic fecundity being lost. Not only did the pollen itself give no indication of having suffered from lengthy exposure, but even in the progeny born of this pollen there was no such indication. Let this comparison with the most delicate and sensitive substances, as will be demonstrated later on, serve to remove all doubt that the reader may still harbor regarding the physiological inefficacy of electrostatic treatments.

5.

Effects of Violent Electrical Discharge

Although it does not directly bear upon the subject that I have undertaken to treat briefly, before closing the part covering static electricity, I believe it to be apropos to give the reader some notion of the effects of violent electrical discharges (sparks, fulminants) because such observations lend themselves to highlighting the natural reaction to be expected, the instinct, one might say, for reparation of the attempted harmful effects desired or occasioned by the violent electrical discharges.

Becquerel, the illustrious French physicist, and more recently Leomstroem, have specifically treated the subject, noting the brown spots and the adjacent necrosis scored by the sparks. Along with them, other scientists have studied the irritability of plants, specifically the contractions of the sensitive plant (Mimosa pudica) under various electrostatic stimuli, and the sectoral limitations of the necrosis established by some types of fulminants.

If, instead of offering a point, a slow discharge of electricity across the arc, (the nature of which was mentioned in section 2) undergoes expansion in the form of a ball, there is no longer a uniform discharge with a luminous fanning out but a series of

11

sparks which rend the air, producing a crackling sound, or even dry little taps of quite some strength when the electrostatic machine is connected up with a condenser.

The spark has the effect of discharging on the plant in one instant, and at a single spot, the electricity that the point would yield instead slowly, by way of the atmosphere, over a vast area.

As opposed to the effluvium, or flux, the electric spark of whatever size striking an organ of a plant causes a necrosis: a type of almost imperceptible scorching, limited to the very start, then, after a few days, spreading and probably flooding the healthy tissue with toxic elements formed in the stricken spot and introduced into circulation by the movement of the lymph.

According to the size of the discharge, the hygrometric conditions, and the intrinsic specific characteristics of the stricken plant, the necrosis is limited to one blister on the leaf, total loss of the latter, or to a stricken branch. Van Thieghen has observed that the weak sparks are not able to damage or even to harm in the least the organs of the plant on which they have been triggered: however, they do render sensitive the contractile leaves of Mimosa pudica, the stamens of Berberis and Centurea.

In the case of strong discharges, under special conditions, necrosis extends along the entire stalks at slow progression and finally takes in the entire sector corresponding to the stricken branch. Outwardly in herbaceous plants it is stigmatized by a vertical brown stripe, which stands out from the rest of the stalk which remains normal in appearance. The plant continues to live with its branch at first necrotic, then dry, stricken. This adaptation is not met with in the case of animals, because, first of all, there is a very sensitive nervous system in which a strong shock, in whatever part of the body it may occur, has its repercussion on the central organs, possibly causing paralysis; moreover, the circulation of the blood carries the blood at great speed from the various organs to the heart and to the nervous centers, poisoning the entire organism in a very short time. For that reason, death is almost instantaneous in the case of animals affected by a strong discharge.

Instead, in the case of plants, the lymphatic circulation is segmental: that is, it progresses vertically from the root position where it originates and is also incomparably slower. In other words, one sector of a trunk can, as a result of diverse causes, suffer necrosis and decomposition without the rest of the plant suffering because of it. In due time, in some species, around the necrotic area there is formed scar tissue that isolates the marred area from the healthy and living area.

And so a spark, and in the case of very large plants a thunderbolt, *under special circumstances,* may injure a branch without depriving the rest of the plant of vitality.

The deleterious effect of the spark or of the thunderbolt does not appear suddenly, because the plant or the part of the plant that has been stricken continues to be kept in a turgid state by the roots, which are never injured by the discharge inasmuch as these roots have available the pathway of the earth, which is always a good conductor, however little humidity it may possess.

The stricken plant thus seems to live on for several days.

I have had occasion to check daily the course of the phenomena in a case of four vines that had been struck by a thunderbolt, lying on iron wires around a country house.

The thunderbolt, knocked down on the house, and fused and partly volatilized the iron wires which supported the four vines; the latter, however, seemed absolutely healthy and normal. Only after two or three days did there manifest themselves symptoms of withering towards noon, and several days later, the leaves, the vine-twigs (the tiny ones) became completely brown and flabby, and assumed the marked characteristic of necrosis. The withering took place only then when the lymph in the affected trunks had been carried by the natural down-flow of the phloem to the roots, had poisoned them, gradually poisoning their functioning.

Undoubtedly the fatal action of the thunderbolt had instantaneously poisoned totally the atmospheric region, all the vine-twigs resting on the iron wires, conspicuously altering not only the tissues but also the chemical composition of the lymph there present, which, pressured from below into circulating as usual into the leaves and to flow off to the roots (remaining outside the current), had poisoned both the latter and the former.

Regarding the fact that this action of electricity does not become manifest at once, more will have to be said again; therefore, I will not linger on it any more now.

6.

Natural Provisions for Preservation

By means of the experiments carried on in the open, you must then bear in mind that the treatments used, even with considerable sparks, do not always yield a homogenous result. It is enough that a very thin veil of dew, a veil not always visible, but one which may exist for a good many hours, covers the organs of the plant, in order to keep them entirely away from electrical action, even if violent.

The tiniest droplets of water that cover the plant become the sole pathway for the exchange of electricity and for its conduction.

It was observed that the effects of fulminations in which is involved a powerful quantity of electricity with an extremely high potential, always prove fatal in plants protected by large rugose barks, difficult to be bathed, such as the oaks, cork-trees, the elms. Among the trees having a smooth bark, such as the plane-trees, Canadian poplars, walnut trees, etc., being easily bathed completely without getting first a drop of rain, the electricity creeps on the outside of the trunk, and only with difficulty has lethal effects.

Analogous phenomena were observed by Franklin in the fulmination of small animals.

7.

Presumed Systems for Drawing off Atmospheric Electricity

Very many have been the experiments undertaken with the aim of protecting plants against the influence of atmospheric electricity.

The presumed transfer of electricity was effected with cages, metallic webs or similar devices of metal wires set in effective contact with the ground and attached all around to the plants to be experimented on. The respective and identical samples to be compared were placed collaterally.

Besides the metallic nets and the wires fastened to the cultures, it was believed that the electricity could be removed from the plants by means of long rods tipped with metallic points in contact with the ground.

I do not consider it opportune to stop now and demonstrate the absolute inefficacy of these appliances, since this is demonstrated by the same reasoning offered for the analogous case of the metal nets.

The results of these experiments are incompatible or zero; in fact, the cages as well as the nets or metallic coverings with meshes of varying thicknesses and sizes, in contact with the ground, do not draw away any electricity from the surrounding atmosphere, inasmuch as the potential of the latter, near the ground, *is never appreciably different from that of the ground itself,* which is zero. These reticulate entities, functioning in an equi-potential medium, have an electrical reaction of zero. They provide shade for the plants, and nothing more.

Their use would be justified in the vicinity of the plants under study if there were an electrified conductor and if it were important to remove the plants from its influence.

The minor discrepancies in the results obtained by various experimenters who have adopted these fictitious protective devices are attributable to inevitable individual differences and not to the slight shadow produced by the reticulations themselves, which may be beneficial or injurious, according to the species and the seasons.

From the meshes of the reticulate entities there undoubtedly passes, if not any electricity, which does not exist in a free state in the air, a vibratory form of the electricity itself, indispensable to plants: light.

8.

Form of Electricity Utilized by Plants

The same nature of electricity and light is nowadays beyond discussion; the latter is said to originate in extremely rapid electromagnetic vibrations. Thus the plants, elaborating their juices by means of chlorophyll, every day achieve a *photosynthesis,* which might be called *electro-synthesis.*

The chlorophyllic electro-synthesis, by means of which the chemical affinity for carbon is overcome, and by means of which there takes place the union of the former with hydrogen, which gives rise to the organic hydrocarbons, is said to re-enter the group of electrolytic phenomena.

However, this quite special electrolysis differs substantially from the ordinary electrolytic phenomenon that we are familiar with. The difference consists not only in the differing quality of the forces brought into play but also in polarity. Polarity is constant during electrolytic baths, while the energy produced by light rays is frequently of the alternating kind, so that their action cannot be usefully conceived of except by granting that the chlorophyll had on these (rays) a power to convert or inhibit during one phase. Moreover, it seems evident that the phenomenon must develop only in the immediate vicinity, nay, upon contact of the granule of chlorophyll; evidently, too, the latter cannot find an artificial substitute!

A source of light other than the sun is only slightly effectual in work with chlorophyll, which is achieved only if the vibrations are *attuned* to the mysterious yet most precise composition of the chlorophyll of every botanical species.

It might seem that illumination by means of the voltaic arc should be suitable as a substitute for the sun; however, that is in no way true as regards plants, which perish in a very short time under such artificial light, because of the ultra-violet rays contained therein, *which are not attuned* to the reception system of plants, bringing about the breakdown and the consequent death of the entire plant. The Cooper-Hewitt lamp, even richer in ultra-violet radiation, kills the plants in a few minutes. And yet the ultra-violet rays do not differ from ordinary types of perceptible light except in the wave length (quite smaller).

For a greater reason we cannot profitably apply electricity to plants, because the means of which we are able to produce it, or, better expressed, to mobilize it, are too far removed from the natural means.

Plants are so constituted as to be activated to develop with the stimulus, *and with that stimulus alone,* by which they are *pre-formed.* Electricity, also playing a large part in their physiological functioning, in the form of light, cannot in any other form be utilized or act as a subsidiary growth factor, or integrator of the usual means.

9.

Soundings on the Difference of Electrical State in the Organs of Living Plants

The question, however, occurs whether a determination may not be possible regarding the transformation of light energy into electrolytic work.

This thought has impelled several scientists to investigate, by means of suitable, sensitive appliances, whether among the various parts of a living plant, in the fullness of its development, there may not exist different electrical charges, proving that electricity plays a part in their life and has a preferred locale in a given part of an organ.

Becquerel has carried on diligent investigations on internal electric currents of the plant. Munerati has done likewise on the anomalous circulation of lymph under artifical excitation of galvanic currents. Davis has experimented on differential electrical charges between stamens and pistils and at the moment of flowering. Warthmann, Burton, Sanderson, Dubois, and Commelin worked on currents in plant tissues, Le Rover and Lemstroem worked on the rise of lymph in an electric field; Haache worked on interorganic currents and on their relationship as to assimilation and respiration in plants. Querton, Errera, Sachs, Guarini and Samarani worked on autogenic currents in plants and their physico-chemical origin, and on the chlorophyllic function from the electro-chemical viewpoints, etc.

Undoubtedly, plants, under the stimulus of solar light and consequent heat, as necessary to the achievement of the maximal physiological phenomenon in the way of assimilation and elaboration, use up, while transforming it, a vast amount of energy. If

17

and when this energy, by one of the many well known means, could be isolated and conveyed to an appropriate measuring device, its total, as anticipated, would be amazing.

However, the immense amount of work accomplished by plants in their chlorophyllatous leaves cannot in any way be added up except perhaps by an incrementary statistical count of growth taken at different intervals. The electro-chemical effect is achieved in each cell hit by the solar radiation, or even by the less refrangible rays of the spectrum, but the electrical action that constitutes its motive force *does not pass out of the cell;* nor, for that matter, does the work there achieved. With the movement of the lymph, in fact, the products of each chlorophyllated cell are transported to wherever the requirements of the species are best served by them as regards the life cycle with its own phases of growth, stasis, and reproduction.

Such study then, was a sterile achievement; against the very meager results obtained, and these at cross purposes, there remains, besides the prejudicial reason explained above, the consideration that within the cellular tissues electrical conduction, when they are in a herbaceous state, does not vary more lengthwise than in the direction orthogonal to the fibers (to the fibro-vascular fasciae). It is therefore impossible to claim that wherever an organ produced at any point a measurable concentration of electricity, the latter should remain there without being dispersed or without moving, at least for the time being, in one rather than another direction. However, a very slight polarity has been registered at times.

Baines[1] cites similar experiments in measuring, with a very sensitive galvanometer, the electrical states (difference in polarity) of different parts of fruits, bulbs, and various organs of plants. He then compares the results obtained with equivalent ones, invariably negative, obtained in a relative vacuum produced with an ordinary plunger-type of pneumatic device. There appears to be the probability that the explorative investigations are affected by polarization, the type of hook-ups, and diffusion. Also when attempting to formulate the complications to which these secondary phenomena may give rise, one must point out that such explorations, effected

---

[1] A. E. Baines, *Op. cit.*

in various live plant organs, between the mesocarp and the endo-carp, between the apex and the peduncle of fruit, etc., fail to give *absolute* measurements, even if at the point of exploration there exists an electric state different from that existing at another point.

The galvanometer gives only the general difference of the elec-trical state of the various regions explored. In each of these regions, there may exist, severally, charges relatively strong and of opposite polarity, which cancel out one another compensatorily: as, for instance, in a high part, the sounding may touch a mass of cells of a weak but homogeneous electrical tenor. Added up by the sounding apparatus that collects them, such homogeneous forces can constitute a considerable electromotor force that surpasses the first type.

Galvanometer readings, therefore, can be retained neither as reliable exponents of electrical states, nor of their exact where-abouts. Only a point-by-point set of cellular statistics could be able to give an irrefutable answer: but that is not practically feasible.

The constantly negative results from the comparison experiments with vacuums, which according to experimental conditions as described by Baines could be only extremely relative, are inex-plicable except by the fact that the imperfect vacuum is a good conductor of electricity, for which reason it offers passage in a short circuit, where there is reason for its being produced, prefer-ably because of the tremendously long winding of the galvanometer used (a resistance of 1,200 ohms).

10.

Deleterious Effects of the Current Passing Through the Seeds

Electric currents directly applied to plants have not had a very widespread use, or at least the results they have produced have not been held by their authors as worthy of mention. On the other hand in a great number of cases, the tests tried on seeds, with current supplied either by a cell, or by other generators of current, are still going on. The goal should be stated as improvement, it being borne in mind that electrical energy can, in some way, be added to the vital, instrinsic energy that every seed encloses. The hope is to be able to imprint with greater ease, by comparison with the adult plants, a few useful changes in the still ungerminated one, assuming that the latter can be rendered more "educable" by artificial stimuli.

I must acknowledge that this group of experimenters is the one that has come nearest to the good way. In fact, in going back to the genital plasma, the creative factor of the seeds, it has been possible to derive modest modifications.

The basic error is attributable to false biological evaluation; to the preconceived notion that the seed is not yet a complete plant, to the belief that the seed can acquire, lose or modify some of its characteristics in the process while it is achieving germination; that outside forces can effect it, with a final tangible influence which would bring out morphologic changes in the nascent plants.

I have been able to ascertain how common this erroneous concept is among even the average well educated individuals, and I want to explain myself.

The seed is only the tiny secret of what the plant will be which will follow it. It is a tiny being, complete in its very part. Its characteristics are already quite well defined, and nothing can change them. These are an assimilated heritage, which the species has been passing down with marvelous precision from the beginning, from the close of Creation, from generation to generation, *immutably* down the centuries, the millenia.

Sexual, morphological heredity, inheritance of a higher or lower vital efficiency, is well determined quite before a seed germinates, quite before a seed matures. It goes back to the moment of fecundation; it is inborn in the ancestors.[1]

The reader will have occasion to revert to this subject, developed more fully in Chapters II and III.

The seeds were exposed to direct or to alternating current, with various potentials; in dry state, wet, or immersed in saline solutions.

Each one would merit separate treatment, making clear the circumstances as regards mass, specific degree of conduction and potential employed in each case, coefficients too numerous for a summary which is intended to be brief.

---

[1] H. De Vries, *Specie e varietà*, p. 691, Sandron, Palermo.

The electrical conductance of seeds increases very little when they are dry. An electric current, to overcome resistance, would have to be a very high potential, not so much to overcome the internal resistance of the true seed but to overcome the very much stronger resistance of the tegumental layers, of the membranes, and of the protective sclerotic tissues.

Never would passage of the current be affected except with batteries of hundreds of cells arranged in series or of accumulators similarly arranged, or else of dynamos capable of supplying currents at many hundreds of volts. Such a current is hardly capable of overcoming the high resistance of the seed, or seeds, a resistance that can oscillate *between highly variable limits,* according to their quality, and their degree of dryness, depending not only upon their desiccation by the sun but also *upon their age,* and in short, not only would it rapidly destroy the vitality of the seeds, but would carbonize them. Whenever the current has passed through a highly resistant medium, it automatically increases the resistance of the latter either by the heating that is induced, or by the creation of a voltaic arc, which provides possible solutions with continuity among the tissues traversed.

A treatment of this kind would undoubtedly be lethal. On the other hand, if the potential employed is not initially sufficient to allow the passage of a current in the seed or the series of seeds under consideration, the current does not pass through. It must be added then, that in many species, and particularly when the seeds are gathered early, an interstice of air exists always between the seed and its envelope, which generally becomes wrinkled, while the seed shrinks in size. Besides therefore, what was mentioned, at the beginning of this section, the electrization of seeds, or stated more aptly, the passage through them of dynamic electricity, is practically unrealizable, cannot be regulated, and proves ineffectual or lethal.

11.

Passage Through a Humid Medium

Whenever the tegumentary envelope is rendered wet, through recent immersion, it affords an easy passage for the electric current, while it is with difficulty that it passes through its seed, which has not had time as yet to imbibe water. If, instead, the wetting (whether of the seed or of the tegument) is of several days duration, the moisture content becomes homogenous, as does, a short time afterward, the electrical resistance.

The moistened seeds have a weak electrical resistance; they can be pervaded also by currents generated by a few batteries, effectively as regards passage through the two cotyledons; not so with regard to the essentially vital parts: the down and the rootlets, i.e., the embryo of the nascent young plant, which is contained rolled up between the cotyledons as provided for by nature.

As to the results obtained by various experimenters, who mainly have had quite a limited objective (premature germination), these results may be summed up as the prevalence in favor of electrization, explainable in terms of the accelerated imbibition of water.

Lastly, there is a limited series of experiments on seeds immersed in saline liquids. In England there has appeared a society—I don't know how important it is—for the electrical treatment of seeds immersed in saline baths and exposed to electrization. The electrolytic liquid is probably sodium nitrate or ammonium sulphate, according to the journal[1] which recently reported the process indicating the results (withheld) as being useful; whereas this cannot be true, as the journal itself had to admit after a note from me.

In fact, in this case there arises a remarkable modification. The seeds are placed in a saline solution, in which conduction does not occur as it usually does. A saline solution, from the electro-technical point of view is an *electrolyte;* it conducts electricity by its undergoing decomposition. Introducing a current into an electrolytic bath, i.e., into a saline bath, gives rise to two opposing currents of *ions:* consisting of fractions of molecules having collectively positive or negative electrolytic charges. The ions have electric charges that are tenaciously bound, and are therefore *towed* by their charges toward the lead-off pole of the current if the charge of the ion is negative or vice versa. No genuine, actual exchange of

[1] "Rivista d'Agricultura" (Agricultural Review) Parma, January 1921.

electricity takes place, therefore, in a saline liquid through which it passes, but only an *interchange* of fractions of molecules and ions, each of which undertakes to carry, so to speak, its own electric load to the electrodes connected up with the generators (cell or dynamo).

Although when wet it is a very poor conductor of a saline solution, any seed is such also if it is very much diluted. The phenomenon of decomposition and of electrical transport occurs therefore *entirely within the saline liquid* where electrical resistance is low. Moreover, if the seeds are very close-packed and the liquid therefore proportionately insufficient, conditions do not change, because the passage offered to the current of ions is always quite great, the ion having dimensions even smaller than those of the molecule. No injury can result if the stream of ions are forced to follow a tortuous path across the submerged seeds in order to reach the electrode that attracts them. Finally, collision between an ion and a seed is, as regards electricity, ineffectual.

A seed in a saline bath through which a current is passing is almost as safe from electrical traps as an entombed man is sheltered from the wind; or as a man in a submarine is not disturbed by any possible ocean current.

The possible usefulness to a seed of immersion in the above-mentioned electrolytic baths is that of absorbing a little of the solution. The sodium nitrate and the ammonium sulphate are two good azotized manures, stimulating the growth of vegetation. But this property has no connection with, nor can it ever be reinforced by the pseudo-electric process the efficacy of which is being lauded.

In Section 5, mention has already been made, among other items, of the electrical treatment of seeds with currents induced at high potentials; provided with Ruemkorff inductors. The item referred to could have been in place here, too, where in brief review there pass the various kinds of currents; but since what was involved was instantaneous currents, one the effect of which is in every way comparable to that produced by sparks, except for polarity, which reverses itself at every spark, it is also not out of place among the large group of electrostatic experiments.

12.

Breakdown of the Plant Tissues Through Which a Current Has Passed

At the end of the eras of the discovery and the first electrical applications of currents there arose in plant physiology the desire to investigate, if possible, mutations in the normal life cycle of plants subjected to them.

It was intuitively felt that a parellelism must exist between the physiological effects provoked by electricity in animals, when it passes through one of their muscles, or one of their vital organs, and in plants. Someone went even further; he wondered whether electricity, considered as a dynamic force, might not be able to combine with a physical force, with chemical stimuli, or with nutritive properties of which plants avail themselves.

Phanerogame plants, in the totality of their organs (roots, stems, leaves and flowers) constitute a second-class conductor, as regards electric currents.

From the electro-technical standpoint the organs of a plant must from here on be considered *complex saline solutions* divided into vesicles, or cells, closely connected with each other. All cells of green plants in reality contain water which contains dissolved in it various acids, salts, alkaline and hydrocarbonate substances. The electricity passing through such cells, transforms some of those substances contained in the cells themselves, rendering them inept for their proper functioning, also, most often (and to various degrees) yielding products which may pollute adjacent healthy cells. The action of the current develops, however, in a different way, if in the baths there are ordinary electrolytes, because of the cellular constitution which takes from the current the possibility of proceeding in its normal course. Not quite in the sense of obstructing the order of the parietal septa of the cells, nuclei, fibers that offer different resistances to the passage of the current, but due to the existence of the lymph canals across which the electricity, which always chooses the path of least resistance, prefers to pass.

The main causes of complications, in the case of currents applied to plants, are consequently two: the chemical breakdown which it invariably entails, and the variable resistance of cellular and vascular structure.

The passage of dynamic electricity, or electric current, is relatively easy in the fairly juicy herbaceous plants, difficult in the ligneous ones, except during the spring seeding, quite difficult in the peripheral cells of the latter, and, in general, in suberous tissues. Applying the electric current to vegetables, which in this instance should be connected up by a good metal contact with the source of electricity, two cases may be offered:

1. The tension of the current used is not sufficient to overcome the total resistance constituting the stretch of fibro-vascular and suberose tissue which it is to pass through. In such a case, the result is zero, even should the current used be intense.

2. The tension is strong enough to overcome the stretch of plant interposed by the electrodes, or lead-off wire. In that case, the latter passes through the tissues of the plant, selecting the path of least resistance, which is generally the zone of exchange, and on its passage breaks down by degrees the saline liquids of the cells and the lymph vessels situated along its way. The immediate external signs of the passage are first rendered visible at the electrodes, with the symptoms of common necrosis. There, in fact, the current, and consequently its injurious effect, is more intense because it is more confluent.

The electricity is transmitted preferably, as has been said, in the lymph canals where resistance is negligible, and, between two points, follows the vector line imperfectly, precisely for this reason. However, in the living plant, the line circulates incessantly, and if the latter is changed, during its passage in an organ, by the electric current, the lymph will carry the consequent poisoning into the organs that it is called upon to nourish. The necrosis, a symptom of the sudden organic breakdown, does not manifest itself all at once, either because the flow of lymph is not very rapid, or because the outer tissues are the last to undergo necrosis, being located in the zone where the conveying operation of the lymph is of minor importance. The posthumous effects turn out nevertheless incomparably greater than those immediately apparent after an application of electricity of this type which, to tell the truth, has been used by very few experimenters. The dynamic electricity or electric current used in this instance does not differ substantially from the static kind except in a quantitative sense and in potential value; for that reason, the observations already offered in Section 5, regarding the extension of necrosis and other secondary causes, are perfectly valid for the applications of ordinary electric currents, with the one difference that in the case of the applications electrostatic treatments the charge tends to slip to the surface, while the galvanic currents are transmitted exclusively to the conducting medium, which in this instance is the stalk, and every humid organ of the plant.

13.

Currents Across Cultivated Ground

The part of the plant below the ground has likewise aroused investigative curiosity as to whether electricity passing over the terrain can aid, by reflex action, in the nutritive functions which the roots are called upon to perform.

It is necessary to premise that in all of these experiments the electricity does not cross nor does it stimulate any roots because of the quite considerable conductance of the terrain compared with theirs; it would be superfluous to repeat here the demonstration already detailed in connection with Section 5 regarding electrical charges, which offer the outstanding instance in this connection.

The most frequent and unwise form in which this experiment has been carried out is that of the copper-zinc coupling. Large plates of these metals are buried deep and connected with an insulated metal wire. . . . Anyone with a little electrotechnical knowledge will figure out at once whether any such system, without the aid to the zinc of any stimulus from acid, and with distances of many meters from one buried plate to the other, can possibly offer an appreciable current, even if it be granted that this were somehow efficacious.

Well, then, instead the experimenters all—and they are numerous —present data indicating that the results were constantly better in the electro-culture than in comparable areas. It is one of the few cases, among the so many various electro-physiological proofs, in which the results are not self-contradictory.

However, one should not therefore believe that the electricity played a useful role in the improvements verified. It is not that some hundreds of amperes of electric energy, which in some case may have developed by the copper-zinc coupling distributed over several square meters of service, is the one that has determined the increase in what was generated and in the product. If in the comparable area of land there had been buried instead of the bi-metallic plate two beautiful rubble stones, or two pieces of any inert substance, similar results would have been obtained.

The profound displacement of the soil occurring from the burying of the plates is indubitably a bringer of beneficial results: the air in the subsoil is the best catalitic agent for the biochemical trans-formations attending plant nutrition.

Nothing therefore is to be credited to electricity.

But even with the use of suitable means, thanks to which there would be made to pass through the terrain a 20-30 ampere current, the results obtained would be no better.

Even if an alternating current is used, without evident benefit, the fact is justified by the premise explained at the beginning of this section.

Of some scientific use, on the other hand, are the laboratory experiments performed in a germinator. Results indicate that seeds adjacent to the pole, or, better said, to the negative electrode, germinate somewhat earlier, this being due not to the current but to the alkaline reaction which the current produced there. It is to be noted, however, that the seeds were not completely buried, but simply deposited on the wet medium in the germinator. From similar experiments performed in jars and in open ground no such results ensued, because the slight electrolysis was not afforded the opportunity to materialize. Among the most noteworthy experiments on currents immersed in the ground, those of Gauthier, in contrast to results by Spencew (sic), are the best performed.

Not to be confused with these experiments are those in which the current is embedded in the ground, through which passes the interpolar current over a metal wire. In such a case, there is exclusively a thermal effect, which can react usefully on the plant if held within reasonable limits of temperature.

14.

Plants in a Magnetic Field

However paradoxical this may seem to an ordinary individual, magnetism may turn out much more useful with plants than is the case with electricity mobilized by the methods known at present. Magnetism could affect plants in two ways: (1) at a set polarity it might (at least it is permitted to suppose so) act by influencing the structure of the vegetative plasma, dialysing out the magnetic substances from the diamagnetic ones, so as to call forth a new constructive order, which would be translatable into deformations; (2) at alternating or pulsating polarity, obtainable with electromagnets activated by alternating or frequently interrupted currents, the magnetism might *induce electric fields* that are diffused, the action of which would have its seat and terminus in plant organs, if placed there in time during the charging of the field.

If the results obtained have not been considerable or productive of useful applications, everything gives reason to hope that further experiments in the field of physiology will lead to worthwhile results, as has happened in Genetics.

We do not have full information regarding the experimental apparatus used up to the present time as to the intensity and the quality of the currents used, the exact distance from the poles of the organs exposed to their action, the value in gauss units of the magnetic intensity, and such other detailed information needed in this field as reference data on the subject.

At any rate, Tolomei, Errera, Reinke, Stampelli, and Pfeiffer, then Bohn and Cheneveau[1] as far as I know, experimented with scant success in the field of magnetism created about plants and micro-organisms, either with insulated metal solenoids, thru which a current passed, but provided with the central iron core, at the

---

[1] Bohn and Cheneveau, De l'action du champ magnétique sur les infusoires (Action of the Magnetic field on Infusoria), "C.R. Ac.. Sc.," CXXXVI, 1903, p. 1579.

post of which was placed the plant to be experimented with, either with electro-magnets or with natural ones. The solenoids do not yield a great intensity of magnetic field, and the experiments performed with these did not yield appreciable results. The application and the experimental groundwork adopted by Stampelli is most noteworthy for its most scrupulous control.

In my opinion, these experiments on plants should be repeated with the criteria adopted by me for influencing the pollen (Section 25 and foll.) in seeking, within the limits of the possible, to obtain a much greater field of intensity than that already adopted and high periodic frequency, activating only with alternating currents.

The experiments carried out with magnets and fixed electromagnets constantly offer one result that is confirmed in more than one way: the deviation of the geotropic axis of the plant, which is normally vertical. Every operational detail would have to be known in order to give a precise judgment of these experiments, which I find in the previously mentioned book of Professor Bruttini. Among the others, there arises the doubt whether with the electromagnets which were used, lying on one side, so that their polar surface is in a vertical position (i.e., parallel to the vegetative axis of the budding plants) constituting a fair-sized mass, may have led the buds opposite the magnet to be deviated not through a magnetic effect developed thereby, but through a helio-tropic effect that was intercepted by a single side.

For a rigorous control, the plants being tested should have, alongside, an object simulating the electromagnet, in the exact position that the latter occupies, from where the experiments are set in analogous conditions also with regard to the light.

Interesting and analogous to my work are the experiments of Tolomei, who has subjected to an intense magnetic field the egg of a hen and a silkworm, obtaining in each case a monstrosity.

15.

Concluding Summary

The concluding synthesis of this chapter aims to stress the fact that electricity has not proved useful to crops, whatever may have been its direct application.

Moreover, neglecting the practical yield that could expect a return only after long and diligent preparation, there is not a single result that justifies encouraging the carrying on of further attempts of an electro-physiological nature.

The rational examination and comparison of the energy spent on electrical devices employed with their actual efficaciousness, the "intonation" between the producing medium and the receiving organ, shown to be existent for luminous radiations as it is for assimilation, are sufficiently convincing as to the fact that in Nature no artificial substitution of methods is easy or always possible.

Every living being possesses an organic constitution of its own, a more or less wide vital potentiality; it possesses from the embryo a totality of set or fixed aptitudes, as well as an intrinsic resistance to causes that might try to modify it or might impede the normal development of its life cycle.

The plant individual, already formed and complete in the seed, develops when it finds the conditions that suit it. Insofar as it is placed at its disposal, it utilizes only what is beneficial to its growth, and languishes if even a single one of the elements useful to any given species should happen to be missing in its case.

Like the characteristic chemical quality and the physical state of the soil, the general physical requirement is predetermined and absolute for each species. Plants which prefer the shade do not grow in the sun; tropical plants do not adapt themselves to our climate; epiphytic species do not live alone, etc.

Whatever extraneous physical force may intervene to modify the specific requirement of a plant is generally rejected by some providential intuition. (Sections 2 and 6). If the force is compelled to act, its effect is invariably harmful or fatal. Electricity, as the physical force, cannot constitute an exception, and the facts demonstrate this. (Sections 10 and 12).

The brief analysis of the experiments in this chapter performed by others than myself has not been actuated by the sterile object of an insipid criticism. I have believed it opportune to inform the reader about them in order to justify the reason for my choosing, in preference to others, which upon superficial examination might seem more brief and level, a way that is indirect and apparently abstruse to affect plants by electro-magnetic means.

The fortunate outcome of my mode of operation is based on the concept that the variability of an organism can be modified only *before its biological functioning has begun,* i.e., before the fecundation that is to conceive it. It is in order that the uninformed reader may have some account of botanical Genetics that the following chapter is presented.

Chapter II

Features of Botanical Genetics

SUMMARY:

16.

Elements of Botany

ALTHOUGH treatment of a single subject based on only one branch of a science may dispense with an introduction covering its elementary portion, inasmuch as the Reader is generally already cognizant, from previous studies, of the material that interests him, it is necessary for a comprehensive treatment involving two unrelated sciences, to provide some elucidation, if not characteristically elementary, yet strictly necessary to anyone not very well informed about problems in genetics.

Limited to this theme, little known in general, the botanical part will not take up much space, and where necessary I have managed to compress the exposition, limiting it to indispensable data, in the most concise form.

The various experiments about which the Reader will find a detailed account in Chapter VI and in VIII concern *artificial in-*

semination, produced with pollen exposed in various ways to specific electrical operations aimed at altering their innermost constitution.

It is known to everybody how the flowers of the Phanerogam plant bear, generally connected at the center, i.e., on the *thalamus* where the corollae converge, the sexual organs that are called *stamens* (male organs) and *pistils* (female organs). The stamens are almost always numerous and quite visible, because they are generally erect and protruding. In their turn the stamens end in special bags (anthers), which, opening up in full blossom, drop or keep the pollen stuck to them, mostly a granular substance, yellowish or orange-colored. The pistils are frequently hidden or slightly visible, because usually they are diaphanous, sometimes coiled up among the stamens, at other times confined at the end of tubular corollae.

The pistils end with an expansion which under the microscope appears finely notched and mucilagenous, and constitutes the *stigma.* The form of the pollen granules is quite varied, and their size also is not uniform. The rotund form is the most common; however, there is no lack of elliptical, ovoid, spindle, trihedral, polyhedric, and conchoid shapes in *entomophile* species. Their surface is generally smooth in the *anemophile* species, which entrust their pollen to the wind because it carries it to the stigmata. It is furrowed, pimply and pointed in the *entomophile* plants, inasmuch as they have been able to catch their bridesman (sic) a species of insects which, attracted by the nectar, accomplish the fecundation while sucking it.

In the *anemophile* species, the granules of pollen have very small dimensions and fall from the anther no sooner than the latter ripens; in the *entomophiles* they attain relatively huge dimensions, even 1.8 millimeters.

Each grain of pollen is enveloped in a fine membrane, as a rule pigmented yellow, which is capable of splitting up in preformed points when the pollen comes in contact with the slightly acid fluid (humour) of the stigma. *Germinal pores* are those points which, after the aforementioned stigmal excitation, but even through the simple effect of the moisture, release the contents (i.e., the *genital plasma,* the male fecundating fluid) of the granule of pollen. The emitted genital plasma fashions extremely subtle excrescences which precisely because of their shape are called *pollen capsules,* intended to penetrate, by way of the stigma, into the *ovary.*

However, the composition of these pollen tubes is not homogeneous, at their apex there are spermatic nuclei called *chromosomes,* the only ones that have a genuine genital function. Upon their molecular composition and structure depend the life and the morphological character of the new organism to the formation of which they are contributing. The rest of the pollen content has a complementary function and serves as the first vegetative impulse and the primitive nutrition of the embryo cell.

It is not superfluous to arrest the attention of the Reader on notions regarding the chromosomes. It is necessary to form a clear idea because on the intimate changes in these *bearers of characteristics* rests the study of the normal and electrical transformational technique of the species.

Upon their composition and internal set-up, always uniquely the same within each species, depends the unaltered reproduction of the species down the ages, upon the possible upsetting of their intimate order depends *mutation* (Section 19).

The vitality of the pollen is quite varied. In some species it keeps for a few hours, and generally it is the coarsest pollen that has a short functioning span; in others, the activity of the pollen continues over a long time. From one year to another it can remain fecund and still yield good seeds but not strong individuals. This is confirmed by my experiments along this line on vine pollen. In order to prolong the viability of pollen for a long time, precautions must be taken to protect it from moisture. In Chapter VI, we shall have to revert to this subject.

As regards the stigma, on the other hand, the functional period for fecundation is always short, and in no way has to do with the self-preservative ability of the pollen of the average species. Generally, the functionally receptive period of the stigma is less than one solar day; in some species, it lasts a few hours; its duration is proportional to that of the flower. In the orchids the duration is very long, but if the flower is fecundated, it withers right away. Such dependence, due to reaction of the ovary, occurs also in other kinds of plants.

17.

On Fecundation

The best time to perform the fecundation in the Phanerogams, when this is to be done artificially, in line with experimental objectives, is from 9 to 10 A.M. in the summer, and from 10 to 11 A.M. in the spring and the autumn. Windy or very warm and dry days are hardly favorable to fecundation because the stigma lacks the needed moisture. Cold and rainy days are less favorable, even if the work is done in a hothouse, because heat is needed for the successful carrying out of the fecundative process.

The maturity of the stigma can be told by its turgescence, by the complete development of the terminal papillae, by their tops, which appear viscid, by the stigmal fluid which covers it and activates the germination of the pollen deposited there.

For the experiments to be described later, it is necessary to inseminate each flower artificially, having previously seen to the *castration* (ablation of the anthers) before they opened up; also essential has been the *isolation* of each castrated flower to keep it from the pronubial insects, or from the wind, which may bring heterogeneous pollen.

Once the pollen is deposited on the stigma, there takes place the aforementioned emission of the pollen materials, which upon special stimulus becomes elongated, worming its way into suitable canals of the *tiny tube*, until it connects up with a terminal cell which closes each of the aforesaid canals. This is the *egg cell* or *cell of the egg*, the existence of which is visibly demonstrated and can be repeated by means of easy research with a microscope. On the other hand, the *mechanism* of fecundation by means of which the co-penetration of the pollen tube in the egg cell takes place is mysterious.

The only thing that is certain is the fact that before reaching the egg cell, the pollen tube carries at its apex the spermatic nucleus already referred to; along with the egg cell, the aforesaid nucleus comes into contact with the *latter's female nucleus*. The contact of the two sex nuclei having taken place, the fecundation is consummated and there soon sets in a rapid cellular build-up. The embryo

35

of the new plant increases and consolidates, utilizing the lymph which actively reaches it and the adjacent preformed tissues that form the ovule. That is how the seed originates. The way in which the latter manages to be formed is *always strictly identical for a pure botanical species* that is fecundated by its own pollen; the case is different, however, if a pollen extraneous to the species or a kindred variety should happen to form the embryo. There is then a hybrid, or a cross, or bastard.

The fecundation is called *autogamous* when the flowers become fecundated by their own pollen, cross or hybrid when there is the intervention of a different pollen.

Plants, and they constitute the largest grouping, which bear on their own flowers male organs and female organs are called *hermaphrodites;* those that have separate male flowers and female flowers but being on the same plant are referred to as monoecious, and lastly those are referred to as dioecious each individual of which bears either only a female flower or only a male flower.

18.

Origin of the Species

Normal reproduction in phanerogamous plants takes place the gamic way, i.e., by means of the seed. Dicotyledon plants can multiply also through scions, layering, flower beds, and grafting; but it suits the purpose best here to restrict the investigation to the only natural means of reproduction, the only one that has any bearing on the study to be elaborated later: a study based exclusively on fecundation.

Pure botanical species propagate by way of seeds with absolute fidelity. Ancient relics still surviving from remote eras bear testimony to the fact that the species existing today do not differ either proportionally or morphologically from those of antiquity and that botanical species do not undergo evolution in any sense of the word.

Conceived by Linnaeus as the ultimate limit of systematic classification, the *species* represents the *biotype,* or elementary systematic unit of morphological characteristics and physiological constants.

The Linnaean species, to tell the truth, were sometimes made up of groups the characteristics of which were not at all homogeneous. Later, other systematizers completed the work of the great initiator by subdividing the Linnaean into *sub-species, varieties* or *races*.

The origin of present species is attributed by Lamarck to variations of pre-existing species. In given eras, succeeding each other, millenia apart, compelled by extreme environmental conditions incompatible with the minimum required for their survival, the primitive species is supposed to have been compelled to change, even to manifest new attitudes appropriate to stop the adverse conditions imposed upon it by changes of climate and soil. In that guise, the changed species is supposed to have supplanted the old one.

However rational the Theory of Lamarck may be, *he admits* the faculty of changing through its own initiative in the guise of adapting itself to its environment, has not yet gathered sufficient factual proof. The phenomena cited by him in support of his thesis were later re-examined, and it was ascertained which are the result of crossed or hybrid fecundation.

Darwin attributed to *natural selection* the modification of the species. An imperceptible but constant modification is supposed to inhere perpetually in every species. The passing from one morphological phase to another is supposed to occur at such a slow rate as to escape investigation. The struggle for existence is supposed to eliminate, among so many constitutional forms to which dissemination can give rise, those individuals least fitted to sustain it.

However, the supposed hereditary variations offered by Darwin are being recognized as requiring to be classified severally as: *hybridization, polymorphism* and *mutation*.

In hybrids or bastards, the combinations of characteristics possessed by ancestors gives new characteristics, new unstable *biotypes,* or awakened characteristics normally hidden in the parents; and precisely the study of unstable hybrid descents should have been the principal argument in criticizing the Darwinian theory.

The Reader will have more ample grounds for learning, in Chapter VII, devoted to hybridization, how through hybrid descent there arises the scission, or split-up, in the specific characteristics constituting the hybrid itself, how from hybrid seeds are obtained the *pure ancestral species,* how the split-up of the hybrids never has any respite except with the complete uncoupling into pure species, transformed absolutely equal to the founding species from which the hybrid had originated.

In other words, the hybrid is only the temporary or transitory, mixture of the two species that comprise it.

19.

Mutation

The *mutations of* De Vries have most recently been brought in to evaluate the hypothesis of Lamarck. Such mutations arise quite infrequently but originate in pure species without artificial stimulation, and hybridization. They are, however, limited to few species.

The internal and external forces that govern the evolution of organisms are normally to be found in a state of equilibrium. From time to time, for some cause unknown, some alterations are reported to take place in the genital elements. Such alterations are thought to be the result of a sharp change or mutation of the species.

De Vries[1] attributes the extreme rareness of mutation, observed by him, strictly speaking, only in the Oenothera of Lamarck, to the fact that the botanical species would not mutate unless forced to do so by external agents, by abnormal condition.

In contradistinction to the hybrid, the mutant does not change any more; it behaves like a new species; its progeny maintains faithfully the characteristics of the progenitor initially mutated. Mutations occur frequently in wild and cultivated plants, and, in the first instance, prevail against competition from original wild types with which they may be thrown together.

The appearance in cultivated plants of isolated types with double flowers, isolates that transmit integrally such a characteristic to their progeny, may be recorded among the mutations. The double Papaveri (poppies), the Althaea, and the Crisantemi (chrysan-

[1] H. De Vries, *Op. cit.,* T. II, p. 655 *passim.*

thema), *Astri Chinesi* (Chinese asters), etc., which faithfully preserve the doubling characteristic, fall into the category of mutated plants. Not so the Violaciocche (wallflowers), which double their corollae only and always under the stimulus of hypernutrition of the seeds.

De Vries has formulated the following laws governing gamic mutations:

1. The new elementary species appear all of a sudden without intermediate forms.

2. The mutant species prove to have an absolute constancy in their progeny.

3. None of the new descendants is of a regressive variety.

4. The mutations appear plurally in the same seed-sowing operation.

5. Mutations occur in every direction, and natural selection acts as a sieve, eliminating *varieties* that are incompatible with the medium.

20.

Spontaneous Variations and Improvements Induced by Cultivation

It is important for the reader to distinguish thoroughly between mutation, just now referred to, which has set characteristics, transmissible to descendants, *somatic variation* due to the medium, or locale, and *meliorative* variation. The first type arises suddenly, analogous to *ionogenital mutation* with which we are to concern ourselves; the second type is altogether casual, and ceases or dwindles with the cessation of the stimulus that has evoked it. The third form of variability, on the other hand, is important. Meliorative variation is not fixed but fluctuating. It is due to the influence of the cultivation medium upon the species. It generally derives from hypernutrition and requires cultivational abundance in order to reproduce anew without detriment to the improvement obtained.

The somatic changes induced by the environment—the altitude, the temperature—are *confined to the individual* acted upon by the aforesaid physical conditions and *limited to the duration of the abnormal stimulus.*

Some Alpine plants, by way of example, and in particular the Edelweiss, change their stature, their color, the pubescence of their foliage and stalk when they are cultivated in the plains. The Chinese red primrose changes the color of its petals at a temperature of about 30° C., becoming white; the change, however, is transitory and if the plant returns to its normal ambient state, at 12-15° C., the flowers once more become red a few days later. Noteworthy differences are seen in the size and color of Dahlias of the same variety according as they are grown on a plain or on a high hill. Also in the Vitae, and particularly in the white varieties, there is a great difference between the beautiful bronze tint assumed by grapes on hills as compared to the same variety which, also maturing early, are pale in the open plain.

The immediate *temporary* changes are probably attributable to the altered proportions between the intensity of light and heat. All plants require for the fulfilment of their vegetative cycle a specified number of calories; in the plain, or better still in the greenhouse, these can be garnered within a much shorter time than at a high altitude, where they receive a greater amount of light for the larger part of their existence.

Probably the ultra-violet rays, contained in solar light in an amount always greater as the altitude increases, contribute to the determining of specific properties of Alpine plants (greater perfume, dwarfishness, skeletal solidity, hairiness, etc.).

The ambient conditions of growth, that is to say good or poor cultivation, a more or less suitable climate, the nature of the soil, etc., would not, according to Weismann, affect the heredity of the species. The stimulative action of the culture would activate that developmental or even amplificatory stimulus of some of the characteristics which the species already possesses. Once the stimulative action of the abnormal development stops, the species returns to normal, seeds of super-nitrated and sturdy plants, replanted in a poor cultural medium, yield plants of normal development.

According to Weismann, the heredity of an individual organism cannot be influenced by its temporary or continued stay in an exceptional ambient medium or culture, nor can it depend on the use or disuse of some of its organs. Every genital cell of an organism, or rather every gamete, would contain the aggregate of *all* and *only* of the hereditary characteristics that comprise its soma, characteristics capable of more or less favorable development according as the cultural medium is more or less propitious.

Moreover, according to Weismann,[1] the possible atrophy, lack, excess, or vagueness, or location of a *determinant* or chromosome or of a part of it would open the way for a mutation of the species.

Among modern theories, that of Weismann is undoubtedly the most alluring. It lends itself to the reporting of new electrobiological phenomena, from which it has received new sanction.

However, in my opinion, it bespeaks a temperament that in no wise is in contradiction to its general lines; a detailed rectification of the affirmation as to the genetic immutability of the species despite the cultural medium. This affirmation is, in an absolute sense, true; but it must be admitted, because the facts are not disproved, that the cultural medium affects the species in *another manner, different from mutation*, which, however, is very important, as the pivot of horticultural and agricultural selection.

It is undeniable that preserving cultivation in a cultural medium marked by excess remains without any genetic effect. Anyone can try this out by sowing, or planting, in good soil a *wild* species (for instance, the tricolored Violet) alongside of an *improved* variety of the same species!

Horticultural improvement *does not substantially change* a species, but it cannot be denied that it habituates it to respond favorably to cultivational stimuli that are lavished upon it. Horticultural improvement owes a good deal to cultivational abundance, that contributes to maintaining and perfecting it, and has great practical importance, particularly for the annual species and for those incapable of agamic reproduction.

Induced changes or *improvements* comprise a group of slow variations due to cultivation; they are progressive, evolutionary

[1]LoPriore, *Genetica sperimentale*. Unione Tip. Editrice, Torino.

41

changes. From these, Horticulture in the first place, as also in a subsidiary way Agriculture, has derived its most splendid advances, above all when superior cultivation, selection, and hybridization have acted in common.

Miraculous are the advances achieved in increasing the size of certain cultivated species: the Chrysanthemum, Celosia, Dianthus, Violet, Aster, Gladiolus, etc. On a more modest scale, but here the selective forces have converged for a useful purpose, there have been obtained improvements in the species of Beets, Barley, Wheat, Oats, as well as vegetables and legumes of various kinds.

Among agricultural plants, the most outstanding example is offered by the sugar beet in which within a few five-year cycles unrelenting selection has tripled the sugar content. Indisputable selection *does not induce new qualities,* but enhances those that the race already possesses, but only to the limit imposed by biological exigency. Among the individuals of a species that reproduces via seed, there are individual organisms that maintain the useful characteristics unaltered, others reproduce in a regressive direction, still others (always very few) in a progressive direction. *These last are the extremists of good will;* it is those few that the selector keeps for the very last sowings. Continued with this criterion, selection reaches a maximum which one cannot top. Individual organisms that excel through their useful quality by that very token become weak, or else poor bearers of seed.[1] The more an organism is removed from the natural conformation of its species, the more enfeebled its biological potentiality becomes. Hence the necessity for evolved races periodically to *breed again with* wild or vigorous species from which to derive robustness, which also is needed because useful characteristics can assert themselves without excessive aid, as is required in the practice of agriculture.

Loughi Di Vilmorin,[2] pioneer in the field of horticultural melioration, in 1850 observed that the hereditary power of a given anomaly did not have as an exclusive exponent individual specimens that could be shown to have that anomaly itself in a superlative degree.

[1] O. Munerati, "Giornale D'Italia Agricola," Rome, January and February 1921.

[2] H. De Vries, *Op. cit.,* vol. II, p. 782.

21.

Mutuality Between Meliorative Stimulus and Cultural Exigency

It is useful to stress that in horticulture, inasmuch as to every plant there is allotted a suitable cleared terrain, with space proportionate to the potential full growth of the plant upon its reaching maturity, the struggle for existence is of secondary importance. Moreover, mediocre organisms find so many cultivation aids as to be able to prosper and reproduce their kind, even though, from the naturalistic point of view, they may be anomalies. The magnificent manuring, the suppression of most of the flowers, the stripping away of the rings, and so many other manipulative operations produce a state of hypernutrition in the seeds of the plants exposed to such treatments. *The hypertension of the seed increases its adaptability to effective cultivation.* If the individual organism was born of hypernutritioned seeds which, offering a meliorative characteristic, are again exposed to the aforesaid cultivational devices, with their seeds used again for further sowing, the incipient improvement will become even better and will be so perpetuated.

The Chrysanthemum is the most conspicuous example of this type.

With sowings following one another in exceptionally well conducted cultivation operations, with a selection directive kept under watch and constantly *holding to a predetermined objective,* then within a few years there is obtained a considerable *improvement.* The objective of the selection can be exclusively directed to the anomalous feature of an organ, which it has been decided to exaggerate, to the development of this feature, to size, to productivity and so on.

Selection is a continuing process of meliorative refinement. Were it to stop in an evolved breed, there would, before long, take place a gradual reversion to the wild stage. Not even effective culturation by itself would be enough to prevent it.

At the same time, and to the extent that rich manuring and cultivation operations modify, with the help of selection to carry it gradually to perfection, the individual organisms of any species or race being perfected become, *all other things being equal, more demanding.* As soon as evolution advances, biological debilitation becomes more marked so that it necessitates the selfsame over abundant cultivational medium which was suited as a stimulus to improvement, for effectively developing the acquired characteristics.

Between productive stimulus to an improvement and the effective development of the race being improved, there consequently exists a *relationship of mutuality.*

In order to obtain from seeds of a race horticulturally evolved a superlative product, it is not enough to get theam; it is necessary to prepare for them a well provided environmentl medium (ample manure, space, food items).

Everything that in Horticulture is a monstrosity is, in this sense, exigent. The *Viola maxima tricolor* (tricolered giant violet), the cauliflower, the pistilloid monster Poppy, are the most notable examples of this.

The more meliorative selection is forced and repeated with the intent of modifying a given organ so as to make it respond ever better to the effective requirements for which it is being cultivated, the more this great vegetative energy which the plant uses up to enlarge or overfeed (hypernourish) the predetermined organ is then lacking as regards the remaining organs. Thus it is well known that the best varieties of vegetables, chiefly cabbages, cauliflowers, etc., that plants with double flowers, with strongly scented flowers, plants from very early fruit, yield few seeds, and sometimes yield none at all. Thus, extreme specimens of an effective characteristic are often sterile.

Sterility is frequent in horticultural varieties of species reproducing naturally agamically (bulbillas, rhizomes, etc.). Some varieties of the hybrid Gladiola produce a vast quantity of bulbillas,[1] but it is futile to look for a seed on such plants.

An analogous observation was made by Ragioneri,[2] the most learned seed-sowing expert of Italy on Ranunculuses and Freesias. Equilibrating biological compensation comes about in various ways and directions.

[1] For example, *Gladiolus Nanceyanum* "Comte Horace de Choiseuil."

[2] Dr. Attilio Ragionieri, *Un bel problema per i biologi, from the* "Bolletino della R. Società Toscana d'Orticoltura." Florence, 1919.

Vine plants with too strongly scented perfume often have imperfect fecundation; the monster variety Bicane, because of its enormous grapes, is susceptible to abortion of these. All these facts and ever so many others go to prove that every organism has a credit balance of vital energy which is reduced in some organs when it is used to excess in other organs of the organism itself.

As occurs in Physics, whenever a force disturbs the equilibrium, since there is no action without the corresponding reaction, so in Nature there is no progress in a given direction without there being a corresponding default somewhere else.

The meliorative stimuli may be summarized under two chief categories and represented as follows:

Meliorative stimuli

1st group *Natural* or *normal* ones	Cultivational operations of the ground Manuring in abundance Bringing in of seed grown in soil of a different type	
2nd group Artificial ones	Hypernutritioning of the seeds	With thinning of the buds and the flowers With anullar decortication, clippings, etc. Cross-fertilization, with pollen taken from terrain other than the one in which the "seed bearer" is grown

Mutational stimuli

Natural-Unknown stimuli, called spontaneous ones.
Artificial-Ionizing or radiant treatment applied to the pollen.

N.B. Horticulture for the production of new varieties avails itself above all of hybridization: but I deem it expedient to divide the subject, treating it partly in Chapter VIII.

22.

Individual Variations

Leaving out of consideration natural variations or those induced by cultivation, there are observed also among individuals born of a normal autogamous fecundation some small variations, particularly distinguishable in the property of vigor and size. But this does not justify the belief that they can be mutated nor permanently varied. What is involved are *individual variations*, due to like causes acting concertedly and which are difficult to estimate exactly as to the part played by each.

One factor may be to insure the faculty of development (i.e., a premature birth of a day earlier can enjoy an advantage over the other seeds placed into culture at the same time) through a larger quantity of fertilizer which a newly born has fortuitously taken possession of ahead of its neighbor, or, ultimately, the intrinsic vegetative property of a seed, more marked in one individual than in another.

Thus a seed can have an exceptionally vital potentiality to its credit, i.e., because of its having been constituted with perfect genital units (genetic cause) or else because of abundant nutrition introduced during its growth, i.e., through a cultivational cause.

23.

Causes Stimulating Variation

It would be superfluous to spend words to illustrate the stimuli of the first group (Section 21); these constitute the basis of every good culture. The improvement that the seed can derive from those stimuli is subordinated to the greater prosperity, to the better vegetative growth bestowed upon the culture.

Among the stimuli of Group 2, the most frequently used is the timely thinning out of the stems and the flowering buds, for the purpose of concentrating a larger quantity of lymph in the tiny buds that are released on the plant. If the partial suppression of the buds is carried out in time and on a large scale, remarkable results are obtained. The giant growth in size of the flowers is immediately observable; but it is not apart from the hypernutritioning of the sexual elements.

The gigantic growth of the flowers is none other than the external exponent of how much is going on in everyone of their parts, even though hidden. In hypernutritioned flowers, even the seeds, must end up hypernutritioned. Inductively it can be admitted that as much takes place in the basic elements of the life of the seed,[1] i.e., in the genital cells of the pollen and of the ovule, in which there must also take place, as is easily confirmed in all the plant cells of the individual plants that have been hypernutritioned, an *expansion*. This *does not disfigure* the morphological appearance of the new organism, because it does not mutate the order of the chromosomes, or genetic determinants, but it *induces* the producing of supernumerary organs, as would be the case with petals doubling in number. A case in point is the Wallflower, which, with hypernutrition of its seed, from single flowers always yields double ones.

An essential condition for obtaining hypernutritioned seeds that will yield doubling is precisely premature clipping or removal of the buds, because in that way there occurs the abnormal enrichment of the sexual cells during their formation.

Not all species respond favorably to lymphatic coarctation, for which reason the process cannot be applied to every phanerogamic plant family, or at least only to a very limited degree. In the Vines, for instance, a too energetic concentration of lymph over the ovules induces such a plethora of humor (i.e., moisture) as to drown it; it promotes dripping in tiny buds, even in the most fecund varieties.

Anellar decortication is generally practiced on fruit-bearing plants for the purpose of arresting, at a point close to the implanting of the fruit, the flow-off passage of the lymph generated, which normally flows down toward the roots. Inasmuch as decortication is performed on the branch that bears the fruit, barely below the peduncle of the latter, as a result the lymph generated by the leaves, finding its passage cut off by the decortication operation, is forced to flood the entire fruit, which thereby becomes very big and matures with several days to spare. The seeds also on their part react to this forced feeding, and the same line of reasoning holds for them as held in connection with the proposition regarding the clipping and thinning of the buds.

If varying the density of seed-sowing, exchanging it from place

[1] Forms the subject matter of following chapters.

47

to place, between terrains of different types, is beneficial for production purposes, as practice demonstrates that it is, I have had occasion to confirm how artificial insemination with pollen from a well-operated culture, *in terrain of diverse chemical and physical composition,* contributes to endowing with robustness and perfection descendants obtained by such a process. I do not know if it is to be attributed to this practice, which I never fail to apply in my crossings of European Vines with American ones, but the fact remains that I have never had occasion to complain, in the Vines from seeds produced by me by hybridization, of the motley lot of miserable varieties that all seed-sowers of this type complain of. On the contrary and without the contribution of any other artificial means (any system of lymph constriction or hypernutrition is inapplicable to the Vine being bound) and employing not very remarkable ancestors of the fruit, I have had the good fortune of obtaining very beautiful new vine plants of pure domestic "blood" (stock) Pirovano crossings and grafts, of the unprecedented robustness of Goliath and Gagliardo.

Every plant absorbs from the soil only those raw materials that are suited to its growth (Section 44). It has been proven, however, that the soil, location, altitude, all have an appreciable effect on the composition, on the taste, on several *minute properties* of the product.

Logically it can be argued that the pollen from a plant grown in soil quite different from that in which the seed-bearing plant was grown, carries within it not only the impress of the species but also some characteristic somatic trait bestowed upon it by the terrain. Conjoining the plasma of the genital cells in the act of fertilization, some benefit may be derived from the very slight difference in the sense indicated above; it may prove complementary and therefore an integrator of perfection.

This principle, moreover, is not actually new; it is quite widely applied in Zootechnique, notably for the strengthening of lactating cows, and merits being seriously considered also in Botanical Genetics. Hitherto, insofar as I know, in this field it has remained almost completely forgotten, as a genetic subsidiary of hybridization.

It is generally predicated a normal procedure to sow over a wide area where the probability will be greater of finding some strain that will represent an improvement over its progenitors. Indisputably it is a good system inasmuch as the probability increases with the number, but it certainly is not the best way to follow, and all the less economical for the purpose of producing variations or improvements. When afterwards the choice is to be made of individual strains which for purposes of fructification must occupy extensive space over the years, as is the case with fruit-bearing plants, I believe it necessary to concentrate one's whole attention on the choice of seed-bearers, and, on the other, of pollen bearers, and to employ, among those mentioned above, those means best suited for producing, even *before* flowering, that plethora of nutritive substances which is suitable for stimulating super-growth of the genital cells, upon which indubitably depends the principle of meliorative variations or the rise of some monstrosity, always welcomed in Horticulture.

As the Reader will have the leisure to see in the following Chapters, the variations that are obtained from the ionolysis of the genital plasma, whether by their forcible separation or through the definite genetic dualism of somebody's matings, or else by the stability of reproduction of the forms obtained, approach much more closely mutations than they do the gradual improvements that have just been examined. In contrast to mutations, the variations produced by ionization of pollen are produced within some species or other. There are, however, some species much easier to vary than any other, especially responsive to one means of ionization rather than to the other.

24.

Concluding Synthesis

To sum up the notions that most closely concern the subject under consideration, it will be profitable to repeat that:

Mutations arise spontaneously, at one stroke, without transitional states in the gamic reproduction of some vegetable species and are stable (or fixed). Improvements are obtained only by cultivation; they get their start by hypernutrition, requiring superabundant culture for the manifestation of their useful aptitudes; they are subject to variation either progressively or regressively, from which it follows that selection continuously governs their regeneration. All species are susceptible of genetic improvement; very few are the species that mutate.

The genetic cause of meliorization is briefly treated in Section 20, and in the exposition of the Weismann Theory, reference was made to his hypothesis as to the origin of mutations; I want now to return to this subject prior to going into the electro-molecular considerations by means of which spontaneous mutations, like those called forth by ionization, I believe can be interpreted.

De Vries has not commented nor has he advanced any hypothesis on the cause that calls forth mutations in any given species. He limits himself to observing that the Violet, Draba and Oenothera seem to be the only ones susceptible of genuine and inherent mutative variations; on a lesser scale there are presumed to be other species with double flowers.

Another noteworthy peculiarity that De Vries offers as evidence in connection with *Oenothera Lamarkiana* (sic), a species studied by him with skill and love, is the following: that the mutations observed on the first sowings of Oenothera were duplicated in successive sowings of the same species, always with the same forms, with equal proportional relationships of the forms mutated.

In the recent past, Reiner put forth the hypothesis that the various forms observed by De Vries in the repeated sowings of *Oenothera Lamarkiana* (dwarf, jigs, short-stems, sparklers, red-vines, broad-leaves) are supposed to be merely pseudo-mutations. The Oenothera is not supposed to be a pure species but a hybrid and for that very reason subject to doubling.

The groundlessness of this point is demonstrable quite briefly:

1. If *Oenothera Lamarkiana* were a hybrid, it would have to represent the only exception, because it would yield only 1.5% of atavistic organisms inasmuch as such is the average percentage of mutant subjects obtained by the famous Dutch botanist, an average that agrees with the results of MacDougal, who repeated elsewhere the experiments of De Vries.

2. If the *Oenothera Lamarkiana* were a hybrid, it would have to double in the two ancestral forms and only in those.

It is improbable for the mutations to arise from causes having to do with nutrition; those mutations appear as often in wild plants, completely without cultivation, as in cultivated plants, and in terrains of widely divergent types.

The mechanism of mutation is unknown. The causes that evoke it are completely cloaked in mystery; but the parallelism between natural mutations and the variations induced by electro-magnetic ionolysis justify the harboring of some hope for a solution of the problem, that cannot be far off.

The familiar artificial stimuli (cutting the tips, afflux of lymph to the sexual organs), not only the attempted absorbing of special catalytic and radioactive substances fed to the plants, have actually failed to stimulate these to mutate. But, on the other hand, it is quite certain that ionization was quite extraneous to the experiments of De Vries, as also to his imitators. It remains to be seen whether among the types of physical energy of which plants avail themselves naturally, there may not be, especially in light (Section 8), physico-chemical combinations that will evoke fortuitously ionic migrations in given points of the plasma.

In Chapter III, the Reader will find a proposed interpretation of the phenomenon of mutation, according to which every visible form probably corresponds to a set internal anomalous mechanism originating in the genital plasma, an interpretation which the experimental results of ionogenetic descent will support.

Why among the so many species observed is only the Oenothera subject to mutation?

Acquaintance with ionogenetic mutations, especially with those caused by ionizing rays, combined with the anatomical knowledge of this particular species, permits, from now on, the advancing of a conjecture which probably hits the truth.

The pollen of the *Oenothera Lamarkiana*, falling from the anthers, remains attached to long filaments; a goodly portion of the former consequently remains suspended in air, where it receives a strong solar irradiation, which can last for several days. In this process, the Oenothera pollen does not lose its vitality; but it is not unlikely that the prolonged light bath has on the plasma an effect analogous to that of the varied ionizing measures. If, during its quest for plunder, an insect smears its trunk with some of the old pollen, hanging from adjacent flowers, the normal fecundation would ensue, and from the seed there would be plants variously mutated, according to the posture with relation to the rays (Section 42).

The imperfect constitution of the sex cells and of their plasma is perhaps quite a frequent phenomenon. The variations possible in such a case would be considerably more numerous than those which we have occasion to verify here, but it is easy to realize their rare occurrence by taking into account the fact that where the resulting molecular structure and the location are quite different from the normal, the plasma would not be able to give life to a new organism. The embryo, stimulated to grow, would be unable to reach its goal. Perhaps a part of the atrophied seeds, small, badly nourished or aborted, which are also to be found in hardy subjects and which we usually discard, could yield modifications of their species could they be viable. Further on, the Reader will find examples of seeds produced by ionolized pollen; seeds perfect in appearance which are not born because of excessive alteration of the male factor effected by the ionolizing treatment.

CHAPTER III

Informational Concepts

SUMMARY:

25.

Fruitless Preliminary Experiments

A FANATICAL CULTIVATOR, bent on innovating, fascinated by the mystery that still surrounds the beginnings of life and the causes of variation via gamic heredity, towards the end of 1899 had undertaken, carefully noting his findings, various types of artificial insemination on different species of plants.

The results obtained, and in particular those rather encouraging ones carefully effected with new vine plants via table grapes, had all the more intensified my interest in and familiarity with the artificial insemination of plants.

Horticulturists are seeking above all, since business requires it so, sensational variations, monsters. Among the stimuli suited to evoking them, I could not forget electricity, which, also not thoroughly known, had vividly attracted my attention in my youth. Meanwhile I centered my attention on the possibility of the application of electricity, about which I had some elementary knowledge, as a possible stimulus to genetic variation, applying it to the reproductive organs of plants; and I have become convinced since then that the life of the new organism begins and becomes stabilized as to its characteristics in accordance with a system, a *well-defined architecture from the moment* of fecundation.

That is how from experiments somewhat puerile, as soon as I had equipped my tiny laboratory with suitable equipment, buoyed up by living faith despite my initial failures, I succeeded in 1914 in getting some modest results.

From the multiplicity and homogeneity of the deformations obtained, from the wholly new appearance of these, I could be certain that they depended exclusively on the special treatment to which I had exposed the pollen used for the fecundation. Since then, confirmations of the original results have been numerous; and, at the present time, there are quite promising proofs that the principle, experimentally confirmed, was generally applicable.

Moreover, not being at that time aware of the electro-physiological experiments described in Chapter I, I was never tempted to predict that electricity could in any way be a force equivalent to those enjoyed by plants (Sections 2, 3, 4, 10, 11) for growth and maturation of their organs.

Some experiments had come close to what was to be the experimental directive of my studies (Section 3) but they ran into, as I have already said, a serious error, that of believing that the electrical treatment of plants which are already mature and complete, or else in the process of germinating, can in some way get to be the modifying agent of aptitudes in the plant.

The seed, as I said in commenting on those electro-physiological experiments, is already a complete being: the little secret of the organism to which it will give the means to develop. In this process the individual characteristic is specific, and is *already determined.* The tiny plant which the seed contains entwined on itself already has a physiognomy of its own, an organic system already set in accordance with the hereditary factors that have combined to shape it; even the attributes of the upper organs (flowers and fruits) are *irrevocably determined,* disciplined according to the system of growth, or increase, already set in motion.

An electric flow of current which passes through a seed could only damage this miracle of perfection and extraordinary dependence, *never modify it!* And the same may be repeated for the germination of seeds under a current or electrical influence.

Every living being is born, it is worth repeating, with an amount of energy, of aptitude, that is a special characteristic of its own. It can happen that because of education, culture, or environmental set-up, its propensities tend to grow, improve, and become stimulated in one given organ; but neither education, nor environmental set-up, nor cures can change a characteristic, be it hidden or apparent, to render intelligent an idiot, increase the size of a pigmy, to make hair grow in the case of a bulb; there *is* no such thing.

And so, cultivation, which also avails itself of very many artificial means, intended to endow plants with greater growth when their organs are hypertrophied, sustains them in the struggle for existence *but does not change them.*

To return to the origin of life, to divert it at its very beginnings, that is the basis of the work. However, to place it on an experimental basis was, for me, and particularly at that time, an almost desperate undertaking. In the first place, there presented itself a dilemma, which, for that matter, is still unresolved, regarding the suitableness of working on the pollen or the ovule. To provide even a coarse granule of pollen with an electrode, was impossible, even less so was it to be thought of to try something of the kind on the ovule. Moreover, what would have been the type and the unit of the *useful* and not *harmful* current?

There remained only to try suitable seeds in their formative stage. Familiar with the behavior of static electricity, which would not have been able to serve the purpose, I applied very weak currents to the very young seeds by means of quite delicate electrodes.

Very soon I had to become aware of their absolute inefficacy, despite my having devised a preliminary operation intended to denude the seed. Figure 1 represents at the left two grapes connected with a delicate metal wire two or three days after fecundation. At the right are seen the grapes themselves deformed and split by the ligature about a month after the operation. The seeds *are* emerging and sometimes are practically separated from the pulp.

Fig. 1

Splitting of grape by a ligature.

This occurs without causing any inconvenience whatever, inasmuch as the cells build up from below as soon as they are split by the fine wire towards which they are thrust, through the rapid growth of the grape.

Without this precaution it is not possible to make a current pass through a seed; unless the latter is absolutely denuded, the envelopes that surround it (epicarp, mesocarp), that constitute the peel, the pulp, the husk, the grape, etc., easily permit of the passage of the electric current, being acid at the beginning of the development of the fruit. The endocarp, on the other hand, i.e., the stone, the inner shell, in a word, the immediate covering of the seed, offers considerable electrical resistance after the first phase of growth. In some plants, then, the seed remains almost isolated from its envelopes, which surround it without touching it. Figure 2 represents a young fruit of a peach tree and a grape, enlarged, at the early stage of growth as seen in cross-section.

The micro-electric current introduced into the young fruits follows the path of the arrows, across the pulpy portion of the fruit, which is the best conductor.

However weak the currents used may be, there are ascertained in the vicinity of the two electrodes two small necrotic points, which, in the long run, poison the surrounding tissues, completely blocking growth and establishing the premature falling of the fruit.

The failure of this experiment, which now seems to me quite

Fig. 2

Young fruit, enlarged, seen in cross-section. The current flows across the
pulp without touching the seed.

naive, had not shaken my faith, and deepening my reasoning about
the cause of heredity, I wondered whether it might not have been
better to turn the force only on the main male element, the pollen,
which also plays a part (nay it plays the preponderant role) in
imprinting the characteristics in the new subject that is about to
be created.

In man, in whom genetic contingencies are studied and controlled more fully, there is a clear confirmation of the fact that the
physiological state, as well as the pathologic and toxic states, can
have an important bearing on heredity. The progeny of alcoholics,
syphilitics, malaria sufferers, offer a sad proof of the aberrant effect
on the subject conceived under such conditions. Whatever takes
place in the human species is to be found, although in a different
form and less obvious in Zootechny and also in Botany.

26.

The Effective Way

This reflection had centered my experimental researches to the
application of electricity on the *male reproductive* organs and

specifically on pollen, which offers greater facility for exposure to *indirect electrical operations*. Certainly these indirect operations could be applied also to the female organs, but aside from the greater difficulty (which can be justified in the study of this technique) reason dictated that the female element, as the one intended for feeding the seed, was better off being left in its natural ambient state.

Artificial intervention, with the means that the Reader will become acquainted with, in the seed in the process of formation, would turn out to be a futile disturbance in the seed embryo, even if only barely formed. The characteristics of the newly born subject are, as was mentioned, already defined; nutrition has no effect other than to continue the growing process according to the pre-arranged aptitude of the egg-cell, which, as a completed and living rendition of the fecundating male element, imprints, governs, and distributes the flow of lymph which incessantly nourishes it.

Life begun may be compared to a train already moving along on tracks. Adverse forces can stop or derail it (and this would be fatal); put it on a *different track*—never. Therefore, something must be done to effect the changeover *before* the run is started. Then it will be possible, so to speak, to run the convoy rapidly on a different line, which is as much as to say *have the variation*.

That is why I have confined myself to drawing profit from Nature's greatest miracle; the miracle whereby a whole life is contained in a few molecules of dust capable of transmitting all the characteristics of its species: the pollen.

The considerations already analyzed regarding Weismann's theory, which, tallying with my intuition, leave no doubt as to the suitableness of operating on the genital plasma of the pollen, which has in it in the most labile form, therefore more easily changed, the principle of life, the hidden characteristics of the new organism.

Consequently, to act on the pollen before using it in fecundation, or better still, on the anthers, while the pollen, in maturing, perfects and *stiffens its molecular set-up;* that is the operation that appeared as alluring as it was difficult.

For the record and for truth's sake, although being acquainted with them, I had not at first thought of using various means of ionization. I knew about the deleterious effects these have, in general, through the molecular disintegration that they provoke.

My first attempts were directed to stimulating through *autogenic currents* an anthogenic effect in pollen, since its diminutive size and delicate constitution made it impossible to effect any direct application on it of current by means of wire or contact. Besides, some electrostatic experiments on pollen had dissuaded me from trying it out in that field. This was further justified by considerations explained in Section 4 as to their ineffectuality.

An external electrical operation had to be devised that would *originate and terminate* in each granule of the pollen itself, an *operation induced,* prolonged for a while, and sufficiently extended to be able to treat a large quantity of pollen, or more than one anther at a time, without removing it from the flower.

Induced electrical reactions are obtained *by reactions* varying the magnetic field in the zone where it is to be stimulated. Magnetic field variations are generated with electro-lodestones or electric magnets, which will get special mention in Chapter V.

But variations in magnetic field are tangibly effective only when produced in bodies like metal that are good conductors of electricity. Foncault has just discovered in these the upsurge of current induced by rapid variation of the field.

However, pollen is not a metal; it does not permit passage of such *currents* as pass through conductors. Even if supplied with electrodes connected with a source of electricity, the latter could not pass through as in the case of metals, but would cause electrolysis (Section 40), as in the case of any saline solution.

Under the stimulus of variable magnetic fields, electrolysis does not occur, as such electrolysis is effected only where there are electrodes (Section 40), which maintain the renewal of electricity. However, there would take place a *rhythmic movement of the constituent particles,* extremely tiny, tending to carry them from one point of the genital plasma to another. These particles which may be influenced by the magnetic field or by its variations are none other than *ions;* and thus the original conception yielded by the phenomenon was modified, brought into a field in which previous studies have revealed extensive kinship of this physical phenomenon with chemical transformations, determining their mechanism, relationships and valencies.

Later on, magneto-ionization of gases, electro-atomic phenomena, the behavior of electrolytes in a magnetic field of which a diffused report was given by the late-lamented Sen. Righi in his last work[1] validated the concept that I had formulated as to the attribution of mutative phenomena.

The pure and simple carrying out of the principle as conceived was not enough. What was needed besides was to get an idea of the value of the forces and above all of their *proportions*.

An ordinary electro-technical problem always comes up in connection with definite, precise terms; it is solved by calculation once the relationships, measurements and values are known. The substance on which work is done is inert, rigid, indeformable, imperishable; but as soon as vitality enters into the calculation, and it is important not to injure it, the figuring no longer suffices. Reference to a species that has already been studied does not help, for every species has a set-up *intimately its own*, just as it has distinct characteristics. Minimal susceptibility and maximal tolerance have limits that are extremely sensitive. Therefore, it was necessary to proceed with tests on each species. To test over and over again, even if only empirically.

When the problem is to explore a field of research that is still unexplored, there always arises the perplexing question as to the road to follow; and if it is difficult to find an orientation in purely physical research, the problem involving vitality, more complex and mysterious, is such as to discourage a man of greater drive.

At first, because of the scanty practical notions as to the fertilization of several plants, through absolute ignorance of the cause-and-effect relationship, the research projects that I had undertaken to carry on presented such a complex of difficulties that more than once I have despaired of ever getting through. And it was a real stroke of good fortune that in 1914, with the dubious experimental bases then adopted, I should have succeeded in obtaining a positive result, effectively reviving my flagging faith.

[1] A. Righi, *Electro-atomic phenomena under the action of magnetism.* Zanichelli, Bologna.

Nature blocks in this field any device aimed at deviating it from the normal; but that is not all. The most serious difficulty, for genetic experiments, is the length of time required; from one to the next at least a year must elapse, to afford the possibility to evaluate the results, if, that is, the plants worked on are annual ones. Moreover, not everything that is sown is born—nor does everything that is born remain undisturbed!

Unfortunately, many lots of seeds, early plants, fully developed plants, owing to various causes, could not be subjected to controls, at the expense of the graduated network of ideas forming the basis for future research projects.

27.

Molecular Arrangements of Genital Plasma

In Chapter II, there were reviewed briefly the possible causes of modifications in gamic reproduction in plants, causes that constitute a complex of *exceptions*, exploited by Horticulture or Agriculture for the purpose of esthetics, food, or profit.

Under ordinary conditions everything is arranged by Nature to block such exceptions, particularly meliorative ones, which selection alone *keeps dammed* up; in fact, vegetable species, or rather wild plants, do not vary much, except for very infrequent mutations, confined to very few genuses.

The normal reproduction of the species without the least change during entire millenia[1] must depend on the constant and rigorously exacted formation of its plasma to the smallest cellular divisions, fecundative elements, perpetuators of their species. It is evident that each of them must be composed of groups of molecules that are *perfectly* alike, and that means *steriochemical and isomorphic groups in the strictest sense of the word*.

It is likely that the cellular arrangement visible through the microscope is not the final ordered subdivision, the ultimate *structure* characteristic of the species. It is necessary that the connections be followed up, and information be obtained also, subordinately,

[1] This is attested to by Egyptian and Greek sculptures and by seeds found in ancient tombs.

on the invisible elements of the plasma of every species. The tiny size of the gametal spermatic nuclei justifies the supposition that they are formed by a not too large a number of regularly ordered molecular groups, or in the regrouping which is inherent in the constitution according to the fixed imprint of the species to which it belongs.

The various *visible* external forms of a plant, of an organism, must therefore correspond to the invisible, ultra-microscopic, yet concrete forms, assembled in the pollen dust, or rather in a small part of this, that is, in the chromosomes and in the nucleus of the egg cell.

Pushing the mental inquiry to the *origin of the abnormal structure* led to the thought that the start must be caused by the *change in the arrangement or of the composition* of the smallest elements that enter into the formation of the genital plasma, and which characterize the species.

The alteration of the chromosomes affects the plasma which is to form the next cells *from the moment of fertilization, triggering the formation of the individual organism on a different basis.* This gives origin to the anomaly.

The beginning of life takes place at contact, and perhaps even through partial or total co-penetration, of the sperm nucleus in the nucleus of the egg cell, the principal cell of the ovary. As a result of the gamic symbiosis of these tiny entities arises the formative directive of the embryo and the seed. The characteristics that are to become visible only in the individual adult are subordinated to this primary and minimal gametic collaboration.

The nutritive juices then that reach the ovary cannot in any way change the structure of the small automatic composition of the embryo, on its way to growing in the pre-established direction.

28.

The Chromosomes from the Bio-Chemical Viewpoint

Before going into the merits of the electrical hypothesis of genetic variations, it will be in place for the Reader to have a precise notion of the proportions of the elements involved.

Above all it is to be remembered that the size of the pollen, at all times microscopic, is quite varied. In tiny species, the pollen is coarse, 1/8 to 1/20 mm.[1]. In most cases, chiefly in the Anemophilous species, their diameter varies between 1/20-1/160 mm.

However, *not the entire* pollen content is transformed *into the pollen sac,* and for this reason alone the sperm element is involved in the fecundation process, as the *bearer of the characteristics* of its species. Without even measuring it, one can easily imagine how small must be the size of each element or chromosome!

Analogously, in the ovum cell, although it varies in capacity, nevertheless always tiny, the essential part in question at the beginning of the fecundation process constitutes only the nucleus. Therefore, size must be measured in thousandths, or in a few thousandths of millimeters; in fact, the sperm nuclei of the species with very fine pollen (Solanaceae, Orchidaceae, Ampelideae, etc.) are hardly visible under a good microscope.

From the sizes microscopically perceptible to molecular dimensions, there is still a great leap; but nevertheless I believed it necessary to highlight the tiny size of the chromosome to give the Reader an exact notion of it (Section 16).

Considering the chromosomes as system-bound molecular groupings, one may explain the immutability of the characteristics that they represent in terms of the *identical* make-up per quantity and composition of each of them in each vegetable species.

The diversity, both chemical and morphological, of the molecular groups characterizing the genital plasma, most distinct as regards different families, is progressively less among the diverse genera and species, to the point where, among varieties of the same species it is reduced to a very slight difference. Should a fortuitous or artifically induced causative element happen to disturb the normal order of one or more molecular groups, to the point of altering the intimate set-up, the *structure of the new organism,* wherein fecundation has taken place, will be *abnormal,* and the seed formed by the abnormal or imperfect gamete *will emerge as a mutant;* it will yield a different plant.

---

[1] Atomic sizes are measurable in 1/10,000,000ths of a mm. and those of the molecules vary in proportion to the number of atoms comprising the molecule.

The appearance of a new variety derived from a pure species is probably the result of an initial imperfection of this kind in the gamete. Deductions from the experiments undertaken by me argue in favor of this hypothesis.

The mutative mechanism is easily understood as reducing for the moment the vitality of the genital plasma, and it may be considered *as if it were an inert organic substance,* that is to say, any aqueous solution, quite diluted, of various organic and mineral salts, compounded into hydrocarbonate substances. From the chemical viewpoint, the genital plasma is none other than a complex of molecules formed by hydrogen, carbon, oxygen and nitrogen atoms *combined* among themselves and partly also with the elements: calcium, potassium, silicon, phosphorus, iron, magnesium, etc.[1]

Atoms of metals possess the greatest number of electric charges, and nevertheless it is very easy to separate out any such charges when at a given time there is brought to bear on them an external electric current or a magnetic field in motion. However, genital plasma is almost free of metallic salts.

Instead, the forces of attraction that keep the atoms of a *liquid* molecule bound together, in relation to the mass of atoms, are powerful ones, by dint of their own proximity within the molecule and the vicinal relationships. In gaseous molecules this is all the more so if the gas is rarefied the force of cohesion is much smaller because of the relatively enormous distance from atom to atom.

While slight magnetic forces, in particular contingencies, are sufficient to disturb the electro-magnetic movements of the gases (Section 34), within liquids there is produced quite a great force, since there can take place certain phenomena of molecular decomposition, resulting from the aforementioned density and greater aggregational force among the atoms. The electric charges are *tenaciously bound to their atom,* so much so that when an electric

---

[1] The molecular grouping, i.e., the tie-up, the consistency of the molecule, is the result of the *electrical charges* characteristic of each atom. Similarly, the location of the atoms is determined by the positive or negative *quality* of the atomic charges held by them; these always tend to oppose one another, so that they neutralize each other, exactly compensating for each other within each separate molecule.

force acts on them, *they prefer to transfer themselves,* towing with them the atom, or an entire group of atoms (as ions) rather than detach themselves from it, or them.

The discoveries made at the end of the Nineteenth Century, especially that of the X-ray, those relating to radio, and the discharges of electricity in rarefied gases, have led scientists to attribute a living form and electric dependence to the set-up and groupings of the atoms.

The atom is pictured as having a positive central nucleus surrounded by negative electric charges (electrons) eddying about the nucleus like planets about their star.

The structure and kinetics of the atom could be said almost to resemble the conformation and the movement of the celestial bodies.[1]

29.

Atomic Statics of Live Plasma

Atoms arrange themselves in each molecule in such a way as to permit the electric forces, or charges, with which they are inherently endowed, to assume such a position of equilibrium with regard to the force of attraction that the charges themselves may be part and parcel of their total electric charge (*plus* or *minus*). There are thus formed almost complex *geometric systems* in which the various atoms assume a fixed position, wherein their valency *comes out electrically compensated for* by the charges of the adjacent atoms.

Such systems are subject to deformation when an electric charge acts on them or activates an electro-magnetic oscillatory or vibratory movement in their vicinity.

Well known are the experiments of Mayer on polymorphism induced by magnetic force on groups of magnetized needles in

---

[1] The reader will see in Sect. 44 that this concept of the atom surrounded by moving charges does not agree with the results of electro-magnetic actions on genital plasma. This living matter, however, is an electrolytic liquid of an *exceptional type,* and it is not my task to make comments thereon.

equilibrium in a field and free to arrange themselves in any direction. To the degree that this happens among bodies magnetized under the influence of magnetic forces, it happens also among bodies charged with electricity where extraneous electric charges are interposed, or else electro-magnetic oscillations are produced throughout the medium. Moreover, the electro-atomic systems of genital chromosomes must submit to this law, in spite of the fact that their vitality leaves us perplexed regarding the development of this phenomenon.

No substantial differences are presented between the effects produced on atomic groups either by electric charges that impinge violently on the atoms (Roentgen X-rays, ultra-violet rays) or finally by the new special action of the variable magnetic field (ionolysis). Strictly speaking the term "ionization" should be used only in the case of the gases.[1]

Later on, the reason will be given for my having adopted a new term for the convenience of differentiation (Section 39), since ionization is determined by the removal of electrons, while ionolysis can be attributed to opposite movement of forces, movements which are determined by the charges of the groups under the action of the electric or magnetic fields.

In the molecules of complex organic bodies, the atoms, by virtue of the electrical and electro-magnetic stimuli explained above, can pass from a *primitive mode of grouping* (Fig. 3) *to another derivative one* (Fig. 4), without the exclusion of any of the atomic components.[2]

Indubitably, where a change of this type is effected in a molecular group of the chromosomes, it occasions a variation of specific character. It is well to warn that Figures 3 and 4 represent systems that are absolutely imaginary ones, outlined in this manner for the convenience of presenting a picture. In the genital plasma, consisting of more than 9/10 water, and rich in colloidal substances, the arrangement might be concretely different.

The large proportion of water justifies the supposition that the

[1] Augusto Righi, *Electro-atomic phenomena under the influence of magnetism*, p. 47. Zanichelli, Bologna.
[2] The physical reason for the phenomenon is explained in Section 39 et infra. of Chapter IV.

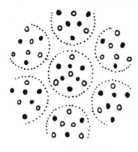

Fig. 3

Imaginary atomic system in a normal chromosome.
The dotted lines mark the perimeters of the molecules. The dots and the small circles indicate the atoms with the distinctive electrical charges.

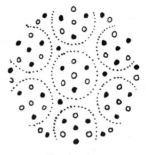

Fig. 4

The same, deformed by ionolization. From the molecules subjected to the test, some ions have become detached, determining a new arrangement of set-up in the atomic groups.

ions produced by the decomposition of any given weak molecular group have a large field to wander about in. That is why there would not easily take place a relinking-up of such molecules to mutate decidedly the chemical composition of the plasma.

30.

Molecular Perturbation and Rise of Mutation

Protracting or intensifying ionolysis—so logic claims and practice confirms—would gradually result in new displacements and ever more complicated combinations.

In the genital plasma, *more than one of these successive combinations* would give rise to a *mutation with a specific character* and for that reason the number of the simple bodies that go into forming part of the genital plasma is relevant; however, the number of the possible atomic regroupings must be vast. According to this reasoning, one would have been led to believe that from a single species there could be derived, by means of ionization, a tremendous number of new rarities and sub-species.

Their number, however, is limited, because not all of the atomic combinations are *compatible with vitality*. If this stumbling-block did not exist, since it is precisely a stumbling-block of considerable weight, ionolytic treatment could make available infinite variations It would be a genetic revolution.

It is not, nor will it ever be possible to carry on a complete anatomical investigation on substances of as delicate a vitality as that of the chromosomes of a microscopic granule of pollen; for that reason, in regard to these, only timid conjectures can be advanced, deduced from observations of perceptible phenomena.

Modern scientific investigation has brought to light an entirely new body of hitherto unknown data, in which electricity, the most recent arrival, has taken the most important place, leading to discoveries of transcendental importance.

With regard to Genetics, an older science, but only recently reorganized, it has covered much ground; but it is still far removed from an exact notion of the *biological mechanism* that governs reproduction.

This natural phenomenon, the most widespread, the most habitual, the most well-known in its exterior features is still the one that conceals the great mystery and remains unknown. The very phenomenon that accounts for our existence belongs to that supernatural category which the human mind cannot understand. What is life? When does it start? What is the mechanism determining the inter-linkage of sexual plasma, how does it develop, and govern subsequent growth, subsequent development?

If it is easy to imagine the dynamism of the phenomena that can be checked physically or that reflect data of experimental facts, on the other hand, it is not easy to conceive of the intimate arrangement of the living matter that we are accustomed to evaluating via an external exponent, sometimes fallacious. Purely physical material knowledge does not sufficiently account for the genetic facts whereby living beings live and reproduce their kind.

The problem of the origin, of the formation of the first living cell, as the incessant increment of propagation, has been faced a great number of times, but has never been resolved.

There is lacking the conception of the vital mechanism. Human intelligence, which stage by stage, gradually and with greater frequency, has acquired dominion over so many natural elements from which it draws most varied energies, has been unable to advance by as much as a single pace the biological thesis of the *beginning*.

The theory of Haecker, the most perfect one for its simplicity, the closest to my way of thinking, among those that I have had occasion to become acquainted with, leaves it, however, with a great gap or vacuum, at its principal point: the *soul* of living things, the veritable fulcrum of existence.

Science can avail very little against the natural evolution of life, against its course and limits.

Whoever might think from hints already given that ionolization, or any other device, can constitute an agent of deformation capable of emulating the harmonious perfection of the Creator, would be mistaken. It can find an application only in the cultivational ambient medium and also in special cases, when simultaneously contributory provisions and a dosage in line with the tolerance of the species accompany the process.

Experimental results confirm this, and if these have yielded results that sometimes were slight, through some refinement and more rarely through opulence, it is solely and always because of biological deficience usefully exploited, above all in hybridization.

I am aware of having strayed a bit, and I ask the Reader's pardon for it; but perhaps it has been useful to express, diffusely, my concept of this point, because I believe that nothing discredits a new theory more than does exuberant enthusiasm inadvertently infused into it by first interpreters.

More than a theory this is a working hypothesis, one which can be advanced to the actual status of experiments.

I have wanted to base it on the modern, current opinion of the molecular world. Perhaps it was superfluous; perhaps it has been imprudent, inasmuch as there is question of the unassailable unknown of vitality.

At any rate, it remains a certified fact that it is always better to consider with magnetic ionolysis, if not in the chemical molecule, then in the physiological molecule (the last particle of *living* matter that it is possible to consider in isolation) there should exist, among the complex and multiple energies where the phenomenon of life materializes, electrical forces, inasmuch as the kine-magnetic forces affect these in an unmistakable way, as will be demonstrated.

31.

Mechanism of Ionolysis — Electrical Hypothesis Regarding Variation

With the problem restricted to variations, it is important as regards constituent molecular groups and chromosomes to highlight a primary distinction between the *normal state,* which may be assumed to prevail *when they are alive* in the plasma itself, and the state while *ionolization lasts,* and the comparison between these two states and that of *inertia or of the death* of the genital plasma.

The characteristic of the living plasma of the sexual organs can be said to exist first of all in the *absolutely fixed ubiety* of the chromosome molecules according to a system so set up as to permit, upon the contact between the sexual nuclei, from the moment of fecundation, an *interpenetrative or collaborative* movement between and/or among these same nuclei, set to form new molecules or new cells. There should also exist an *integrative dependence* equally among the groups and among the single molecules constituting the two states, i.e., the sexes. Everything leads to the belief that the molecules of the *live plasma are integrally whole,* arranged in predetermined positions, and remain irremovable in their ubiety in line with a specific structure.

The integrity and rigidity of the molecular pattern of the live matter (rigidity not absolute (Sect. 33), but which can, for a very short time, be considered as such) is suggested further by the fact that the final division of said live matter (to whichever realm it may belong) within the furthest limit of visibility, appears in *rigid forms,* with special characteristics of its own, even where gelatinous organs are concerned. Moreover, from the very concept of the existence of any living particle there issues one element of construction, one building-block of a living structure.

Insistence has already repeatedly been placed on the immutability of the species, on the absolute precision governing the reproduction itself of the series; I believe that these statements will suffice to justify the aforementioned hypothesis, fully in line with what follows herewith.

When an ionolyzing medium acts on living plasma, the molecules of the more labile molecular groups are decomposed into *ions*. There take place very minute oscillations, collisions, repercussions, new make-shift and quite unstable reconstructions, then new breakdowns. The *molecular structure*, inasmuch as it depends upon atomic electric charges, undergoes continual deformations during the process of ionolysis. Dispersed ions and more frequently fragments of ions more closely gathered, cluster about adjacent molecules, affecting their already shaky equilibrium complicating and increasingly diffusing the breakdown.

The molecular structure of plasma, miraculous as the tiny representative of a life, is harried, upset, maltreated, and finally it collapses. That is a synthetic picture of the effects produced by ionolysis. The collapse corresponds actually to the loss of vital potency. The edifice collapses, but the substance is still all there; it lacks a connective element. It has been demonstrated that a grain of pollen in this condition can still *stimulate fecundation* of an egg cell and sometimes yield seeds, even if only abortive or imperfect ones.

It can also yield vital seeds if the sudden ionolyzation is not excessive. And this is precisely the exploitable phase.

That is why the ionolization process should not be pushed beyond a given limit. It is not the work of a pickaxe or a catapult that is needed but that of a scalpel. However, in some species, the resistance of the actual molecular edifice of their chromosomes is considerable; tenacious resistance is offered to strong ionolytic treatments for many hours; and unless quite a great breach has been made, the effect does not appear in the new generation.

The transportation of ions throughout the inner molecular structure does not imply modifications in their universal statics. Therefore, there are no visible, immediate deformations in the ionolyzed chromosomes.

Lines of research tending to this means of ascertainment, which also would serve as the best control regarding the existence of genetic variations resulting truly and solely from the ionolysis of the genital plasma, have not yielded, I am assured, proven results.

Also, in castration of mammals by means of X-rays, there is no effect immediately visible in their sperm; there are, instead, posthumous and macroscopic deformations in the genital organs.

Reason would dictate that kine-magnetic forces or those of electronic projection (Sect. 37), as well as those employed in the ionolysis of the genital plasma would react on the atomic electric charge, so that every argument regarding ionolysis should be restricted solely to the ratio of the aforementioned charges, their relative nearness to each other, the magnetic force being brought to bear, and the velocity at which this force rises and disappears.

As has been well observed by my very dear friend and valuable adviser Professor Remigio Banal of Turin, who with modern physical and mathematical doctrine combines a very sharp biological insight, the ionolysis of live plasma, according to the aforementioned and quite probable rigidity of the molecular arrangement (characteristic of its constitution), requires, in quite a variety of ways (i.e., by way of *physiological ions*), ions composed of considerable masses of molecules, belonging to the *physiological molecules* (molecola fisiologica) (Section 30), primitively integral and vital particles detached from the idealized ultimate, vital mechanism. Their detachment, or even only their displacement by wear and tear, would militate completely against any *aedile of the species.* Here, moreover, is an authoritative statement by him apposite the matter, drawn from his correspondence:

". . . I should also clarify for you one thought of mine that could not be confirmed at this time however well founded it may be, but which is very alluring. It is the one whereby in my mind I always connect most closely your investigations with the most essential and urgent problem in life. Matter is only the substratum of life: the vital functions are reduced to an extremely complex system of action and of forces. Let us simplify: let us get down to the chromosomes. These are particles still divisible, that have their chemical constitution, but that also possess the movements and the elements of life.

"*However, these particles are extremely complex, are, that is, comprised of smaller particles, aggregates of molecules less vast, less complex, but which also possess—one may be permitted to consider—the primary elements and movements, or actions, of life. Continuing this mental process of subdivision, the final stage is the chemical molecule, and after that the atom. At a certain point we may be permitted to think of linking up with a group or system of molecules which like this one possesses the elements, and within which exist and act on a simplified and reduced scale the energies, or forces, of combination and of multiplication, from which life results; but, besides, a system of molecules such that it reaches the point where there ensues a division thereof into simpler parts, and the latter no longer possess the aforementioned elements and characteristics.*

"*If for mutual understanding, we call this system that of the physiological molecule, we may be permitted to consider that the constituent and distinguishing characteristics of the species pre-existing in the pollen, and subject to changes in response to ionolysis, have their roots in this, but nothing else therein. And then it must be admitted that the ionolytic actions penetrate and develop in the physiological molecule, determining the new set-up of the (chemical) molecules or of the groups of the latter that form it, and variations in the forces that activate or link up these molecules or these constituent groupings.*

"*If this line of reasoning is correct, it is the part of wisdom, in interpreting of the ionolytic factors involved, to coordinate the terminology therewith.*

"*But here arises another consideration.*

"*All the constituent particles of the bodies being considered by us, the atom, the chemical molecule, the physiological molecule, are not only matter, but they are systems of one or more particles of matter, and of forces.*

"*In the physiological molecule, some of these forces (or systems of forces) are such as to constitute the ultimate elements of vital energy. If the molecule itself decomposes, if these systems break up, there are left stumps and trunks hav-*

ing a chemical or mechanical existence of their own; but there is no longer any physiological existence, no vital capacity.

"Now the facts demonstrate that ionolysis is able to react on these systems and to modify them without taking away from their vital capacity, i.e., making room for newly provided systems in a form other than that of the vital capacity referred to.

"Consequently, we may act, react, activize, exert influence on the ultimate elements which make up, and in which is rooted life. . . ."

32.

Comparison Between Living and Inert Plasmas

I remind you again that plasma is a viscous liquid prevalently composed of water, which holds in solution small quantities of salts (Section 27) and in suspension hydrocarbonate substances. Having available large quantities of pollen of a single given species, one could analyze its precise chemical composition. But supposing it were possible to imitate, or *scientifically to re-make the genital liquid,* and produce an artificial liquid from the identical elements and physiochemical characteristics?

Intuition at once suggests the futility of such a project. However perfect this might be, it would not be such as to *infuse vitality* into the imitated substance.

At this point it is well to stress the well-substantiated nature of the hypothesis presented above, attributing the *prerogative of molecular integrity* precisely to the genital plasma. Through this integrity, it is differentiated from a synthetic chemical product intended to imitate it; such an artificial product would be *permanently and completely ionized,* like any other mixture of diluted saline solutions.[1]

---

[1] Bartoli and Arrhenius were the first to discover that in saline solutions there do not exist any salt molecules, but ions, at a distance from each other, generally in motion and transiently held in place by the interaction of their charges.

In fact, ionizing living genital plasma to the utmost degree, as has already been mentioned, converts it into some sort of inactive liquid, which, moreover, not having undergone any injuries from ordinary physical causes (cold or heat), nor for any other apparent reason, has lost its vital potency.

Is absence of ionization therefore the indispensable condition of life?

33.

Ions in Solutions

Ordinary ionizing agents, while they prove effective in gases, which they render partially conductive as a result of the atomic upsetting effect they provoke within their molecules, have no perceptible effect on saline or electrolytic liquids. Not because these intercept the Beta- or Gamma-rays, but because of their being *"natively"* ionized as a result of being in solution. The ions can have the most varied sizes, positions and motions. Generally, they consist of media of molecules or fractions of molecules; but there exist also *large ions* formed by clumped molecules having, in general, an electric charge that is characteristic of them and guides them.

In ordinary solutions, they are activated by translator movements in every direction, without any type of motion predominating. There occurs an almost continuous automatic agitation as a result of which, within the saline solutions, there is generated a decomposition and a re-integration of the molecules. No outward sign shows this work-complex since forces in balance, still functioning, compensate for each other.

Within the genital plasma, too, there are bound to occur *some movements*, and undoubtedly these are generated actively during and after fertilization; but in contrast with ordinary solutions, those of plasma must be *in arrangement* and dependent, *concentrated among themselves*, and occur, rather than among the ions, among the large nuclei of molecules constituting the physiological molecule (Section 30). The dependence of the intermolecular movements within the vital substance should also be extended to the thermic actions which probably aid it.

In Chapter VI, there is an allusion to the ambient conditions essential to the successful achievement of fertilization; this is achieved within very narrow limits of temperature. This is true of vitality in general.

Many tropical plants, although adult, die at 8-10 degrees centigrade, i.e., without the intervention of the conspicuous phenomenon of freezing, which might only too well justify the death; they die, most likely, through a defect of thermic movement that tropical species require, as a complementary factor of their vital process.

These reflections give rise to a new concept of interdependence between matter and movement, a concept tending to compare vital functioning to a machine in action.

It is insufficient for the machine to be perfect and complete in its entire mechanical set-up; for it to keep moving it must have at its disposal the type of energy suited to its needs.

The same must hold true for the whole plasma of each living species; so true is this that each of these species requires climate, humidity and soil according to its predetermined set-up. The physiological movements which probably have their base in the plasma (it is not likely that they are very active before fertilization takes place) are not completely observed; but they may remain negligible compared to those extremely rapid ones induced electro-magnetically or by means of electronic projection with which molecular decomposition is set in motion.

Summarizing the subjects treated in this Chapter, it may be concluded that:

1. The life of a new organism begins in the parents and in normal life incorporates exactly the specific characteristics of the latter.

2. Mutations, or variations in characteristics, arise through abnormal constitution of the gametes, prior to fertilization.

3. The atoms of living plasma and their groupings or ions are endowed with electric charges, just as in inert matter. Vitality, that mysterious *quid*, which has its renewal base in the genital plasma, does not in itself constitute matter, nor may it be assumed to be a secondary substance; rather it results solely from the fixed set-up of the physiological elements constituting the plasma itself in

such a way as to be able to participate in a complementary capacity between the sexual elements.

4. The gametal structure may be compared to an extremely tiny geometric structure, always identically equal in each sexual cell of the same species and of the same sex.

5. Ionolization disturbs the molecular stability of the gametes through its effect on the electrical charges of the atomic groups, effecting, along with the molecular breakdown, the collapse of the gametal structure, characteristic of the species.

6. To a moderate degree, modifying with ionization the molecular arrangement of the chromosomes, effects proportional modifications in their molecular architecture and consequent morphological changes in the progeny.

7. The genital plasma during and after fertilization is coordinated with, and dependent upon, the thermic movements determined by the outer environment. The probable slowness of physiological movements permits its being neglected as regards electricity, which is immensely speedy.

8. Living plasma, immune to any and all molecular separation, lends itself to demonstration of the fact that a special type of ionization (ionolysis) penetrates to the core of the liquid electrolyte placed in a variable magnetic field.

However much the electrical dependence of vitality may seem at first a revolutionary concept, the admission can seem acceptable and justified as soon as it can overcome the obstacle of one's previous mental attitude.

Observation of the most common phenomena connected with the behavior of visible and tangible bodies moved by slow forces like those familiar to us, inadvertently induces in us an erroneous preconception in our judgment of exceedingly tiny things and of the electric forces that govern molecular cohesion and atomic science. I find it opportune to remind the Reader that I do not claim to have exhausted the subject, nor even less to have made a contribution of great weight in explaining my opinion of the effect of electro-magnetic treatment on the arrangement and structural concatenation, or linkage, of the tiny particles that transmit life.

Physical, materialistic knowledge, even if aided by philosophical cogitations, does not suffice, nor will it ever suffice, to solve this most lofty problem. To hope to solve it would be an irreverent and light-minded claim. The Reader, from his observation of the experimental data, will be able to convince himself, however, that the genetic behavior of the descent of ionolyzed pollen is quite interesting, and may well merit attention, also as an index of a useful road to future research projects.

CHAPTER IV

Means of Ionization

34.

Mechanism of Ionization

UP TO THIS point use has been made of the terms "ionolysis" and "ionization" in a generic sense, and only in those senses that apply to genetic breakdown, which they occasion. Stress has been laid on why ionization modifies the molecular state of the gases, while it has no appreciable effect on electrolytic liquids. However, the Reader must know, at least in brief, the means likely to produce this physical phenomenon.

Ionization in gases and ionolysis in genital plasma are variously derived but unequal severally as regards their variative capacity in the effects they induce in the plasma itself; each ionizing excitation has its own breakdown operational characteristic regarding one specific species rather than another. However, the results taken universally prove that any type of ionolization is more or less effective, and that differences are due rather to individual sensitivity and to attunement to the means employed.

As to comparative ionizing values obtainable in the genital plasma, and the effects obtained in gases, *there exists a parallelism* but not *proportionality*.

The widely noted non-conductance, or insulating property, depends solely and permanently on the atomic and molecular distance that characterize them, and on atomic statics.

With rarefaction there is increased conductivity of gases, although the molecules undergo a greater thinning out. The molecules remaining more easily separated in ions, have aided in their achievement, i.e., transporting electric current from one electrode to the other under the impetus of the opposing charges.

The Geissler tube, containing rarefied gases, shows the effect of diffused and silent discharges which are produced by the action of the gaseous residue remaining in the tube. The luminosity of the latter under electrical excitation is caused by the collision of electrons, ions and molecules engaged in carrying electric charges that move in opposite directions at top speed, at the expense of energy supplied to the electrodes.

In gases at ordinary pressure, the discharge finds instead considerable impedance in the quite greater compactness of the molecules.

Gas molecules at ordinary pressure, when struck by ionizing radiation, lose the stability granted them by the atomic electric charges, in other words, break down into ions, which tend to link up with complementary ions and electrons in order to re-establish new molecules. The electricity profits by this agitation, *the ion turning it into a vehicle*, which, in order to dissipate itself, moves away from the conductor, where it would be held back by the gas, which normally acts as an insulator. This phenomenon is better carried out between two oppositely electrified conductors. The swarms of ions coming from either pole occasion a slow discharge via conduction. That is why gases which at ordinary pressure are non-conductors, become conductors of electricity once they are ionized.

In the tubes of rarefied gas as well as in gases at ordinary pressure affected by ionizing rays, molecular division *is quite different from that which occurs in electrolytic liquids.* In gases, molecular scission occasions the formation of *ions* and of *electrons,* while in liquids there never exist isolated electrons (electric charges not amalgamated with any mass of matter).

Hence the necessity of adopting the new term "ionolysis" for the purpose of differentiating between the phenomena. "Lysis" in as much as for every magnetic impulse a separation is produced between the positive and negative ions.

Terminology is still a thankless job. Sometimes, however, one happens to create a brief term, with precise and special meaning, which serves to distinguish a phenomenon of similar items without the need for distinguishing adjectives, that would always have to be repeated. That is why I have decided to call *ionolysis* the rhythmic displacement actuated in the genital plasma by variations of the magnetic field.

In the seminal nucleus of the pollen, the ionization actuated by irradiations breaks also, as in gases, the molecular connections, but through the greater adherence and incomparable thickness, or compactness, of the atoms in the liquid molecules, the ion cannot transfer itself very far. Its colliding with adjacent molecules can, however, cause new combinations, some one of which may remain. Hence the stable alteration, the biological imperfection that is then translated into a mutation.

35.

Ionization in Gases and Its Measurement

Ionization in gases is easy to verify and may be estimated by deducting it from the dispersion of electricity which it provokes in the electrized elements, or else by the conduction it offers to the electricity between two electrodes.

The most convenient and economic way to ionize would be offered by heat; but in the special case of pollen, such a method is not to be thought of, because the degree to be obtained is too far from that needed to maintain vitality.

The measurement of the ionizing force is effected via the electroscope, with observation of the index of discharge within a unit of time, or else via the galvanometer, by comparison of the entity of the deviation produced by the passage of electricity between two flat plates, parallel, face to face, with a given, or standard, electromotor force.

The ionizing thrust in the molecular systems can occur through the *violent projection of isolated electric charges* (electrons), which break the static equilibrium by the mutual attraction of the atomic charges, or else by a special system of exceedingly rapid electromagnetic vibrations (X-rays and ultraviolet rays), or lastly by rapid variation of the magnetic field. This latter, which does not ionize gases, has shown itself to be the best for the ionolysis of pollen.

Among the stimulators of ionization I believe it to be *apropos* to offer first some informative comparison regarding vibrators, giving precedence to X-rays.

36.

X-Rays

The reader can find in any treatise on Physics[1] the various aspects and the reason for the transformations which the electric discharge undergoes whenever it passes through a glass tube provided with electrodes, from which the air or the gas it contains is gradually extracted.

In the Roentgen-ray tube the vacuum is pushed to the maximum, beyond the millionth of an atmosphere; the degree of conductivity of a gas thus extremely rarefied becomes quite poor. The few gas atoms remaining can no longer provide for the transport of the electric charges, as happens to moderate rarefactions in the Geissler tubes (Section 34).

When, however, the electrodes, with which the glow-lamp is provided, bring electricity with a very high potential, the potential in one effort overcomes the obstacle and spreads out. But it no

[1] The best and clearest: *Electricity in its principal phenomena*, by G. Marchi, Hoepli, Milan.

longer follows the normal route, does not seek the shortest route, does not move towards the pole of the opposite sign; instead it leaves the negative electrode (cathode) normally on the latter's surface, whatever may be the position of the positive pole (anode), and where it strikes the glass of the lamp, it generates a greenish light.

The cathodic electric flow, almost always invisible in an ordinary Roentgen tube, is attributable to separated electric charges, devoid of matter, and the mass of which is infinitesimal even compared with that of the atom. These electric particles are set in very rapid motion and in connection with the state of motion they constitute *cathode rays*.

These do not propagate outside the tube that generates them. Besides generating fluorescence within glass and various other substances, they cause heat; rising orthogonally to the surface of the cathode, they lend themselves to being concentrated, giving the latter a suitable concave form.

The concentration of the band of cathode rays is made to converge on a highly heat-resistant plate opposite the cathode and diagonally inclined toward the cathode rays. This plate, which is joined on its back with another metallic mass, or is connected with water which draws off heat from it, is called *anti-cathode*. Against its obliquely placed platinum plate, clearly visible in Fig. 5, the cathode rays are halted, and from their collision originate Roentgen X-rays, which are prevailingly reflected in a direction perpendicular to the surface of the anti-cathode, easily pass through the glass (it must not be leaded-iron) and in general all the specific light substances that they encounter on their way, even if the latter are less transparent for ordinary light.

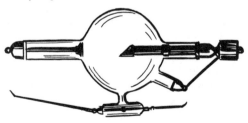

Fig. 5
Roentgen ray tube.

This property can be used to advantage in radioscopy and in photographing the invisible, it being well known in both fields. X-rays produce a most vivid fluorescence not only in glass but also in quartz, diamond, various silicates, etc., and a very vivid fluorescence in platino-cyanide of barium. Their potent action on photographic plates is well known to all.

For some time past, X-rays have also been used therapeutically in skin ailments, not only in epitheliomas and fibromas, on which they have at the same time a resolvent and a disinfectant power. Their action on benign cancer neoplasties is very much analogous to that which takes place in the genital plasma inasmuch as in therapy too the decomposition of the molecule must be kept in view.

The more the gas in a Roentgen-ray tube is rarefied, the greater the penetrative power of the rays that are produced, to the detriment of their quantity. Speaking technically, the tubes that are quite emptied are referred to as *hard* and are employed in radioscopy and radiography of vertebrae or deep-seated organs to reach which the rays must pass through considerable thickness of semiopaque matter such as muscles, blood, intestinal substances. Hard tubes lend themselves only poorly to ionolization of pollen, which, obviously enough, permits the passage also of rays of low pentration, such as those produced by *soft* tubes (these being only slightly emptied). These are precisely the ones that will be adopted.

The brighter the ampoule, the greater is the indication of its effectiveness in the treatment of pollen. In comparative precision experiments, the intensity of radiation as well as the time must be taken into account and measured with Waler, Benoist or Belot radiometers, etc.[1]

The Rühmkorff coil is useful in exciting Roentgen ampoules; a vacuum tube must be inserted in the circuit to exclude the reverse charge which blackens the glass of the ampoule and soon makes it useless. Overlong exposure must be avoided because this heats the soft tubes excessively to a point where the anti-cathode becomes red-hot. When this occurs, the ampoule is ruined.

The ionizing effect of X-rays is due to electro-magnetic vibrations

---

[1] F. Schincaglia, *Roentgen-Technique*. Hoepli, Milan.

at high frequency which accompany propagation, as has already been said. This property allows for duration of the vibrations and their transmission through solid elements of minor molecular composition, and it is impervious to light.

When the electro-magnetic vibrations of X-rays penetrate the genital plasma, they cause an atomic reaction in the molecules and consequent relaxation, then atomic disintegration, or ions, totally comparable to those occurring in electrolysis, to which reference will be made under Section 39, when discussing magnetic ionolysis.

37.

Radio-Active Elements

Radioactivity, which was first discovered by Becquerel and successfully developed by Monsieur and Madame Curie, consists in an additional property possessed by certain elements, particularly by uranium and thorium. The atoms in radioactive elements are not entirely stable as those in other elements, but are liable to disintegrate suddenly and violently one after the other, in a series of explosions. The fragments constituting these exploded atoms are hurled in all directions at great speed. It is such fragments in motion which constitute the separate Rutherford radiations, and are so classified:

1. Alpha-rays, which consist of bivalent ions of helium, a gas element with positive charge.

2. Beta-rays, which are formed by simple incorporeal electric charges, possessing extreme velocity; they are entirely analogous to those in the Roentgen ampoule which constitute the cathode rays; and like those, produce X-rays; the β-rays produce secondary radiation when colliding with the molecules of elements encountered in their passage.

3. Gamma-rays, which are very similar in their behavior to X-rays; with the difference that they form *within* the molecules which come into contact with the γ-rays.

The α-rays may be stopped by a thin metal sheet; they are likewise hindered in their propogation process by the air and therefore their influence is restricted to a brief area surrounding the radio-active element. They are deflected by a magnetic field, or by an electro-static field. They cause ionization, but are excluded in the treatment of pollen, since they are harmful to its germinative faculties.

The β-rays penetrate any gas and all dieelectric elements without any considerable attenuation; they are stopped only by metal sheets of remarkable thickness, but lose very little of their power when penetrating the fragile aluminum filter excluding the α-rays. The ionization caused by the β-rays is extremely powerful also because it is never severed from the simultaneous formulation of γ-rays which form both in the ionized matter and in the air surrounding it.

This makes their effect quickly deleterious, since the molecules are both disintegrated by the β-rays which exercise something like the effect of a missile on them, and at the same time are shaken by the simultaneous local formation of γ-rays, which already, in themselves, possess considerable ionizing power.

The radio-activity of uranium and thorium is extremely weak, and has no practical influence for the purpose of the ionization necessary in disintegrating the molecules of genital plasma, but by a series of chemical processes, together with the aid of selective devices, which both formed the glory and made the fortune of the two Curies, it has been possible to isolate a substance in the former, or rather more in uraniferous pitchblendes, which is endowed with four million times the amount of radio-activity found in uranium: *radium*.

Metallic radium is not found in commerce, but only salts of radium; that is to say, the bromide, which is deliquescent, and therefore more difficult to use, and the sulphate which is insoluble and can be applied, with special glues, to any kind of surface, by previous specification, when ordering from the firms supplying it.[1] Radium salts are not sold loose, but in very thin, welded vials, or else caked inside small silver cylinders or capsules, with accompanying inspection certificate. The purest salt costs, at the current rate of exchange, about 2500 Lire per milligram. Radium emanations,

[1]My radium apparatus came from the Paris 'Banque du Radium.'

which are radio-active in themselves, must not be dissipated, so it is always advisable to keep radium capsules closed until needed for use.

Very recently, various secondary products endowed with radio-activity more or less transient in nature, have been obtained from thorium. The most notable of these is *mesothorium,* which is specifically more radio-active than radium initially, but loses much of its valuable power as it grows older. Five years after preparation, its ray emission has dwindled to half its original power, and continues then to decrease at a lesser rate. But it costs considerably less than radium. Mesothorium also emits α, β, and γ-rays and must be protected the same as radium, if its emanations are to be preserved. It is essential that both these elements be handled with precaution, at least insofar as their radioactive surface does not come for any length of time in contact with the skin. It is also dangerous to keep radium or mesothorium capsules in one's pockets, since the β-rays emanated by them may easily penetrate their metal casing, and cause reactions later, (such as radio-dermatitis), which are very difficult to cure.

The molecular disintegration caused by the rays is not remarkable at all, considering the extreme tenuity of the elements concerned,[1] which are considerably smaller than the tactile papillae and nervous fibrils; though their prolonged action of molecular laceration will cause organic disintegration.

Modern therapy has exploited this deleterious characteristic to its own advantage, using it to weaken and combat the development of cancer. Who knows whether there is not an incentive in iono-genetics to substitute electro-magnetic ionolysis beneficially for ray-ionization which is still extremely expensive.

Any pollen which is to be subjected to radio-active salts should be placed at least ½ cm. from the radiating surface, so as to receive a homogenous and not too strong radiation. If greater intensity is desired, then it may be placed almost, or actually, in contact with it for an extremely brief period, the aluminum diaphragm being put between it and the salts to intercept the α-rays

---

[1] The dimension of the electrons, forming the 6-rays, is as follows: .000003 million parts of a millimeter.

which would destroy its vital faculties in a few months. I use the device seen in Fig. 6, and insert the pollen in a thin mobile baffle

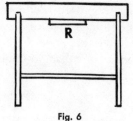

Fig. 6
Device for radium treatment of pollen.
(Natural size)

capsule (the pollen may be in a thickish layer) and lower onto it the silver lid to which the radium sulphate, caked on a fragile ebonite plate in R. is attached. Fig. 6 seen here is reproduced in its actual size.

38.

Ultra-Violet Rays

Though considerably less influential in ionization of gas, ultra-violet rays have proved to be powerful in stimulating variations in genital plasma. They are caused by high-frequency electro-magnetic vibrations, of relative power; but they differ from X-rays inasmuch as they may be restrained by many different elements, among which are water and common glass.

In gases, ultra-violet rays ionize particularly the molecules adjoining the solid elements upon which they are concentrated; but in liquids, their action, which so far has been exploited in the destruction of germs, is restrained by even an extremely superficial stratum; any solid substance, even if transparent, with the exception of quartz, will arrest them completely. The extremely fine pollen grains are penetrated, providing they are spread out in one single layer; it is not easy to attain this kind of layer; but it can be achieved with a little patience, and the use of extremely close silk veil-net sieves.[1]

Ultra-violet rays are not perceptible to the eye; the luminous sources which contain them in great quantity may at times have a purplish tinge; but this is not a reliable indication upon which proportionate calculations can be based.

The effective ionolization of plasma by ultra-violet rays is probably caused far more by the intonation of the high frequency vibrations, and consequently the extremely short wave length with the molecular system, which is only slightly different in size, than by the intrinsic effectiveness of the electro-magnetic energy which they also convey. Hence the difference in proportion of effects of their ionizing influence in gases and in plasma, in comparison with X-rays and those emanated by radio-active elements.

The principal sources of production for ultra-violet rays are the electric spark, the voltaic arc, and the mercury-vapor lamp.

In order to have rapid action, the spark must be produced at no great distance from the object; in the case of pollen, a distance of 4-5 cm. is sufficient to irradiate a surface of about 16-20 cm., which is enough to spread out a thin layer of pollen, sufficient to fecundate 2-3 flowers.

If a larger surface of radiation is required, one has only to increase the distance between the layer of pollen and the *spark gap measuring tool,* or *deflagrator,* between the extremities of which (Fig. 7) the sparks fly. It must be pointed out that for each spark, the effect diminishes as the area of distance increases, and this must be taken into account in comparative experiments, and the time exposure increased, so as to establish an average.

Fig. 7
Device for treatment of pollen by ultra-violet rays produced by sparks.
(Natural size)

[1] The silk fabric known in the trade by the name of 'crêpe de chine' is useful for this purpose.

A long duration spark is not effective; on the other hand, it is extremely important instead that sparks occur at high frequency. With the use of suitable converters, one can obtain from 1000 to 1200 sparks per second with the electrolytic switch, or better still, with a high frequency cycle alternator (Fig. 25). In this case, a vivid, permanent blaze, like a flame, will be seen between the poles of the measuring tool. Even though these are of brief duration, such a rapid succession of sparks will give out such heat to the electrodes that these will become incandescent in a very short time on their side nearest to the spark, if metal background does not provide the necessary cooling process. So it is necessary that the thermal part of the apparatus be equipped with broad, reasonably thick electrodes. It is also necessary that it is beveled in devaricated sense, as seen in the illustration, so that the light may shine all over the small surface below, where pollen has previously been spread out on an isinglass plate. Despite these precautions, the extremities always become red-hot, and should be made of platinum, if the device is to function properly, especially if the number of sparks exceeds one thousand per second.

The voltaic arc, produced by two retort-heated pieces of carbon, also is rich in ultra-violet rays, thanks to the effect of a powerful electric current of low potentials. I have never used it for pollen; but it must certainly exercise an influence, if the following precautions are taken: 1. A distance of at least 1 meter from the arc, to prevent the fierce heat emanated by it from damaging the pollen; 2. no glass or any other element must be placed between the arc and the pollen, because glass and other substances of transparent nature will allow luminous rays but not ultra-violet rays to pass. Twait, in Britain, and several others, in Germany and elsewhere, have experimented with the action of the voltaic arc on vegetation, with uniformly alarming results; in a short time the plants all died of the necrosis provoked in all their leaves by the radiations. This mortality will not be provoked if the lamps are protected by glass globes, for the reason above stated.

The mercury-vapor lamp of Cooper-Hewitt is the most intense source of ultra-violet rays; and since their production by this apparatus does not give rise to intense heat, it is suitable for the ionization of pollen. But the time of exposure must be very short, since ultra-violet radiation by the Cooper-Hewitt lamp is powerful; the instructions already given previously in connection with ionization by rapid sparks may apply here for the layer of pollen.

The mercury-vapor lamp consists of a quartz glass tube, emptied of air, proportionate in length to the stimulating current at disposal; the tube ends in two bulges in which the electrodes are welded, and a proportionate quantity of mercury as well. Under a rapid initial inclination of the lamp, the mercury causes contact between the electrodes and the consequent vaporization of the mercury itself as it passes through the tube. When the lamp is brought back to its normal position again, the thick mercury vapors maintain the electric contact between the poles.

The instrument used in magnetic ionolysis forms the subject of the following section; with adequate transforming equipment, it may easily be used for production of rapid frequency sparks, so anyone who wishes to use it may, with but a small additional expense, forego the purchase of a Cooper-Hewitt lamp, because rapid ionolization may equally well be obtained by a series of high frequency sparks, without any excessive waste of current.

The calculation of the ionization value of ultra-violet rays is particularly difficult in view of the number of factors involved: explosive distance, frequency of sparks, the intensity of the current provoking them, the distance of the sparks from the pollen, and finally the specific tolerance of the pollen itself.

39.

Electro-Magnetic Ionolysis

This is a special form of ionization which should not be confused with the magnetic ionization process discovered by the late lamented Senator Righi,[1] in a gas with electric currents running through it in a *stable magnetic field*.

I stumbled upon electro-magnetic ionization or *ionolysis* purely

[1] Aug. Righi, *Op. cit.*, Chapter III.

by accident; indeed, I might say, through insufficient knowledge of the behavior of currents in the genital plasma. The observation was made possible by the vital properties of the plasma, for it would not have been possible in any non-vital electrolytic liquid (Section 32).

Even in the days of my early experiments, I was not unaware of the fact that electricity cannot pass through, nor in any way move in any liquid without affecting it; I was not unaware that the atoms charges in liquids are irremoveably connected with the atoms themselves, and that these, formed in ions, prefer to move because of their own charge, sooner than abandon it to some extraneous electric energy acting on it. But I became confused by the essence of pollen grains, which unlike the electrolytic baths, are devoid of electrodes. I then believed that a grain of pollen, if put in a *variable* magnetic field, could be penetrated by *induced current* (apart from electric resistance at any variation of the field, as though in its place there were some grain of metal filing. (Section 26).

With this preconceived notion, I had begun some initial experiments with electro-magnets activated by intermittent currents, or alternating currents at 42 cycles, used for illuminating purposes. In comparing these with later experiments obtained with ultra-violet rays, X-rays and radium, which were already known means of ionization, what had been doubtful in my mind now became certainty. After mature reflection and fresh confirmation, I was convinced that the variation in the magnetic field *caused a special ionization* in the pollen, comparable to that obtained by the various rays. This is, precisely, *ionolysis*.

Already in section 31 I referred to the advisability of extending this definition to *all forms of molecular perturbations of ions in vital colloids.*

Every ionizing system causing ionization in gases may provoke ionolysis in electrolytic liquids; the difference consists in this: the active agent in gases causes disintegration of the molecules into ions (atoms with positive charge) and electrons (negative isolated charges), while in genital plasma the molecular disintegration always produced *pluriatomic ions* with positive charges and likewise ions with negative charges. I think therefore that the new term, ionolysis, is justified. Before entering further into the matter, I think I should give a few clarifications concerning the behavior of liquid ions in electrolysis.

40.

Relationship with Electrolysis

In 1800 Carlisle and Nicholson discovered this phenomenon, caused by the passage of electric currents through liquids which act as conductors in consequence of the presence of acids and salts. The famous Faraday pursued the study and gave a scientific explanation for it in 1833.

Under the impulse of the electric current penetrating electrolytic solutions, the various ions, floating adrift, are divided into two large factions, animated by contrasting motion. The ions formed by the molecular groups which have an excessive positive charge *in their composition* converge on the negative electrode; those possessing a *prevalently* negative charge converge on the positive pole. The word 'ion' does not signify any determined quantity of atoms or of matter; it may consist of one single atom, or a large number of atoms; it may be half a molecule, or part of a molecule. Its quality is determined by the distinctive charge it contains and which gives it direction and mobility when it comes into collision with the electric current.

When two rheophores are put into communication with an electric generator, (battery, dynamo) in any liquid conductor of electricity, small gassy bubbles will be seen, issuing from the aforesaid rheophores immersed in the liquid, and which in this case are called *electrodes*, a word common to other devices to which reference has already been made.

The liquid which decomposes under the passage of electricity is called an *electrolyte*.

Electrolytes cover all the acid or saline liquids, in which category one must also include the seminal colloid of pollen, which forms the object of our experiment.

In the same solution the number of ions present in the electrolytic liquid will increase with the temperature (the thermic action affecting both atoms and ions). The encounter between ions of opposite type may generate new neutral molecules, just as the collision between them and the ions may produce new ions.

So some *electric life* does exist even in inert electrolytes; it is, one might say, a constant pattern of marriage and divorce between the lesser constitutive groups. Nothing reveals this to us, because the sum total of the various motions, occurring in all possible directions, are exactly compensated, without exterior emanations.

41.

How to Generate an Ionolysis

Electrolysis is not directly connected with ionolysis, but it can offer some notion of electric correlation. In electrolysis, as in all other kinds of ions, it occurs in a *continued* manner, with a *constant direction toward the* electrodes, whereas since there are no electrodes in pollen and therefore in ionolysis, the electric movement caused by the variation of the magnetic field *is not at all centralized,* but acts homogeneously upon the whole volume; its action is contained in the briefest time periods, and always with a rapid inversion of direction and therefore of movement.

Every time that the magnetic field changes value, that is to say, when it increases or diminshes, electric energy liable to react to any variation in the field is generated; this energy may be beneficially manifest in metal, but it doubtless exists and is active in any environment, and even in a vacuum. When the variation in the magnetic field is intense and almost instantaneous, that is to say, when an electro-magnet progresses from magnetic saturation to the state of annulment in the fraction of a second, the induced electric energy in the interpolar space, or in the space immediately surrounding an isolated pole, becomes so powerful that it exceeds the considerable power of cohesion in some molecules of the plasma. In the moment of maximum variability of the field, the entire area between the poles (Fig. 8) is polarized.

In respect to each molecule, the action of the *variable* magnetic field on the atomic charges is such that it can exercise an effect

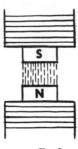

Fig. 8

The dotted line represents the virtual lines of magnetic energy established between the Poles N S during the activity of the electro-magnet.

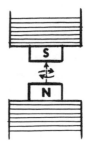

Fig. 9

The curved horizontal arrows represent the directions of the electric current in the interpolar space, induced by the variations in the magnetic field.

identical to that which would exist were there two especially electrified electrodes exchanging their polarity constantly, at brief intervals, on the two sides of the molecule.

Different magnetic forces, different valences, and complex marginal action of other groups are involved in the assemblage of the molecular masses, so that some groups may be less bound irrevocably to the position assigned to them by the structure of their species (Section 29). When the induced electric power produced by the variation of the magnetic field influences a molecular assemblage of weaker constitution, it splits it up, as has already been said, into two ions of conflicting nature. The mobilized ions encounter other molecules, more or less forcefully allied, in their path, and their impact on them facilitates ulterior ionolysis, and possibly the formation of new, electrically balanced groups, or of *new molecules.*

The effectiveness of ionolysis is probably due to the presence of some inconstant element in all plasma, the initial disintegration of which causes a wide-range disarrangement even among the more solid molecular masses, within a short time, by reason of its impact, although these molecular groups would not split up even under prolonged exposure to a variable magnetic field. This occurs in the |

same senses that an initial spark may gradually cause a flame to leap higher and higher, or a stone may cause a landslide.

The plurality of experiment results strengthens this interpretation, as may be seen in Chapter VI and VIII. At each brusque variation in the magnetic field (Fig. 8) the positive mobile assemblages situated in the field are urged to move in one direction, while the negative masses are pushed in the opposite direction. Since the variations succeed one another at great frequency, it is probable that their influence is channelled into more or less slight *vibrations,* which nevertheless in due course succeed in driving some of the molecular masses from their initial position, when harmonizing with their inertia.

The original distinction between ionization obtained through radiation and ionolysis consists in the *absolute form* of the former, while *graduation* is possible in ionolysis.

Indeed, ultra-violet rays, X-rays and γ-rays cause vibration at *constant* frequency: they have characteristics which have been experimentally recognized as constant and always identical. The rays of radium cause collision, which bring about secondary vibrations. Each type of ray diminishes in intensity in proportion to the square of distance, in conformity with the rules of rectilineal propagation. The intensity of the rays is attenuated; but this does not mean that their vibratory or impulsive form with which they are endowed, is affected, nor that it changes its frequency. *On the contrary, in magnetic ionolysis, the genital plasma* may be subjected to an extensive variety of alternations, which vary frequency within extremely wide limits.

Analogously to what occurs in metals exposed in variable magnetic fields, the *intensity* in ionolysis, is *proportional to the variation of the field in unit time;* precisely as occurs in every phenomenon of electric induction. There are two limits for every type of pollen; one of minimum *frequency,* beyond which the pollen is not ionolized, even though the excitant current is very powerful, and the magnetic field extremely intense, because the variations occur too slowly; the other is of *minimum magnetism.* With magnetic intensification devices (Sects. 48, 49), introduced in the construction of apparatuses for the treatment of pollen by electro-magnetic methods, this coefficient may be entirely, or almost entirely disregarded; but it must be taken into account in connection with high frequency (Section 59) in which magnetic force of small size is employed.

42.

Some Reflections on Susceptibility

While molecular disintegration may occur in every direction in ionization by rays, the forces influencing the molecules and their assemblages in magnetic ionolysis only work *in two directions* (perpendicular to the magnetic flux). Like electric currents, or charges in action, they produce perpendicular magnetic fields along their circuit, and a reverse variable magnetic field (which might be comparable to a magnetic entity in rectilinear motion passing from the contact to the infinite), causes electric disturbances *in a direction perpendicular to its line of force.* So also in the case of plasma, ionolysis occurs under the influence of *oscillations* in a plane *perpendicular to the line of force,* and never otherwise, as the arrows in Figure 9 indicate.

The possibility of electro-magnetic ionolysis in plasma is subordinated to three main requisites:

1. The existence of weakly assembled molecular masses which may abound in plasma or be lacking in it, according to the species and age of the pollen.

2. The *intonation* between the cycle frequency affecting the field variation, the distance, the disposition and entity of the vital mass, which permits gradual *amplification* of the oscillating vibrations, until an atomic group has been forcibly moved from its natural position. It is only logical that, just as there is a *critical point* of dissolution in fusion and other physical phenomena, there must also be one for each type of molecular group of plasma.

3. The position of weak groups so that they may benefit by the variation in the magnetic field, which acts in an orthogonal sense to it.

The above deductions are prompted by experience, and explain the difference in behavior of pollens of various kinds. At first, such behavior seems completely paradoxical. Some species of plants, especially those with coarse-grain pollen (pumpkins, gourds in general, malvaceous plants and convolvulaceous ones) react well to low frequency cycles, that is to say, to relatively mild variations in the magnetic field; other species react only to high frequency or acute variations of the field; again others manifest a *definite genetic dualism* under the same treatment, which leads one to suppose that the position of the chromosomes in respect to the direction of the magnetic current, that is to say, in respect to the lines of magnetic force, (Fig. 8) is not extraneous to the phenomenon.

Thus, identical conditions of ionolizing treatment will yield different results from one type to another, and noticeable from one species to another; one might say that each of them has its own caprice, if such a word can find a place in scientific calculations.

43.

Causes Which Facilitate Magnetic Ionolysis

As a general rule, the species having a short-life cycle have pollen which is particularly sensitive to any kind of ionization, whether by ray action or electro-magnetic ionolysis. The reason is probably due to the rapid growth of their organs, which are destined only for ephemeral duration, and therefore flaccid, weak and only slightly fibrous; the upper organs too (flowers and their parts, not excluding the pollen) are generally distinguished by this same specific characteristic of limpness in gametic constitution. In this case, it is not surprising that the molecular articulation, generally considered rigid in genital plasma, is lacking in this kind of cohesion.

As for the intonation between frequency, atomic mass and interatomic distance, the present phase of investigation does not permit us to form any opinion. Logic would seem to endorse the above hypothesis, but there are some by no means negligible factors which do not permit us to isolate single attributions with any certainty. Further on, this will be dealt with in greater detail.

The translation of ions, when detached from the supposedly integral vital molecules, seems to take place independently from the mass of pollen.

Analogous results might be obtained under the same pattern of variation in the magnetic field, whether gross pollen or extremely fine grain pollen is under treatment, one might then consider nothing other than the relationship:

"ionolysis=variations in field."

But it is not that way in practice.

A rapid frequency of time unit sufficient for operating an appreciable genetic modification in extremely fine-grain pollen of certain solanaceous, compositae, or ampelid plants is sometimes lethal to the coarse-grain pollen (relatively speaking, it must be understood) of such plants as the convolvulaceous, malvaceous, cucurbitaceous types, etc.

It was recently demonstrated that the coarse seminal cells of the mammiferous species are rapidly drained of vitality by ionizing systems, which would not suffice to achieve the same effect on fine pollen of vegetable species.

Animal azoospermia leads one to hope that by regressive modification of action tending to provoke it, analogous results may be obtained such as those which I obtained with vegetable pollen.

The larger mass of coarse-grain pollen encompasses a greater quantity of lines of force. If the ions moblized within the plasma could group all their action and become endowed with great mobility, then it might be supposed that the manifest correlation between the susceptibility and the size of the pollen might be attributed to an energetic ion current, uniting all the individual impulsive forces, like electric batteries in series ranged in a ring; but the phenomenon cannot develop along these lines, both on account of the compactness of liquid molecules, and the fact that the variation of the field does not provoke only one, but two currents, identical and opposed to each other.

Only continued experiments on many different species and on a wide scale will permit even a tentative explanation.

44.

Possible Isolated Action of Magnetism

Among other causes which play a role, or which one might suppose exercise influence in ionolysis, and are extraneous to ionolization by rays, one of the principal ones is the effect of magnetism in itself.

Among other elements, salts of potassium, phosphorus and iron are found in the composition of plasma. The former are diamagnetic, that is to say, having a tendency to reject any magnetic attraction; iron, on the contrary, is attracted to a magnetic field (Section 14). Iron salt is likewise attracted, but in a much lesser degree.

A permanent magnetic field, with constant polarity, no matter how intense it may be, does not modify the molecular order so as to cause appreciable genetic effect, as may be seen from the experiments I carried out contemporaneously with other means of ionolysis.[1]

In experiments of ionolysis with variable magnetic field, the ionizing effect is not proportional to magnetic intensity. When magnetism has attained its maximum value in the electro-magnet, ionolysis is nil, while it is most pronounced when the magnetic field is inverted, or annulled, because it is precisely then that it attains its maximum variation in absolute value. If then, magnetism had an effect all its own, this would not be isochronal with ionolysis; but it might perhaps influence molecular rearrangement.

The reader will appreciate that the matter is complicated on account of the various causes which are superimposed, despite phase difference; but it cannot be entirely excluded that the magnetic field, independently from its variations, adds or subtracts

---

[1]Iron compounds form a very small part in plant and pollen composition. By cultivating plants in ferruginous soil, and administering appropriate solution of nitrate of iron to them, I thought I might contribute positively to the enrichment of the organs, *not excluding the pollen,* of such plants with iron.

I was probably mistaken, because absorption of any substance is subject to contemporary assimilation of other complementary elements. In fact, nothing of advantage was gained, as far as ionolysis was concerned, by a pollen presumably richer in iron content. (Section 46).

value to or from the effectiveness of the variations, or that it confers a specific character on the definitive order of molecules, when ionolysis occurs.

For according to modern concepts, atoms consist of a stable central nucleus and are surrounded by electrons gravitating around them like satellites, so it would seem evident that a magnetic field, particularly when highly intense, would have a deformative effect on the passage of such electrons.

Electrical charges in motion may be considered extremely flexible conductors permeated with electric current along their passage; the variable magnetic field with set polarity should wrench, displace from their normal plane, the electronic orbits.

If this did occur, with great intensities there would no longer be any need of variable magnetic fields in provoking ionolysis, and deformations, of various kinds, might be observed in genital plasma subjected to treatment in a stable field.

My knowledge is not so extensive as to permit even a conjecture on this important subject; but it is a fact that experiments carried out with a stable field proved ineffective for genetic purposes, and I think I should point this out.

45.

Secondary Action and Rearrangement

In evaluating the secondary effects produced by the magnetic field, one has to consider an accessory phenomenon verifiable in any and every electrolyte liquid.

The liquid surface of any electrolytic situated in a strong magnetic field, will modify its level appreciably, under the effect of the motion of ions translated from the field. Magnetic displacement of ions is still greater when the electrolytic liquid is contained in very slender tubes.[1]

During ionolysis, the magnetic field is enlarged, diminished and inverted constantly; if iono-magnetic displacement occurs in pollen

[1] Augusto Righi, *Op. cit.*, p. 352.

plasma, it must be alternating and oscillating, in dependence on the excitation cycle, or the rapidity of interruption in the magnetic field itself.

It is not easy to estimate the magnitude of this impact, its eventual traumatic effect on the chromosomes, and its possible contribution to the variation of their arrangement (therefore on their progeny), nor may one advance any hypothesis, since the value of vital cohesion of the minimum elements is unknown.

The analogy between ionolysis and ionization justifies the doubt that the mobilized ions will be rearranged, so that the respective molecules of which they formed part are reconstructed, after completion of the perturbation provoked by the ionizing action in plasma. A similar reactivation must occur in ionolysis, as has already been verified in ionization; but it is probable that (Section 34) the *exceedingly displaced* ions are partially rearranged among themselves where they happen to be, forming a new type of molecule. In any case, there is an undoubted effect of relaxation, which in relationship to vitality is expressed in *debilitation of the specific characteristic* of which the pollen is bearer. This will be dealt with extensively in Chapter VII, regarding hybridization.

The ionolysis of pollen might be compared to a riot taking place in a closed room between couples dancing and couples standing still. Once the cause of the confusion has been removed, all the persons concerned are still present; a few couples will have broken up, some male partner (ion) will still be beside his companion, and will take hold of her again, to pair off with her once more (molecule), while another—an extremely rare occurrence—(Section 29) will resume dancing with another partner, and while a few other elements will wander listlessly.

46.

The Addition of Iron

If it is to benefit by a homogenous intensity of a magnetic field and its consequent variation, pollen should be spread in one single layer over the polar surfaces of an electro-magnet. For various technical difficulties, this is not possible to achieve with the necessary precision.

To give a concrete idea, one might calculate pollen grains as presumably 1/10 of a millimeter in size. The stratum in immediate contact with the iron of the magnetic pole will be subjected to the full effect; the second stratum, situated at the 2nd distance (2/10 of a millimeter) will benefit four times less; a third stratum at the 3rd distance, will benefit nine times less, and so on.

Were ionolysis *proportionate* to the magnetic intensity to which each grain of pollen is exposed, widely different results should be observed among the progeny of the pollen in the three strata referred to above. This frequently does occur; but it does not follow that the differences depend exclusively hereon (section 42), firstly because in the electro-magnets for pollen the field is relatively homogeneous, owing to the vicinity of the two poles, which affords compensation, and secondly because in each instance, there are more than 4000 gauss of magnetic intensity.

Nevertheless, I wondered whether it might not be beneficial in attenuating the effects of this diversity of field, due to the varying distances of the pollen grains from the polar surface, if metallic iron were finely scattered over the pollen itself. There is a powdered iron in commerce, consisting of tiny fragments which are still susceptible to even greater refining by screening.

If it is not anfractuous, the iron does not damage the pollen, because as soon as the iron-pollen mixture is put between the poles and the current acts on the electro-magnet, the iron particles are magnetized by its influence and range themselves in close, thin columns parallel with the lines of magnetic force connecting the two poles (Fig. 10).

The pollen nests between these filaments held upright by magnetism, so that each grain of pollen is surrounded by a magnetic substance in which magnetism increases and diminishes, according to the rhythm of excitation; and in this way, although its distance from the *magnetic matter* may not be identical for all grains, it is at any rate a negligible variable.

Between one cycle phase and another, or during an interruption, the tiny iron filaments are not disintegrated, thanks to the

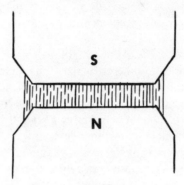

Fig. 10
Column arrangement of iron powder
in a magnetic field.

residuum of magnetism, so even though the exposure is prolonged, the pollen is not damaged.

The addition of pulverized iron to pollen could not only equalize the intensity of the magnetic field, but intensify it, and consequently intensify ionolysis in pollen, since the magnetic *area* surrounding each pollen grain *varies*, with an inverse ratio to the excitation of the magnetic field.

The results obtained belie this calculation. With rapid frequency, ionolysis is less effective when iron is interposed. This is not because its fragments, by absorbing magnetism, leave less of it to act on the pollen, (because it is not so much the magnetism as its *variation* which determines ionolysis). But the iron fragments mingling with the pollen between the poles, are *metallic.* Their magnetic susceptibility does not prevent the formation of reaction currents within each of them, which tend to oppose variation in the magnetic conditions every time the excitation current summons it.

In this way, the powdered iron does obey the dominant magnetism of the lamellar nucleus, but each grain of it offers a hostile magnetizing force, produced by the Foucault currents formed within it, to combat it. As a whole, the effect of these single currents constitutes a debilitating forces, inasmuch as it is opposed and isochronous to the exciting current.

As long as the powdered iron is put in, low frequency alternative magnetic fields are beneficial, but the opposite effect is obtained by high frequency cycles or very frequent interruptions.

In Section 44, I mentioned unsuccessful attempts to administer iron salts, with a view to enriching the pollen by this superlatively magnetic substance.

A hasty calculation might lead one to believe that a special nutrition diet might stimulate the variations in progeny, since the seeds of treated plants would absorb heterogeneous substances which they would not usually receive. But this is difficult to put into practice.

Unlike animals, which are protected from partaking of harmful or toxic nourishment by their instinct, sense of smell and taste, and diffidence toward any new kind of nutrition, plants are obliged to live where they are born or transplanted; but they possess another providential characteristic: the faculty of selecting those elements which are useful to them (chemotropism) and of repudiating that which is useless, unnecessary or harmful.[1]

It is only necessary that one element, beneficial to vegetable development, be abundantly present in the soil.[2] The plant will absorb it only in the rightful quantity corresponding to the proportion of other available elements. The same theory may apply to the administering of radioactive salts, as recently utilized.

Summarizing the arguments presented in this chapter from a purely practical viewpoint, it will be seen that magnetic ionolysis offers the advantage of the possibility of gradual progress over the system of ionization by rays. This offers the possibility of exercising influence over genital plasma without destroying its vitality.

By gradual attempts, increasing frequency and intensity, the critical phase will be found by acting *only on the secondary elements* of the true, extremely delicate and specific mechanism which is the continuator of life, *saving its principal structure* which, it would seem, is not respected when rays, especially when radium

The reader will find listed experiments mainly in the field of rays are employed.

[1] Unless these are treated with concentrated saline solutions, which provoke plasmolysis in the absorbent root cells.
[2] Liebig's law of minimums.

magnetic ionolysis in Chapters VI and VII, because they figure among the most successful and easily carried out.

An approximate element of comparison might here be cited in advance, namely that the percent of germination of poppy seeds, for example, obtained from radium treated pollen, does not attain nearly the level of those obtained from pollen exposed to magnetic ionolysis for an identical period of time.

Magnetic ionolysis would therefore appear to be the more suitable form of disintegration by which the undeterminable, but intuitively ascertained, phase midway between life and death, may be reached; the sole form which may be practically exploited for the appointed goal of mutation which already, because it is susceptible of perfection, promises to yield practical results far superior to those already obtained.

Chapter V

Electro-Magnetic Apparatuses for the Treatment of Pollen

SUMMARY:

47.

Elementary Notions of Electro-Magnetism

A CONDUCTOR (metal) acting as circuit for an electric current, generates a magnetic field in a direction perpendicular to the current. If a metallic wire, duly isolated, is wound in many parallel springs, the individual magnetic actions produced by the passage of the current unite in a direction perpendicular to the springs. This creates a more intense *magnetic field* within the spring. Intensity will be in proportion with the product of the *number* of springs activated by the quantity of electricity passing along the metal wire. If this is wound in several layers of springs on a spark coil with interior cable, of insulating material, and a soft iron cylinder is introduced into the cable of the same spark coil, the magnetic field will be all the more intensified, and by reason of the *magnetic permeability* of the iron, *two magnetic poles* will form at the two extremities protruding from the spring. The whole magnetic flux produced by the springs along the cylinder stem from the central iron nucleus which is conducted to stream toward them. This causes *magnetization* of the iron, and inducts two opposite poles called South Pole and North Pole, in comparison with the equally magnetic poles of the needle in the compass.

But such magnetization of the iron is only *temporary*, because soft iron loses its magnetic properties, which it acquires during the passage of the *energizing current* through the *winding* of metal wire conductor, when this is interrupted.

Iron is far more sensitive to magnetism than steel, therefore electro-magnets are far more powerful than the common steel magnets, since iron possesses greater magnetic permeability, and imbibes a greater quantity of magnetism, so to speak; furthermore, steel magnets do not have poles at their extremities, but considerably closer to the center.

The area surrounding each pole is known as *magnetic field*, while the electro-magnet is active, and its intensity decreases proportionately to the square of distance from the poles.

When the electro-magnet has its nucleus curved over it, instead of being rectilinear, with corresponding winding, so that the two poles are face to face, (Figs. 15 and 16), that is to say, two identical rectilinear and coaxial electro-magnets are brought into close contact, so that they are interchangeable, or one had better say, complementary, the field is still more intensified. The area between the two facing poles is called a *tube of force,* and is virtually encompassed by the connecting lines of the perimeters of the polar surfaces. (Fig. 8).

48.

Auto-Induction and Magnetic Hysteresis

When the current in the circuit of the electro-magnet is interrupted, the soft iron nucleus loses its magnetism, apparently on the instant; but in reality, it does so with some very slight delay due in the first place, to the rise of spontaneous currents within the winding, known as *self-induction,* or *auto-induction,* which tend to preserve the magnetic condition of the nucleus about to lose it. An analogous self-induction current initially counteracts the passage of the activating current when the nucleus begins to be magnetized, since in this case, it is converging from the opposite direction toward the activating current itself.

Both these self-induction currents are practically instantaneous, and they tend to preserve either the state of inertia or magnetic polarity of the electric-magnet.

When the current is interrupted by a very rapid switch, several hundreds, and even thousands, of volts per second are necessary to reduce to a minimum the effect of these reactionary currents, which resist variations in the magnetic field at each interruption or resumption of the current, attenuating the impact necessary for maintaining its intensity if the desired ionolysis is to take place.

Independent of the self-induction currents, the iron nucleus is, so to say, reluctant both to acquire and to lose magnetism, once this has been acquired, and this is yet another reason involved in the delay of magnetism on the excitation current, due to *magnetic hysteresis;* this delay is not perceptible to our senses, but it is long in relationship to electricity, which is propagated at the velocity of 300,000 kilometers per second.

A third detractive element hostile to exploitable energy is represented by the induced currents, situated inside the iron nucleus; they are directed in the opposite direction to the influential current passing through the winding, and they help to demagnetize the iron in which they are generated, diminishing its magnetism in moments of variation of the field; they are known as *Foucault currents.*

These currents are not only harmful for the above reason, but they are also dangerous when the electric current is either interrupted or reversed several hundreds of volts per second, for in this instance they are so strong and frequent that they overheat the nucleus considerably.

All these disadvantages are eliminated by the formation of electro-magnets for frequently interrupted or alternated currents with *lamellar iron.* Each iron plate for such a purpose is previously varnished on both its surfaces or compressed between small sheets of isinglass. Negative currents can no longer form, because the passage of their common circuit is obstructed in several places. At the same time the nucleus is no longer a magnet, but consists of a large number of small, elementary magnets isolated one from the other, with homonymous poles almost contacting when the electro-magnet is activated. Just as complementary poles are attracted one to the other, so do these homonymous poles exercise the same attraction; they are drawn to reciprocal repulsion. Should the filaments securing the plating at the ends suddenly yield, while the electro-magnet is in action, they would tend to open out, like a fan. Since this is not possible, the homonymous polarity of each plate influences its neighbors, repelling the magnetism toward the neutral area of the nucleus, which is situated half-way along the length of the nucleus.

This accelerates neutralization of the magnetic field when the electric current is turned off. The iron lamellar nucleus never becomes hot, and reacts promptly, without any waste of energy, to the variations of the activating current. It is more necessary than ever that the iron nucleus of electro-magnets should not become hot in an apparatus used for treatment of pollen; so it is advisable that, apart from being manufactured of well-insulated lamellar iron, one should strongly recommend to the manufacturer[1] that the winding be well calculated, so as not to provoke heat exceeding 10 degrees higher than the temperature of the environment. Since such an apparatus is mostly used in summer, no matter how little the winding may be heated, the nucleus will inevitably feel the effects after some little time. If 45 degrees centigrade are surpassed, the vitality of the pollen is endangered.

49.

Electro-Magnet for Anther Treatment

Electro-magnets are built in many different ways; but the three forms described here below, which differ substantially from others

[1] In electro-technical calculations, it is not considered important whether the winding material attains 60 or more degrees centigrade when the apparatus

solely by reason of the purpose for which they are used, are mainly suitable for the treatment of pollen.

The electro-magnet seen in Fig. 11 consists of a square metal bar with two rings which encompass it perfectly, sliding along it;

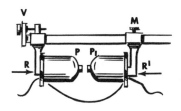

Fig.11
Rectilinear electro-magnet with adjustable induction coil suitable for treatment of anthers.

one of these is activated by a lateral V-screw which causes it to slide along the bar, the other may be clamped to the bar in any desired position by an adjustable hand vise. Two stout brass extensions are solidly coupled to the rings, and to them are attached perpendicularly, the two iron plate cores which are seen protruding under P,P'. Two (R,R') spools are threaded onto the cores which are rigidly joined to their supports, and on these spools the winding is arranged so as to constitute a polarity contrary to the P,P' poles in which direction the winding declines, so as to leave freedom of movement in operation, and not obstruct visibility of the object which is to be put in the area between the poles. This apparatus is generally used for ionolysis of anthers, of flowers in bud, to influence the pollen ripening within them. If experiments are to be made in the open country, then the winding should be protected by a stout stratum of rubber tape, likewise the connecting wires, which are encased in rubber tube or isinglass. From the few experiments recently made, this process seems highly promising. It has given rise to significant and strange modifications

---

has been functioning for some little time; there is a tendency toward obtaining the maximum intensity of the magnetic field compatible with the available electro-motive force.

without any damage being done to robustness or fertility, which is generally deficient in the extremes of ionogenetic mutation.

The device is extremely simple to work in ionizing anthers, and one of the more easy instances is shown in Fig. 12.

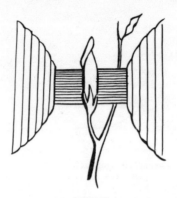

Fig. 12
Wallflower bud between the poles of the electro-magnet, for treatment of its anthers during the final phase of their development.

Treatment may last for 2, 3 and even more days. Any considerable intensity in the magnetic field is impossible, but there is the advantage of being able to influence weaker plasma, probably in the moment when its specific structure is passing through its final phase.

In practice, the greatest difficulty consists in securing the required solidity to the electro-magnetic system, so that, in its motion, it does not cause damage, for it might even lacerate the extremely delicate bud held between its polar surfaces. Where very big flowers are concerned, the lines of force may converge from the magnetic field, provided that few milligrams of powdered iron are put very carefully near the anthers within the bud itself.

The apparatus may be activated with currents of low and medium frequency cycles, interrupted by a mercury switch. If it is to be activated by broken currents with the electrolytic apparatus, or with alternating currents at 500-600 cycles, the winding material should be less, because of the greater impedance caused by it. (Section 51).

112

Complementary polarity is not necessary in ionolysis of the pollen; in fact, it may be expedient that the facing poles be homonymous, if the electrolytic switch is to be used, because this facilitates prompt demagnetization of the lamellar iron nucleuses, and the inducted effect is more forceful, even though the field does not attain too great an intensity.

50.

Electro-Magnet for Pollen, with Secondary Winding

The effectiveness of the ionizing effect provoked by variation of the magnetic field may be measured. Knowledge of this represents a first sure foundation and prompt reference of great convenience, since there is no need for endless calculations which become almost impossible when the electrolytic switch is used (Section 57), because its variations are irregular, highly frequent and disturbing and if there is not perfect synchronization between the generator and the platinum point which serves at one and the same time as switch and rheostat, self-induction will paralyze or diminish its positive effects.

Since ionolysis is always strictly proportionate to the induced effects, it suffices to have a measure of the induced effect, in order to ascertain its value, once the cycle frequency (Section 58) or interruption frequency (Section 56-57) and the time of exposure are known. The effect induced by variation of the field may be deduced from the length of the spark, produced, for this purpose, between the extremities of *secondary winding* in insulated tape of extreme thinness, which encompasses the original winding, that is to say the excitation winding. The quicker the variations of the magnetic field, the greater is the potential disparity occurring at the extremities of the secondary winding. In order to measure the spark adequately, these extremities must be put into contact with the *spark gap measuring tool*, consisting of two metal coaxial stems, terminating in two small metal balls and two handles of insulated material which help to move them. Also the small columns on which

113

the whole thing stands are insulated. The spark gap measuring tool, mounted on the same base as the apparatus, is easily discernible to the right of the magnetic apparatus in Fig. 13.[1]

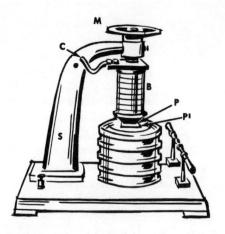

Fig. 13

Vertical electro-magnet for treatment of pollen, particularly suitable for interrupted currents.

This table also shows what a very solid structure may be found in the rectilinear apparatus for magnetic emission used in the treatment of pollen. In this apparatus two identical superposed spools have well insulated an iron lamellar nucleus; one of them is attached to the base together with its nucleus, which is hardly visible in P. It is not discernible because it is completely surrounded by the secondary A-winding in copper wire of 0.1 millimeter, insulated with silk and puttied over with paraffin.

The other spool, B, may be raised and lowered by the handle M which controls the motions by a clamp, pivoted on a stout supporting cast iron lever, solidly screwed to the base. In C, a reversal

---

[1] The spark gap measuring tool should be used for occasional rapid measuring. It must not function during the treatment of pollen, because it would detract energy from the inductible ionolysis.

device allows control of polarity in P and P' so that there may be homonymous poles or complementary polarity, as required, according to the needs of each individual instance.

The original winding should be in proportion to the intensity of the current which is to pass through its metal section; the stratum of winding on the spools will be determined by the available electro-motive energy. Every good manufacturer knows these facts, which depend on the cycle or rapidity of interruption required.

As we have already said, the length of the spark in the measuring tool is in proportion to the positive effectiveness, that is to the efficiency of ionolysis.

In this apparatus too, the extremities of the two cores are beveled in the center, so as to intensify magnetism; since this is susceptible of concentration, when converging on a more restricted surface, as in the case of electricity.

The cores must not terminate in a point, as in electricity, but should be beveled in a perpendicular sense toward the laminas. Iron lamellar cores are quadrangular, instead of rounded, and the previously compressed plating will be beveled as seen in Fig. 14.

Beveling should not be excessive; it is expedient to have a slightly larger field, having a polar area for each surface, while very little is gained in magnetic saturation beyond a certain limit, easily attained by appropriately activated and well constructed electro-magnets.

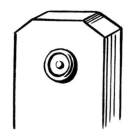

Fig. 14
Magnetic pole in lamellar iron, for electro-magnets used for pollen. Beveling and connection of the laminas.

The nucleus of the lower spool, A, is enclosed on a perfect level with the edges of the two concentric spools, both primary and secondary, which also are covered by a very smooth ebonite sheet in which the upper extremity of the nucleus is perfectly enclosed.

The B spool is lifted by a clamp and pollen may be easily spread on the lower polar surface in perfect correspondence to the pole. Before activating, that is to say, before turning on the current in the apparatus, the upper spool is lowered again until its pole, protruding well from the winding, is almost in contact with the pollen. In any case, due notice will be taken of the distance between the two polar surfaces, so as to estimate the maximum value of the field, expressed in "gauss."

The above apparatus of magnetic emission, is particularly suited for action by interrupted currents, since it is more able than others to reproduce noticeable fluctuations in the magnetic field, corresponding to the brusque interruptions of the activating current, and the advantages set forth above help to avoid, within the limits of possibility, all deadening action which would curtail effectiveness. When a mercury switch is used (Section 59), a condenser is inserted to shunt the contact plug screws which facilitates rapid magnetization and diminishes the spark produced by the extra-current, while the primary circuit is interrupted; the spark deteriorates contacts.

51.

Electro-Magnet with Circular Nucleus

If alternate currents, produced by dyamos generating alternate, or alternating currents, such as those commonly used for illumination purposes, are desired, then *electro-magnets with almost closed* magnetic circuits, such as may be seen on page 118 and 120 (Figures 15 and 16) are better indicated.

Alternating currents vary continually and gradually, both in potential and intensity; for each *cycle* (Fig. 21). Commencing at zero, the current increases until a maximum is attained, and then gradually diminishes again to zero; at the same time that polarity is reversed, the current again begins to increase and, after attaining its maximum in *reverse phase*, again descends to zero to renew the initial course, and so on.

All this takes place within the space of one cycle, so that an alternating current of 42 cycles passes through 42 such complete reversals in one second; it is projected 42 times in one direction, and as many again in the opposite sense. In 84 cycles, between one inversion and the other, no current passes through the circuit.

Analagous to 600 cycles, there are 600 revolutions in one direction and 600 in the opposite direction, with 1200 inversion cycles. Figs. 21 and 22 show the diagrams of the above-mentioned currents.

There is a synchronous and proportionate magnetization in the iron nucleus of an electro-magnet activated by the aforesaid alternating currents; and it increases, diminishes, is annulled and reversed, etc., in correspondence with the progressive and regressive inversion phases of the activating current. Since the variation occur with *relative slowness* and regularity, no matter what the frequency of the cycle may be, the device used in electro-magnets (Figs. 11 and 13) to exploit mainly the fluctuations in the field, due to rapid interruption, is no longer necessary; it is desirable that the nucleus have the minimum continuity solution.

The nucleus for alternating currents too, must be carefully insulated by lamellar iron. In the apparatus reproduced in Fig. 15 the C-nucleus is circular, all in one piece, and consists of plating previously sheared to the shape of a C almost closed; it is interrupted by the space of 2 millimeters between P and P', and slightly bevelled to concentrate a greater quantity of magnetism.

Under section 50 are instructions how to proceed in this connection.

Winding must be estimated on the basis of the potential (voltage) of the current used. If this is high (usually illumination currents range from 100 to 160 volts), it must be *reduced* to 25-40 volts, for normal-sized apparatuses, which can be used for currents of from 40 to 50 cycles without strong reactance.

It must be pointed out that rheostats should never be used, still less should one have recourse to liquid resistance in diminishing potential, when the electro-magnet becomes heated after long use, because liquid resistance deadens the impact of variation of the

Fig. 15
Electromagnet with curved nucleus, for alternating currents.

current, which should be advantageously maintained well and decisively. Liquid resistances especially deaden the effect of the *reverse impact* of the alternator, which corresponds to the maximum intensity of the inductive effect.

There are excellent speed reducers on sale which waste very little energy, and readily reduce the line potential to that already mentioned as adequate for the above described electro-magnets. Should the electro-magnet become considerably hot after several hours of application, then a controllable *inductive resistance* may be inserted in the circuit which will help diminish the intensity of the current without interfering with the elasticity of its pulsation.

This type of electro-magnet, which stands firm and vertical on two stout lateral supports inserted in the base which holds it tight, is easy and economical to construct; if it is to be used for currents of 500 and more cycles, then it should be ordered from a specialized workshop. Insulation between the iron lamellas in the nucleus must be thorough for high frequency cycles, and the winding accurately calculated on the basis of voltage and impedance, which becomes extremely high.

Since the interpolar area is smaller and the poles are immovable, the pollen has to be inserted between them laterally. First of all,

118

ıt is put on a very thin slab of isinglass, within the circle outlining the projection of the polar perimeter, and the stratum should not exceed 1 mm. in thickness. Then the mica slab is made to slide into position, in exact correspondenc to the polar surfaces, in which the upper P will be less fully wound, as may be seen in Fig. 15, to facilitate operation and visibility.

The small slab of mica will then be secured on the slab of ebonite, T, which is precisely level with polar surface P, thus avoiding any eventual slipping. It must be understood that the circular form of the nucleus is not essential; rectangular or square shapes are equally efficient.

An approximate measure of the induced effect may be applied, too, with this type of electro-magnet.

By introducing a metal disk into the interpolar area while the electro-magnet is excited, it is possible to calculate the increase in heat produced within a certain period. A calorimeter would be required for exact measurements of this kind.

Any metal may be used for this purpose, but aluminum is preferable, since it heats more easily and does not melt.

If the electro-magnet is excited by currents of 500-600 cycles, then the aluminum disk, because it is extremely light, is blown away under the effect of the magnetic field created by the autogenous currents forming within the metal disk; these currents are displaced in phase by the activating current.

The disk must be kept still throughout the time of exposure. If a nickel disk, or some other such alloy (for example a one or two lira piece) is used, then it need not be kept steady, since this is already done by the magnetism developed by the electro-magnet. But there will be lesser increase in heat.

52.

Electro-Magnet with Mobile Lever

Pollen is not always extremely fine and easily handled; there are some relatively coarse types, with the grains sticking together, knotted together in small lumps (for example, Oenothera, Hibiscus,

Ipomoea, Cucurbita, etc.), which are difficult to spread out, for with such pollen it is almost impossible to form an orderly, uniform stratum without handling such a fragile and delicate substance excessively. Any laboratory lacking much equipment might prefer to vary the intensity of the magnetic field with the same current that is available to it.

The electro-magnet in Fig. 16 is very suitable for this. Its nucleus, which must be of insulated lamellar iron, is of rectangular shape and divided into two parts. The larger, shaped like a U, has its horizontal section enclosed in the base, and its vertical sections are surrounded by the spools, A and B. The A section, terminating in a customary beveled manner (Section 50) in P' ends completely level with the solid ebonite slab; this contributes to the connection of the apparatus; the B section is longer, and enclosed in C with the mobile lever, L, which can be moved to any position required by the thrust screw, V. This mobile lever ends in P with a projection at right angles, likewise beveled in the usual way, that is to say perpendicular to the laminas.

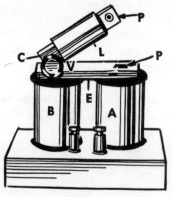

Fig. 16
Electro-magnet with mobile lever.

The hinge is the most critical part of this apparatus; it should be made in such a way that it does not interrupt the continuity of the magnetic circuit, but at the same time it must prevent the passage of any Foucault currents. These two conflicting requirements cannot be satisfied completely; nevertheless, a way to deal with them quite satisfactorily has been found, because the electro-magnet is able to function even under 600-cycle currents.

The two protuberances on the cores which have to interpenetrate to form the C hinge, are constructed so that on the one side the iron laminas are completely absent, while emerging significantly on the other.

The laminas on the one side of the nuclear extremities, which are to act as hinge, have been alternatively shortened, that is to say the 2nd, 4th, 6th . . . 30th, and the 1st, 3rd, 5th etc. on the other side. In this phase of operation, the nuclear extremities look like two thickly tined rakes. Before being varnished and dried, they are cautiously fitted together, accurately bored and linked with the thrust screw, and insulated from the iron of the screw with suitable material.

It must be pointed out that before inserting the mobile lever, reels A and B are threaded into the vertical cores and connected in a manner producing conflicting polarity in P and P'.

This apparatus should be equipped with subsidiary winding on the lever, L, to conduct the magnetic flux developing from reel B to the polar extremity, P, since it has been observed that if this winding was absent, there was a great dispersion of magnetism at the hinge, which was very damaging to the process.

The pollen is set on the small slab, E, by lifting the mobile lever, L; and when the operation is completed, it is lowered again, establishing contact with the pollen, if one wishes that it benefit by the maximum magnetic intensity; if lesser intensity is required, then it will be kept slightly at a distance from the pollen. There cannot be too great a distance between poles, however, because in increasing the magnetic range, the current in the winding becomes stronger than usual and heats it; if the distance between pole P' and pole P is to be considerably enlarged, then inductive resistance must be inserted to balance the diminished reactance of the winding.

These electro-magnets have their advantages and drawbacks; the secret lies in knowing how to control them. In most instances, the rigid core type (Fig. 15) is preferable, especially for comparative experiments, because an exact idea of the intensity of the magnetic field may be obtained simply by reading the ammeter.

In both the models here reproduced (Figs. 15 and 16), the core has a square cross-section, measuring 2 cm. per side, a thickness of 30 cm. and 38 cm. in length. The bevelled section shortens the core from 4 cm.^{2} to little more than 1 cm.^{2} at its polar surfaces; a sufficient area to expose thousands of pollen grains.

In summarizing requisites and attributes, one may say that ionolysis of pollen depends on three primary conditions which must be borne in mind when constructing electro-magnets:

1. Production of an intense magnetic field.

2. The variability of field with time; this variation must be clean and decisive, abrupt, that is to say, not deadened.

3. The conditioning of the iron core so that it will not become heated over 45 degrees centigrade, not even under conduction of the heat produced in the winding.

Since the mass of pollen is microscopic, the quantity of magnetism influencing each grain is extremely limited; therefore it is necessary to produce a strong magnetic field, even beyond the *magnetic saturation* generally estimated by the manufacturers who measure it by its action on iron.

Details are given in section 58 on variation of field and comparison between certain values.

53.

Compound Ionolization

The reader will find reference to experiments carried out with radioactive ionolizing systems and electro-magnets in combination.

The very spark feeding the spark gap measuring tool in the apparatus seen in Fig. 13 may act on the pollen spread out in a *very thin* layer on the mica slab on the lower polar face of the apparatus. To do this, the little balls of the measuring tool are moved, and the current of the secondary circuit is conducted to form a spark within the tube of force (Section 39) between the magnetic poles P, P', which diverge, as can be seen in section in Fig. 17.

Two insulated metal supports, A and B, ranged symmetrically about Pole S, both end in identical points like those seen in Fig. 7.

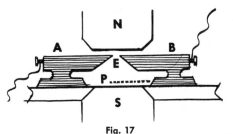

Fig. 17

Extra-flat spark measuring tool, applicable to electro-
magnet seen in Fig. 13, for compound ionization of
pollen. (Natural size)

The wires are connected with the tips of the induced winding, wound around the rods of the measuring tool, and the sparks then flash in E, illuminating the pollen P below with ultra-violet rays emitted by the electric discharge.

Each spark flashing in E is *isochronous with the maximum variation of field,* which means concomitant in effect with ionolysis (Sections 39 and 50). The small supplementary apparatus seen in Fig. 17 must not be inserted in a direction branching off from a condenser, because the dry, crackling sparks which would then ensue would scatter the pollen, pushing it toward the edges.

An analogous device in which the detonator, E, is replaced by a support for a radium capsule, likewise provides compound ionolysis in pollen.

It must be remembered that β-rays emanated by radium are deviated by the magnetic field; thus, in the instances of major intensity of the field, they do not affect the pollen, while they act undisturbed during the reversals in the field. So their effect is isochronous, in connection with ionolysis and with that of the electro-magnet, just as occurs in the spark system just described, although this is motivated by another cause.

54.

Vast Range of Exploration Work

If a complete assortment of alternating currents were available, one could attempt a series of experiments on botanic or cultivated pollen, commencing with only a few cycles per second increasing to maximum frequency (500,000 cycles).

Hopes for profitable action are rooted, in my opinion, in the possibility of undertaking a vast exploration of this kind, repeating it on various species, since, when controlled within the proper limits of frequency and cycle, ionolysis seems to be the electro-magnetic form least deleterious to vitality, as will be demonstrated later (Section 61 and following).

But the problem of the extreme variation of susceptibility in a genetic sense, is not entirely solved by determination of the cycle or the method of interruption considered more suitable; for another highly important factor is involved, the time unit, or duration of exposure. This can vary considerably, being generally in reverse proportion to the intensity of the magnetic field and its rapidity in variation.

But the electro-biologist is not concentrating solely on a maximum genetic variability, especially when he works with a special criterion.

It is essential that some middle way be found which may satisfy both mutative requirements, without excessive reduction of the vital power of the species; in other words, greatest care must be taken to contain within the lowest degree possible that biological debilitation which usually accompanies the more outstanding specific mutations artifically induced.

A *complete* experimental test *on one single species,* even though carried out summarily, would require:

For electro-magnetic ionolysis of pollen

a) To excite by alternate currents with multiple cycle ranging from 100 to 1000 cycles — Tests 10

b) As above, ranging from 1000 to 10,000 cycles — " 10

c) As above, with 5 analogous high frequency variations, up to 500,000 cycles — " 5

d) Excitement with interrupted[1] currents ranging from 100 to 3000 interruptions per second — " 30

Total 55

[1]Interrupted currents have the advantage of a powerful, abrupt variation in

For each of the 55 tests, based on the frequency of cycle, by 5 degrees of intensity of the magnetic field, one would have:

55x5=275 tests.

But since the exposure time also has to be considered, with 5 units as above, we would have:

275x5=1375 tests........1375

For ionolization of pollen by rays

e) With X-rays, produced by 3 ampoules (normally soft, very soft)   3

f) With β-rays of radium   1

g) Ultra-violet rays   1

_____
5

which become 25, with 5 different degrees of intensity for each, that is to say, 125, if 5 time exposures are observed for each, as in the previous tests   125

So for each species a total number of 1500 tests would be required.   1500

If combined treatments (Section 53) are to be added to these, one may well imagine that the figure would become exceedingly large, thanks to all the possible varying combinations, even though these were curtailed.

One also has to consider that each group experimented with requires some extension, because the larger quantity one experiments with, the fewer will be the causes of error in evaluating the progeny. So if at least four flowers are used in the test, it is readily understood how time consuming these would be, performing them in only a few days, and reserving only the noonday hours for pollination.

At the time of bloom, the work would be excessive for one single

---

the magnetic field which is far greater in power, and therefore in effect, in one _single sense,_ corresponding to each interruption on the instant when the electric circuit _is_ opened. Figs. 42, 43, and 44 (Chapter VI) show how rapid interruption obtained by the Wenhelt electrolytic switch causes highly special and most varied characteristics in poppies, which differ considerably from those obtained by other means, in which the variation of field occurs by alternate, _equilibrated_ opposition.

person to perform, because it includes castration of the seed-bearers and their preservation, the gathering of pollen, its distribution beneath the apparatus, fecundation and labelling.

So the premise contained in the opening pages of this book, namely that in the interests of ionogenetic research, extensive co-operation and specialization of the work is more necessary than ever, is not exaggerated.

The definitive and complete experiments should be preceded, a year before-hand, by minor tests of preliminary nature, carried out with few but powerful methods of ionization and ionolysis. When the results are known, some of these tests may be eliminated, if they yielded uncertain success in their outcome.

55.

Continuous Current Generators

It would be superfluous to engage the reader, even if unversed in the matter, in describing the infinite varieties of electro-motives (batteries, accumulators, dynamos) or the special advantages that each of them offers.

According to circumstances, one may use quite indiscriminately any type of generator which may be most convenient; the apparatus will be ordered according to the choice made. But it should be pointed out that, on the whole, only batteries operate small electro-magnetic apparatuses, and signify heavy maintenance costs; the Bunsens, which are among the most active, emanate noxious fumes which oxidize metal, irritate the respiratory organs and perhaps exercise, over a period of time, a deleterious effect on the vitality of pollen; they do not give a constant current and they deteriorate rapidly.

Accumulators are far more practical, especially if one has a workshop, institute or plant which can recharge them with continuous current; if this were to be done with batteries, it would be strongly inadvisable to use them, all the more, because they require recharging at least once a month, even when not in use.

The ordinary continuous current for illumination purposes may be used, lowering its potential, which is usually between 140-150 volts, by any kind of resistance, until one obtains a suitable potential for exciting the switches, whether these are rotative or electrolytic. In the use of direct current, inductive resistance is not required, but some rheostat may be useful.

Electro-magnet switches need currents of 10-15 volts; 50 volt currents are needed for mercury switches, and from 50 to 90 volts for electrolytic switches.

Alternating currents can be converted into direct currents, operating with a motor-dynamo, or may be rectified by magnetic devices activated by mercury or with electrolytic cells. The former are delicate, while the electrolytic cells offer problems of maintenance and are subject to saline efflorescence which becomes clotted on the plate, and spreads to the contact plug screws and connections, especially if the cells are left idle for any length of time. Although direct in the same sense, a current rectified by electrolytic cells or other rectifiers, is not homogeneously intense, but varies in its undulating rhythm peculiar to alternating currents.

The best practical solution for places equipped with alternating current for lighting remains the electrogenic generator, consisting of a motor activated by alternating current, coupled with a dynamo giving continuous current.

The electrogenetic converter groups are expensive to buy, but they are not worn by usage nor disuse, and will always be worth at least half of their original cost.

Among the few experiments made with direct currents, I did not obtain any modifying results in the progeny produced by the pollen subjected to them, as stated already in section 44. Direct currents produce a magnetic field of unvarying intensity, for the entire duration of their circuit around the winding of the electro-magnet; therefore their direction is constant, and polarity is stable. It is not necessary that the nucleus be of lamellar iron, but should it be so, this does not alter anything.

If results have so far not proved successful on pollen, this does not mean that other experiments may not be put to the test, especially on organs (perhaps on anthers) in process of development, in which magnetism might influence the extremely tender aggregates of the plasm.

56.

Hammer and Mercury Switches

Switches deserve detailed mention as integral parts of the electro-magnets described under section 49 and 50.

Excitement of an electro-magnet for ionolysis of pollen may be obtained:

A. With rapidly interrupted currents (Figs. 11 and 13)

B. With alternating or sinusoidal currents (Figs. 15 and 16)

Of these the most simple and economical is the small hammer switch, consisting of a small spool with central nucleus of lamellar iron, with only a few layers of winding of thickness equal to that of the electro-magnet with which it is inserted in the circuit of a continuous current generator (battery, dynamo or accumulator).

Opposite the extremity of the core protruding from the spool, and about 1 mm. away, there is a small soft iron disk attached to a small flexible metal strip (spring) in which a small platinum disk is inserted. Connected with it, when the spring is in normal position, is another platinum point, controlled by a screw to which it is rigidly welded. The screw in turn is upheld by a thin metal column which stands, like the spool, on the base of the apparatus. When this is in action, the current passes from the small metal column through the screw and the two adjoining platinum contacts, through the winding of the spool, emerging at the contact plug screws. But its passage makes the iron nucleus magnetic, so that it attracts the small iron disk facing it at close range; so the spring is deformed, detaching the platinum contact from the point to which it is attached. This interrupts the current. But the spring soon resumes position, the two protruding tips again unite, re-establishing the current, and consequently the magnetic condition of the nucleus and so on.

Interruptions are all the more rapid when the vibrations of the spring are less extensive, and the shorter will be the moment of inertia of the little hammer, or iron disk, while the spring will be properly rigid.

This model will give as many as 30 to 50 interruptions per second. The switch may be applied laterally to any kind of linear electro-magnet of the type in Figs. 13 and 14, similar to what is done with the small model Rühmkorff coil; but in the specific instance of pollen, any quivering of the electro-magnet must be avoided as far as possible, for this is harmful to the stable position of the pollen, especially when the apparatus is standing on a shelf or surface which is not entirely even. That is why, like any other switch to be described later on, they should be mounted on a special shelf if they are to work properly, and the table or surface on which the electro-magnet used for treatment of pollen is to stand, must not vibrate at all.

The small hammer switch can be used up to 15-20 volts, and with currents of 2-3 amperes; with higher charges, the platinum contacts become red-hot because of the highly frequent sparks of self-induced currents, and are either quickly worn out, or their action is affected.

The contact plug screws are connected with suitable electric energy (condenser) to attenuate the deleterious effect of the self-induced current sparks.

High potential is not required for the usual dimensions of electro-magnets used for ionolysis of pollen, since their coils have little reactance; nevertheless, other types of more rapid switches, which have the additional advantage of not requiring constant surveillance, as the hammer switch does, should be used in exploiting currents of 40-50 volts.

These would be mercury switches both electro-magnetic and rotative. The latter hold up under extensive usage without needing any special care, no matter how treatment may be prolonged. The only necessary precaution is frequent cleansing of the mobile part, the mercury and the vessel containing it, because with time, these become covered with a blackish coating, which hinders the 'slip' and is harmful to the insulating effect of the liquid in which the interruptions occur (gasoline, or alcohol).

Mercury switches work well with direct currents of any voltage, and yield about 100 interruptions a second, with steady regularity, even under strongly charged current. There are several different types, all based on the same principle: centrifugal energy generated by a motor activated by a shunting of the activating current to a rotating drum, and to the mercury and the insulating liquid above

Fig. 18
Rotative mercury switch.

it, projects the mercury, which is particularly heavy, against the walls of its vessel, leaving a cylindrical-conical void in the area of the axis where a metal section, equipped with small vanes, rotates at high rapidity, the vanes contacting the mercury for extremely brief instants. These fleeting contacts with the vanes (which contact a pole) and the mercury (connected with the other pole) cause highly frequent connections and interruptions of the current.

57.

Electrolytic Switch

There are two known types: the Wenhelt and the Simon; the latter is used less because its interruptions are slower, and it is suited to a steady current speed; to compensate for this, it functions fairly well on alternating currents. The Wenhelt is capable of functioning with currents ranging from 50 to 60 volts, and is controlled by the inductance of the rectilinear electro-magnet, similar to that seen in Figs. 13 and 14.

Intonation of the electro-magnet with the Wenhelt switch is extremely important, because, as already mentioned, the self-induction wastes considerable force.

The Wenhelt switch, like the mercury switch, must be connected in series between the generator and the electro-magnet. It consists of a glass vessel containing a solution of pure sulphuric acid in distilled water, of the specific weight of 18-20 Beaumé. There are two electrodes afloat in the solution; a lead sheet which must be in contact with the negative pole of the generator, and a platinum point welded at the tip to a metal rod, shielded along its entire length by a porcelain tube of conical shape, as clearly seen in Fig. 19.

Fig. 19
Electrolytic Wenhelt switch.

The tip of the platinum point, which is metallically connected with the positive rheophore, may be controlled by an insulating screw over the porcelain tube, immediately beneath the contact plug screw. The more the point protrudes, the greater will be the intensity of the current passing through the winding; in a word, the platinum point works as a control, because the Wenhelt switch is inserted *without a rheostat*, which is sometimes necessary with other types of switch.

The widest possible variations in frequency of interruption can be obtained with this apparatus, if one takes into account that the higher the potential and the *less* protuberant the point, the higher will be the number of interruptions in the time unit; but one attains a limit which can not be exceeded, both because the electric resistance increases as the point grows shorter (the high point is reached when there is contact between the point and the liquid), and because the all too frequent interruptions do not allow time for the nucleus to demagnetize between one interruption and the other.

In order to obtain the maximum yield from an electro-magnet connected with an electrolytic switch, the layers of winding on the spools must not exceed four in number, and if high intensity currents are used, there must be a device to operate the winding layers either in parallel or mixed combination. In this case, treatment must not last longer than 10-15 minutes, because the acidulated water becomes heated by the strong currents, and the phenomenon of interruption is no longer regular at high temperature. For long treatments, one needs several spare tanks, or the liquid should be left to cool between one treatment and subsequent complementary ones. Otherwise the tank must be very big indeed.

Contacts between the two spools, and the electro-magnet must be equipped with *commutators* (Section 50) to confer conflicting or homonymous polarity to the activating opposite poles. It has been observed that homonymous polarity yields far more noticeable effects on the circuit than the complementary polarity, with equal amperage, although the interstitial tube of force acquires double value with it. The reason for this has already been mentioned under sections 48 and 50, when speaking of the construction of electro-magnets.

The Wenhelt switch also works with alternating current; but the platinum needle is rapidly worn out. There have now been electrolytic switches in commerce for some time, which are of the Wenhelt type, for alternating current, and equipped with varnished iron tanks, with an aluminum lamina for the electrodes, and an iron point, protected by a porcelain tube, from which it may emerge from a few millimeters to 1 cm. Instead of sulphuric acid, the solution is of Seignette salt.

These types utilize only half of each cycle and yield as much as $\frac{1}{4}$ or $\frac{1}{3}$ as much as those for direct current. A great deal of the current is wasted in heat. Furthermore, it is never possible to achieve perfect intonation with the electro-magnet, because the current varies every instant both in quantitative value and potential.

Interruption is not obtained by mechanical means in other types of electrolytic switches, but by electrolytic and thermic effects combined. The effect of the current covers the point in contact with the liquid with gaseous bubbles, and in that section of the circuit where resistance is highest, a puff of steam forms, thanks to the considerable potential, which for a moment insulates the point from the liquid; but it soon wets the point again, and so it continues.

Electrolytic switches absorb a great deal of current, as compared to electro-magnetic or rotative switches; but their results are considerably more conspicuous, *when operated by someone who knows how to use them effectively.*

They do not require special care, and never go wrong, but their good functioning is connected with several different factors. Nevertheless, even an amateur with but little experience of electrolytic apparatuses, would only have to control the protuberance of the point, starting at a minimum when experimenting, were he to take the trouble of repeating several experiments undertaken by me, or of attempting other similar ones. He would then activate the polarity commutator, the socket in series, in parallel or compounded with the winding, until hitting upon the fusion between the various factors so as to obtain the longest spark by the spark gap measuring tool.

He must then observe how much the point is protruding, as well as taking note of the registrations of the ammeter and the voltmeter, for future guidance; he will not be able to work without the latter apparatus, if using potential energy.

The spark measuring tool serves in making preliminary evaluations; it must not be left to work continually when working is protracted at length, but it is as well to consult it from time to time, especially when the water in the tank begins to grow hot, because it instantly registers any alteration in the normal condition of the apparatus.

It must be observed that while the intensity of the magnetic field in gauss is easily calculated with direct and alternate currents, simply by reading the ammeter, when the number of coils and the nuclear section are known, a similar calculation is not possible with interrupted currents, especially when using an electrolytic switch. Not only are the interruptions irregular with it, but even during the course of the treatment, and controlling them so as to maintain the exciting current at constant amperage, the frequency, clarity and extinction of the interruptions vary considerably, particularly because of the heating in the electrolytic liquid in the tank.

So it must again be stressed that the best basis for measuring comparisons, remains the length of the spark measured by the spark measuring tool: the principal rule of interrupting treatment, and then resuming it or continuing it with a new tank, when the ammeter begins to oscillate and there is no longer the frantic characteristic discharge flame between the globes of the measuring tool.

58.

Alternate and Alternating Currents

The dynamos producing alternate current or alternating current, may very well be used for direct excitation of electro-magnets, particularly of the type with closed magnetic field (Figs. 15 and 16).

In alternate currents the electric flux varies continually at equal rhythm, and with it the magnetic flux of the iron cores; so interruption to provoke variations in current is no longer necessary. Alternators invariably consist in a mobile part and a stable part connected one inside the other; the variation in current is produced by the forced and rapid translation of electro-magnets ranged in a circle, with alternate polarity, the polar surfaces grazing the electro-magnets, equipped with lamellar cores and adequately connected with the winding, as they gyrate. This generates induced currents which increase gradually as the inducing poles diverge from the corresponding poles of the current induced, attaining maximum value when half-way between the poles, and diminishing to zero with the consecutive resumption of the polar contact. The current is annulled when the poles of the induced circuit are perfectly level with those of the inductor circuit; then the opposite phase sets in, in analogous development, producing contrary current and terminating in contact with the opposite successive poles where direct current is again resumed, and so on.

The more poles there are and the swifter their rotation, that is to say, the tangential displacement of the inducing circuit poles in respect to those of the induced circuit, the greater will be the cycle frequency in the time unit.

The same thing occurs when the poles of the inducing circuit are steady, and the induced circuit acts as rotor.

A complete transfer between two consecutive poles, commencing from the neutral area, is known as *cycle.*

Each elementary action produced in the spools' circuit occurs with prearranged connection with the others, so that the current may stem from an alternator in tension (*series*) or in quantity (*parallel*) according to the way it is used. It must be remembered that connection in series will always be required in high frequency alternators, because the rapidity of the cycle increases reactance, which can only be surpassed by extremely powerful electric motive forces.

Frequency of 42-50 cycles per second which is generally used in the interests of technical utility, is rightfully prevalent, since it gives the greatest results in transformation; but the variations of field are too slow to have effect in ionolysis of pollen, except where very coarse pollen is concerned (section 30 and following).

High frequency alternators are necessary for very fine, powdery pollen. Ionolysis can be effected even on finest pollens, with the most tenacious molecular arrangement with special alternators varying from 500 to 600 cycles.

Fig. 20
Small 600-cycle alternator.

There is no equivalence nor proportionality existing between the positive effect and the product of numbers expressing the product of the time unit (duration of treatment) by the frequency of cycle.

Therefore it does not mean that with equal intensity of magnetic field, the ionolytic action of two electro-magnets, one excited for

135

15 hours by a 40 cycle current, the other for an hour by a 600 cycle current are equivalent, although the products:

$$15x40=600 \quad \text{and} \quad 1x600=600$$

lead one to imagine equivalence.

It is enough to look at Figs. 21 and 22 to be convinced of it.

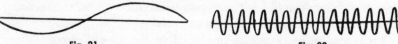

<table>
<tr><td>

Fig. 21

Sinusoid of alternating 40 cycle current (in 1/10 of a second).

</td><td>

Fig. 22

Sinusoid of alternating 600 cycle current (ih 1/10 of a second).

</td></tr>
</table>

They reproduce the sinusoids of the two currents in 0.1 sec. on two identical abscissas. If one were to take 15 parts of the former, this would not increase the *steepness of the curve* which represents the value of the current, and consequently of the field variation.

Today one can buy small and utterly perfect models of alternators of 500-600 cycles such as the one seen in Fig. 22, which are used in radio-telegraphy.

They are connected with suitable motors, and with a change of pulley, one may obtain variations in frequency within fairly ample limits.

If no change in velocity is needed, the motor can be coupled coaxially with the alternator, thus saving space and power.

The number of cycles which may be obtained per second is extremely high; in big, special alternators as many as 10,000 cycles have been obtained; the velocity required by such an apparatus is immense, and iron would not withstand the terrific centrifugal force produced in the rotor without buckling. Thus this has to be built of steel, to the evident detriment of effect in respect to the absorption of power. But this is still not the extreme limit of frequency obtainable.

59.

High Frequency Devices

The Tesla device in which the property of the condensers is utilized, since they confer an extremely rapid oscillating rhythm, known as *high frequency*, to the electric discharge, obtains electric oscillations in the order of one million per second.

These oscillations which accompany the apparently instantaneous phenomenon of the spark, are produced by rapid currents, and the magnetic field they produce is extremely weak, because of the enormous impedance to their propagation. Only a very slight *intensity of field* develops in the central cable of the primary circuit of a Tesla solenoid, both because of the few lines of force converging in it, and the deficiency in nucleus (iron does not react to such rapid variations) which absorbs and intensifies them, conducting them to the poles, as in the electro-magnets just described.

For the rest, the vibrations produced by X-rays and ultra-violet rays are even more frequent, and nevertheless are effective, indeed are often lethal on all types of pollen; while magnetic ionolysis only occurs when a minimum value limit is attained in field variation, no matter how strong its intensity in absolute value may be.

A complete Tesla device is not required for treatment of pollen; it is enough if a large inductor, such as a Rühmkorff coil or a closed magnetic field transformer, according to whether it is excited by interrupted or alternate currents, is connected to a proportionate condenser, C, connected outwardly with a large, thin spiral of metal tubing, I (inductance), inserted in the circuit with a spark gap measuring tool or detonator, E. The pollen, spread over a rectangular slab of ebonite mica, is slipped through the spiral, and feels the effect of the highly frequent variation of the magnetic field induced by the extremely rapid alternate currents which pass through the spiral every time a spark flashes in E. Each spark produces *a train of electric waves* which gradually extinguishes itself, under the effect of the oscillating discharge.

I have worked out a modification of the usual device in the treatment of pollen; the primary circuit is deformed, as seen in Fig. 23, at I. The turns of the aforesaid circuit, connected with the deflagrator and condenser, are more tightly wound and the solenoid is flattened to procure the maximum possible intensity of field.

A still more perfect system of high frequency is offered by thermionic tubes, which produce persistent waves ranging from 200,000 to 400,000 cycles per second and intensify them.

Inductances applied in series to the Poulsen arc and the Cooper-

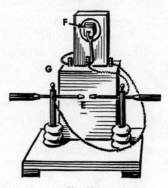

Fig. 23
High frequency device for treatment of pollen.

Hewitt mercury vapor lamp, which act as extremely rapid switches in respect to the circuit feeding them, would come under this category.

CHAPTER VI

Iono-Genetic Mutations in Horticultural Species

60.

Critical Point of Susceptibility and Limit of Tolerance

DURING the two previous chapters reference has been made several times to the necessity of *limiting* the duration of ionolysis, and of *tuning* this to the species upon which genetic modifications are experimented.

Just as it is necessary to proportion the device in any machine or mechanical gear to the activating force and the task in hand, so is it necessary to attune the exciting electric force to the apparatus in which it is to perform its action efficiently; it is likewise reasonable to admit that appropriate *measure* is required, both in quantity and frequency, if the extremely delicate work of modifying any vital order is to succeed, without destroying the essential biological requisites which give it existence. Facts prove this.

The business of dosage is, unfortunately, an extremely risky one, for which there are neither exact rules, nor presumptive ones; for the time being, only a empirical classification can be made between species of coarse pollens sensitive to slow cycle ionolysis, and species of fine pollen which are genetically deformed only by frequent alternations of magnetic field or by ethereal electro-magnetic vibrations produced by various kinds of rays. (Section 36, 37 and 38).

The reader may immediately form an idea of the unfortunate selection of means by observing the results of inappropriate ionolization in three different botanic species, in no way connected with each other.

Figures 24, 25 and 26 represent three fruits produced from treated pollen in which the treatment destroyed the unknown requirement corresponding, theoretically, to the sweeping architectural lines (Section 29, 30, 31) of their specific molecular structure; these lines must necessarily remain intact if the vitality of the embryo and seed are to be preserved.

Inappropriate, excessively intense or excessively prolonged ionolization of pollen does not prevent the continuation of fecundating power, in most instances. As has already been said, the chemical composition of genital plasma is not modified (Section 32) in ionolized pollen, and only the disorderly molecular arrangement differentiates it from its normal condition.

The excitement of the fecundating act may still occur, even though genital plasma has been discomposed, and once the egg cell has been stimulated to fecundation, the vital humours are excited, by reflex, to flow to the tissues pre-arranged to form the various parts of the fruit. This develops, and its development may be normal, somewhat less and at times—which seems paradoxical —even more than usual. But invariably the seeds will sooner or later miscarry.

The development in the fruit may differ widely, according to the treatment and disposition of the fruit; we have *abortion* in the fruit of Indian corn, grapes of *reduced size* in the vine, *over-developed* seed-vessels in opium poppies. In none of these three instances do we have seeds.

The strange discordance in the case of the poppy, might be explained by the flow of latex which the act of fecundation recalls to the ovules; no longer able to nourish the seeds because they have miscarried, the latex flows back into the mesocarp, causing it to thicken, as one can see in Fig. 24, producing opium secretions on the outside.

But in the vine, the lack of formation of seeds causes an automatic reduction in the afflux of sap in the pulp of the fruit. In the face of the xenia phenomena observed by Mendola and Bouschet, it would seem that in the vine the seed apparently has control, so to speak over the nascent plasma surrounding the embryo, to the extent of infusing partial pigmentation to it, which are peculiar to the paternal variety.

Vine pollen, which is hardily resistant in preservation, is no less resistant to slow cycle magnetic ionolysis,[1] which does not seem to exercise any significant effect on its specific properties; but though it does not lose its fertilizing qualities, it is no longer able to produce seeds after an hour and a half of *light* ultra-violet radiation. Fig. 25 shows us two bunches of Maddalena Reale, identical at the moment of fecundation, which were produced artificially with pollen of the Lady Finger species. On the right an almost general miscarriage was verified, due to ultra-violet rays treatment, while the bunch of comparison grapes to the left is, so to speak, inviolate.

The corn cob in Fig. 26 was fecundated with normal pollen in its lower half, the stigmas having been carefully divided into two parts (before they were insulated from extraneous fecundation) and with pollen ionolized at length in the upper half. The photograph shows evident results.

These are the extreme results of unsuitable or over-prolonged ionolization; a shorter exposure period of minor intensity will cause partial abortion, or with progressive diminution of the 'intensity, frequency and time' combination, we find seeds which in appearance are well developed, but do not germinate, or else seeds of normal appearance which when shooting, produce abortive, short-

[1] It will resist under a month-long treatment with excitation at 42 cycles, and still produce vital seeds.

lived plants; lastly, we find perfect seeds which bear well formed plants with some variation of the upper organs. It is these which arouse our interest.

The deforming iono-genetic action is therefore a complicated combination of hyper-delicate factors, and success depends on selection of them, the proportion and duration.

First series of experiments made by the author.

61.

Mutation in the Double Opium Poppy with Fluctuating Magnetic Field

Just as I was about to start describing the experiments shown to you in connection with ionolysis of plants, and was arranging them so as to stress their genetic consequences, I found myself somewhat undecided as to what method should be followed, and what priority I should give to this or that series of experiments.

Overcoming my initial perplexity, I decided to divide them into two categories: the first covering the experiences of genetic variations obtained on *pure species,* or races, fecundated with their own pollen and subjected to various systems of ionolization; the second dealing with the larger number of experiments concentrating on restraining the individuality of the masculine element in cases where it proved dominant *in hybridization.*

I then decided to describe both in the one and the other instance, and in chronological form, the various experiments carried out on each species, so that the reader could follow the different phases of evolution which commenced with the first uncertain idea and grew more and more assuring through the tuition of failure, extending successfully even to plant families and species which in the beginning, when I was only applying slow cycle magnetic ionolysis, had seemed to be refractory, that is to say, genetically unalterable.

In the interests of brevity, I omitted the utterly negative experiments, which were particularly numerous in the initial stages.

I thought it as well to give some technical details on the preparatory or operational process for each different batch of experiments, to convince the reader of the serious nature of procedure and offer guidance to anyone feeling inclination to repeat, or better, to develop, the delightful work of experimentation.

EXPERIMENTS ON THE HORTICULTURAL SPECIES

Double White Opium Poppy (*Papaver sonniferum album pleno*).
The first verification of the effectiveness of ionolization in a variable magnetic field dates back to 1914, in connection with this variety, which, from a genetic point of view, may be considered as stable as the pure botanic species.

Both in this and subsequent experiments on poppies, the preparatory process and operational procedure followed the following rules:

In each experiment the buds intended to act as seed-bearers were prepared, having been chosen from the better constituted ones. On the same morning in which the buds evinced imminence of bloom, they were delicately opened very early, their petals being moved so as to isolate the ovaric seed-vessel at their heart.

With small pincers the anthers and petals round about this seed-vessel were removed, and the petals again closed about it, so as not to expose the extremely delicate stigmas, which were still gelatinous, to the rays of the sun which would have ruined them. The buds were then put into small bags of transparent paper, where they came to bloom in safety from the eventual visitations of 'wedding-happy' insects which, instinctively attracted, would have provoked fecundation with the heterogeneous pollen with which their wings are soiled after previous visits paid to flowers in the same area.

Toward noon, when the petals that were well opened and the stigmal papillae swelling, feather-like, on the edges of the little cap of the ovaric seed-vessel, testified to the maturity of the female organs, the procedure of fecundation began. This is done by soaking a very soft brush, or a fine quill into the pollen which has already been gathered, and applying it to the stigmas. When the artificial fecundation is completed, the buds are again put into

143

their protective paper bag, and the manner, entity and duration of the treatment received by the pollen is duly registered.

For each group of experiments the pollen is taken from one flower only, or at least from the first flowers blooming on the same plant. The best time to gather the pollen is in the morning, not later than seven o'clock. The anthers of the flowers which are about to open are delicately lifted and placed on a fine sieve of silken veiling drawn very tightly. When exposed to the sun for a few minutes, they open their lattice cells and let the pollen drop, the pollen being easily gathered, after a light shake, on a small plate or *shiny* paper, possibly black in color, held below.

Absorbent paper is to be excluded completely, because much of the pollen is retained for comparative experiments, a thin layer of it being put into the appropriate pollen-container, which consists of a double-bottomed box in which the lower part contains an electric lamp with metal filaments of 5 candle power.

Fig. 27 shows a section of a pollen-container. In the upper part are two lattices on which the sheets of shiny paper with the pollen are put.

The lower part becomes somewhat warmer than the remainder (2-3 degrees centigrade) because of the lamp which is always alight inside it, heating it just enough to prevent any steam from forming in the upper part, during the night or in consequence of any sudden fall in the outer temperature. At times an imperceptible veil of dew suffices to clot the pollen of some species, making it quite useless.

A slight but indispensable ventilation is obtained through the holes in the sides and lid.

Such severe control experiments are by no means superfluous, especially in the interests of comparison between ionolytic pollen treatments carried out with slow cycle excitation which are spread over several days. Quite apart from artificial alterations, the pollen will modify its genetic disposition solely in the process of aging. (Section 61).

The first experiment of the series was as follows:

a) Comparison: Fecundation with pollen gathered 4 days previously.

b) Fecundation with pollen spread for 4 days on the upper polar surface of the electro-magnet seen in Fig. 11 and *excited day and night uninterruptedly* by alternate current at 42 cycles for 4 days. Maximum intensity of magnetic field 4000 gauss.[1]

c) As above, in the interpolar area. Maximum intensity of field 6000 gauss.

Results

a) The plants born of the seeds of this controlled fecundation germinated regularly, and had a normal stature and development, upright bearing, straight stems (Fig. 28). They bloomed at the usual time, and the flowers were well developed, of pure white color.

b) Plants identical to the above; with slight increase of development and heads (seed-vessels) somewhat larger. Stems were slightly more curved in some of the plants, as though bending under the weight of the flower.

All plants were of homogeneous constitution and faithfully continued to reproduce by seed.

c) Regular birth and development. Plants were very much taller and apparently stronger than those used in comparison. They flowered a few days later than group a) and b). Flowers were larger and slightly more yellow than the others; seed-vessels very large. At the end of their bloom, the stems bent, becoming flaccid, sometimes sinusoidal or helicoidal in attitude (Fig. 29), perhaps because of the abnormal seed-vessels and perhaps because of the longer resistance of the yellowish petals on the flower. Such characteristics were found, in a more or less accentuated degree, in all

---

[1] The *gauss* is the unit of magnetic measurement and corresponds to one magnetic line of force per cm.[2] of polar surface.

The value of the field intensity expressed in gauss must be considered as proportional to the moment of maximum intensity (Section 39) of the exciting current which in technical terms is known as *working value*.

For the above reasons (stated in Section 42 and 46) the field intensity could not be uniform except in an exceedingly limited interpolar area. Since this is not possible, the measures of the magnetic field stated for each experiment express the maximum intensity effecting the pollen.

individual plants of this group, which reproduce quite well by seed, but retain the anomalous forms to a large measure in their progeny.

Of the four main characteristics in the mutation brought about in their species in the experiment c) (gigantism, tardy bloom, yellowish petals, curving of stems), the last seems the most enigmatic and sensational. It is also the most unstable; it is not found in equal proportion in all the individual plants, nor is there a homogeneous response in the different stems of the same plant (Fig. 31A).

So one has to surmise that it is a patent property which manifests itself to a greater or lesser degree, according to circumstances and exterior causes. The same applies to turgescence, which the burden of dew that is deposited on the plant in abundant measure during the nights which follow on rainy evenings, seems to further, while the curve of the stems is prevented by dry and windy weather.

Proof of this has been obtained by planting the seeds used in comparison in the experiments described above (which were repeated in 1918), in the ground during the fall season, and which blossomed the following year, which was memorable on account of its persistent spring drought.[1]

The stems were only slightly bent, or not at all, although many of the seed-vessels retained their close petals, even though they were withered, until July, (Figs. 30 and 31).

The gigantism induced by slow cycle ionolysis in group c) contrasts with the overall effects of ionization which are debilitating, as will be shown more specifically in Chapter VIII.

Probably the taller stature is due to the *retarded flowering* of the plants of this group. It is an obvious fact that flowers, and consequently fruit and seeds, are *passive organs in the process of vegetative increment.* From the moment they sprout on the vegetable axis, the better part of the sap and other reserve matter stored away within the plant, is assigned to them; the plant only works for the organs destined to reproduce it.

In many species, flowers and seeds absorb all the nourishment existing in the plant which withers, to yield all its juices down to

[1] Not one drop of rain fell during 1919 from the end of April until the end of June.

the last drop, to the multitude of new existences (seeds) which it has formed. The plurality of annual plants follow this admirable law of loving devotion.

Among these is the poppy and the ripening of its seed-vessels does in fact, coincide with the death of the plant.

It is understood that the more a plant delays in forming buds (and the poppy certainly does not constitute any exception), the more it will develop. For it is true that this development can be produced at will in any species by repeatedly destroying the secondary buds and stems, which resprout. So it seems that the delay in blooming, verified in iono-born plants, favors the greater growth of the vegetative axis.

During the different blossomings of white opium poppies, produced with ionolized pollen, I was able to verify how the tenacity of the petal was proportional to the yellowish or greenish tint which the flower takes on under the effect of ionolizing treatment of the paternal genitive plasma. The yellowish petals are difficult to detach from the flower; the greenish ones are even more constant, and remain in flower for about a week, while they fall during the day following their bloom, in the plants used as comparison. This is a positive quality which, however, is prejudicial to the production of seeds, at least insofar as the extreme green quality is concerned.

The curving of the stems would seem to be independent of the intensity of the anomal lutescence or virescence; in fact, ionization experiments by rays combined with magnetic ionolysis have produced *straight, thick-set and dwarfed* plants with short stems and large flowers of a fine and *definite green*, although somewhat pale (Section 64). But there are also instances in which the most outstanding characteristics of genetic deformation are found combined, so that with ultra-violet rays one finds *extremely twisted stems and greenish flowers,* (Fig. 40).

Subjecting pollen to magnetic slow-cycle ionolysis, as in the cases just described (b and c), some little time is necessary to obtain any noticeable genetic modification (3-4 days). To gauge the influence of the aging of genital plasma, independently from ionolization, I fecundated several somniferous poppy seed-vessels of the double white variety, in 1920, with pollen of their own variety, which had been taken respectively 6 and 10 days previously[1] from the first flowers of the group and preserved in the manner already described.

I have obtained plants somewhat taller and later in bloom than normal ones, with pure white flowers which showed some slight tendency to flaccidity, while some of the stems of the secondary axes were twisted. So in some instances, the aging of plasma will producè analogous effects to those of light ionization. Vine pollen may be preserved from one year to another (Section 43) and the debilitating influence due to its aging is even more apparent.

Rapid-cycle ionolysis (Section 62) shortens the stem, and one finds several off-shoots of stems far lower than usually found in that variety, but without any deformation of the stems.

In judging the cause of the twisting brought about by ionolysis in group c) independently of anything else, one is led to believe that the duration of the treatment has contributed greatly thereto, though it is also found in cases of very weak but prolonged ionolysis.

In order to establish the minimum amount of time sufficient to cause genetic modifications of any entity, I later pursued the experiments described below.

d) Fecundation with pollen exposed in a fluctuating magnetic field at 42 cycles, for 24 hours. Maximum intensity 4750 gauss.

e) Id. also for 24 hours, maximum intensity 6000 gauss.

f) Id. id. intensity maximum 8000 gauss.

g) Id. for 40 hours. Maximum intensity 6000 gauss.

h) Fecundation with pollen mixed with finest shredded iron; 40 hours exposure, as above. Maximum intensity approximately 15,000 gauss. In this experiment, compared with experiment g) the same apparatus (Fig. 16) was used, with the identical area between poles and analogous excitation. The greater magnitude of the field expressed in gauss is only approximate, and due to the introduction of iron which was distributed by brush as indicated in section 46 (Fig. 10).

i) Fecundation with pollen produced under the influence of variable magnetic field by alternate currents of 42 cycles, the bud

---

[1] The maximum compatible with endurance of the fecundating power.

being placed between the rectilineal electro-magnetic poles of Fig. 11, commencing four days prior to flowering. The anthers were therefore completed and opened under the influence of the variable magnetic field. The intensity of the magnetic field was extremely weak, because of the distance between poles. The approximate intensity of the field was 700 gauss.

Results

d) No difference from the control group.

e) As d.

f) As d.

g) Slight deformation of some stems, and a few flowers lost their petals somewhat late. Otherwise normal.

h) Flowers are slightly yellowish in this group and the petals are tightly attached to the stem, at times enduring until the seed-vessels have ripened (Fig. 30).

The mixture of iron in the pollen was definitely favorable to ionolysis.

i) This experiment proves that the precocious action of ionolysis on pollen in a process of ripening results in significant modifications very different from those which one may obtain on ripe pollen by far more powerful means, even though the magnitude of the field is relatively weak. Results obtained with recent cucurbita and althaea experiments confirm those obtained with this group of poppies, and lead one to hope that in the future, ionolysis of the immature anther will prevail over that of pollen, mainly because, no matter how protracted the treatment may be, it does not deprive the progeny which it originates, of its robustness.

All individual plants in this group are greenish white in flower, the blossoms are big, lasting, and well doubled, with highly contorted stems and plants much smaller in stature than those in the similar group (c), previously described. They blossom 8-10 days later than normal. Fig. 31 shows several flowers of this type, with their characteristic closeness of petal which lasts even while the seed-vessels are already well on the way to maturity.

62.

Mutation With Frequent Alternation of Magnetic Field

Rapid-cycle electro-magnetic treatment of poppies yields results considerably different from those obtained by slow cycles; indeed the opposite effect is obtained in regard to the height of the plant.

I therefore thought I had better list the rapid-cycle ionolysis experiments separately, coordinating them according to the customary rule. For this group too, observations are based on the morphologic differences of the variety of type, which remains always the double white opium poppy; I am therefore omitting the control experiment which the reader will find under section 61 (Fig. 28) for his reference.

A. Fecundation with pollen placed in the interpolar area of the apparatus seen in Fig. 15. Exciting current 400-500 cycles. Maximum field intensity 3250 gauss. Treatment lasting one hour.

B. Fecundation in the identical conditions as above, with powdered iron mixed with the pollen in proportion of $\frac{1}{3}$ to the total volume.

C. Fecundation in identical conditions as A, treatment protracted to one hour and a half; intensity of field 3250 gauss.

D. Fecundation as in the foregoing, with pollen mixed with shredded iron. Equal time exposure.

Results

A. Homogeneous group formed of somewhat dwarf-like plants, strong, large, well doubled blooms, white, rarely tinged with creamy yellow. Early flowering, characterized by almost simultaneous opening of secondary stems and principal axis; petals closer to stem than usual, very little dissimilarity from normal. No curved stems (Fig. 32).

B. The introduction of shredded iron in the interpolar area which already proved beneficial in experiment h) (Section 61) with *slow variation of magnetic field* (42 cycles) was not quite so beneficial in this instance.

In sections 46, 47 and 48 it was already explained how, by increasing the number of cycles in the exciting current, a point is reached when any further increase in the rapidity of magnetic field variations has a detractive effect, because reactionary currents are produced in the iron shreds; these counteract the magnetic variations, destroying their effect. Plants in this group are almost normal in height; nevertheless, one finds pale yellowish flowers occasionally; seed-vessels are lightly flattened and furrowed as in experiment a) already described.

C. Not a very homogeneous group as regards height and size of flowers. The more anomalous among them are very low in stature and bush-like in structure, in a most singular manner. There is no longer any difference between central axis and secondary off-shoots; flowers are no longer gradual in order of blossoming, all the many small flowers opening their buds at the same time, in the same degree. Each plant might be compared to a bunch of flowers (Fig. 33A) stuck in the ground.

All stalks (which are numerous) originate from the main stem of the plant, because the vegetative cone is shrivelled (diminished to only a few centimeters) and enormously swollen, so that the stalk of the plant seems to disappear entirely.

Two extreme samples in this group, somewhat tardier than the twins, have no stalk at all; in its place there is a tangle of enormous, twisted leaves, between the axils of which sprout a few thin and weak stems which bear double white flowers, with a green heart and fimbriate edges tinged with pink, which is very interesting. It does not come across too well in a photograph. In the other flowers of this curious flower-bed, the color of the flowers is white or yellowish; toward the end of flowering many pink-edged flowers appear. The ovaries and seed-vessels are somewhat deformed, and in one case, there was a monstrous seed-vessel, curiously contorted in shape, on one of the later secondary off-shoots. The petals fold tightly about the seed-vessels. While the majority of the plants forming this group flower prematurely, the extreme cases of deformation flower normally, or even later than usual.

In this group too, the curved stems are rarely seen, but they are, at times, distinguished by an abrupt curve.

The more singularly varied plants have no seeds; it is also observed how some of them die easily both before and after blossoming, before completing their whole vegetative cycle, and these are plants with the more swollen stalks. The seed-vessels are flattened within plants already having undergone mutation and are furrowed, in the less varied examples, by parallel undulations.

D. Again in this group, the addition of iron in the interpolar area together with the pollen has fully confirmed the results obtained from group B so the same deductions may apply. But they differ from group B insofar as one observes a more pronounced curve in the stems, which is, however, considerably less than in the plants processed in experiment C. The seed-vessels are flattened and furrowed, often having petals which remain closely folded over them until the seeds are ripe.

It was only possible to ascertain that the green character induced by ionolysis may be transmitted, like any other specific characteristic, to the progeny from two plants with greenish flowers from which the seeds had been taken prior to artificial fecundation, with the customary preservation. This is an interesting observation which is confirmed by several other experiments, and it proves that the iono-born plant is *mutated in all of its plasma,* so that its progeny continues to instil the anomalous derangement, from which it was artificially created, into every organ.

63.

Mutation with Pulsating Magnetic Field

I have put together all experiments in connection with the use of interrupted currents with electrolytic apparatuses producing pulsating magnetic fields, giving priority to those of low frequency, produced by 40 volt exciting currents. As the reader will see, the former do not yield results proportional to the amount of energy used, which on the whole cannot be estimated exactly (since then there were no electro-magnets equipped with measuring tools (Section 50) (Fig. 13) which evaluate the induction produced), and which is strictly subordinated to the harmony of the various factors of electric circuit, impedance and self-induction, as was stressed repeatedly in Chapter V.

The few experiments described here below are a compendium of many more, undertaken with criteria of gradual testing, many of them being unsuccessful or, even when they did yield seeds, lacking in possibility of control, for various reasons.

Here again, the experiments were made on double opium poppies having white flowers.

I. Fecundation with pollen subjected to pulsating magnetic field, placed between the polar opening of a rectilineal electro-magnet (Fig. 11), with polarity in series, and alternating (40-volt alternate exciting current, 42 cycles), interrupted by electrolytic Wenhelt switch apparatus. Duration of treatment: 3 hours. Maximum field intensity: 6000 gauss.

II. Fecundation with pollen treated as above for 6 hours.

III. Fecundation with pollen treated with pulsating magnetic field in the manner described above, but with 80 volt exciting current. Duration of treatment: 20 hours.[1] Maximum field intensity: 3400 gauss.

IV. Fecundation with pollen as above. Same duration of treatment. Maximum field intensity, 5000 gauss.

V. Fecundation with pollen placed between the complementary poles of the rectilineal electro-magnet, with spark gap measuring tool, (Fig. 13) with spools in series. Alternate exciting current 42 cycles, 80-volt, interrupted by Wenhelt electrolytic switch. Duration of treatment 90 minutes. Maximum intensity of field, 9430 gauss.

VI. Fecundation as above with introduction of powdered iron.

N.B. Experiments in which the current was interrupted by a small hammer switch are omitted, because they were inconclusive.

Results

I. Homogeneous group, somewhat low stature in plants, with a few instances of half-doubled flowers. Normal blossoming. Despite the slight and brief ionization, several flowers were found to be

---

[1] No poppy pollen would endure such long treatment alive; but in the case of No. III and No. IV there was no intonation between electro-magnet and current; so the field variation was not regular, nor did it proceed with the proper rapidity.

lightly greenish or straw-colored; a few flowers were edged with pale pink toward the end of the blossom time. Flattened seed-vessels, very varied in shape.

II. Great abundance of plants, all somewhat low in stature. This group too, showed about one fifth of their number to be definitely taller, and with semi-double flowers, as in group I. Two were robust, but the plants were low with very curved stems and greenish flowers, while several other examples had rounded petals instead of fringed edges. Flattened, misshapen seed-vessels. Despite prolonged treatment, no outstanding demorphistic characteristics were observed.

III. Very homogeneous group; hardly distinguishable from comparative sample (Fig. 28) in regard to stature, which is only slightly lower. Flowers are all white, as in the type species. Straight stalks and seed-vessels almost normal, but slightly smaller than usual (Fig. 34).

IV. The greater intensity of magnetic field caused this group to be dwarfed in all individual plants of which it consisted. But it did not alter the shade of the flowers, as occurs with abrupt ionization (see experiment V), owing to the previously explained discordance between electro-magnet and exciting current. Several mature plants of this group are seen in Fig. 35.

Experiments III and IV show that the effectiveness of the process of ionolysis does not depend on the time exposure, but above all on the rapidity and abruptness of variation in the magnetic field.

V. A perfectly clear judgment on the development of height in this group is not possible, since the plants in it are somewhat thickly planted together, so that they are apt to push upward in search of room and light. A comparison with the original control variety, and with the previous groups shows that they flower somewhat late. The most outstanding characteristic is the prevalence of flowers with rounded edges in petals (the petals in the mother variety are finely fringed).

The flowers, which are very compact, look like white double peonies; and the petals are folded so closely about the thalamus that they remained on the plant for over a week; before falling, many petals became veined with pink toward their edges. In some instances, the seed-vessels still retained their close-lying petals when mature (Fig. 36).

The peony-like corollas gave rise to seed-vessels of varying size; but instead of being oval and flattened, such as are generally obtained with other systems of ionization, they were thin toward the tip and broad below, like pears. The opercula are very small, wedge-shaped and resemble very often the roofs of Indian pagodas; but at times they are completely absent. In one case, the seed-vessel was reduced to a mere strip, far narrower than the peduncle on which it stood vertically (Fig. 36 to the lower right). In a few cases, which were the most tardy and fragile in this group, a curious phenomenon was verified. After the normal bloom was over, and the petals fell, rudiments of petals were seen to shoot from the open lips of the seed-vessel, at the top of the ovary, there being no operculum, and the seed-vessel seemed to be well advanced toward maturity. In Fig. 36 three of these monstrous instances of petaloid carpels are seen, which as far as I know, has never been found in any species of cultivated poppy.

Fig. 38 reproduced in natural size an extreme case of petalody which, like all the others, is absolutely sterile. The anomal seed-vessels do not have the proper sectional divisions in their interior, and in place of seeds there are semi-transparent, gelatinous blackish balls measuring about $2\frac{1}{2}$ to 3 millimeters in diameter, unevenly distributed over the interior wall.

The curving in the stems is not homogeneous, but frequent, in this group, of which both the general and specific abnormalities are undeniably important.

If similar results could be obtained agamically on multiplicable flowers, instead of on annual plants, such as those on which I have been working until now (so that the results might be seen within a brief period of time), this would be a valuable and lasting step forward.

VI. As might easily have been imagined, instead of furthering the ionolysis of the pollen, the addition of iron debilitated it considerably, so that this experimental group, treated with an identical process as the foregoing one, can be compared to the second group in which the action of the ionolizing force is considerably lessened.

On the whole, the results of experiments with interrupted current confirm that quite uncommon mutations can be obtained with a pulsating magnetic field.

Besides one phase prevailing over the opposite phase, electrolytically interrupted currents have an advantage over alternating currents, in the case of living plasma; they do not have a constant rhythm. Since the phenomenon of molecular disintegration is admittedly determined by the intonation of velocity with which the field varies and the composition of the atomic groups of chromosomes, it is obvious that the probability of advantageous effect on chromosomes is undeniably increased, with consequent development of mutability, by using the electrolytic switch which allows irregular, and therefore assorted variations.

64.

Mutation with Ultra-Violet Radiation

Ionization by rays is very effective in the morphological consequences it entails in the progeny, but the violation it causes in the atomic structure of the genital plasma provokes grievous abortion of the majority of the seeds.

Because it offers an extremely interesting comparison of differentials, I have included several experiments in compound ionization produced by the contemporary action of rays and a variable magnetic field, in this section.

The subject treated is still the white opium poppy with double flowers, and the following were the experiments:

a) Fecundation with pollen treated by ultra-violet rays with spark flaring between the tips of the apparatus seen in Fig. 7, fed by the gap-measuring tool with which the short circuit electromagnet is equipped (Fig. 13). The exciting current is alternating, 42 cycle, interrupted with Wenhelt switch. Length of spark 3 millimeters. The small pollen-bearing slab was 30 mm. away from the spark. Duration of treatment: one hour and 30 minutes.[1]

---

[1] In experiments a) and b) the pollen was passed through a very fine silk sieve onto a thin mica slab, in a very thin layer, before putting it into the apparatus, so that it might benefit as much as possible by the radiation. (Section 38.).

b) Fecundation with pollen placed in identical experimental conditions, in which the magnetic field also took part, under the same synchronous effect of the exciting current. Duration of treatment: 1 hour 30 minutes.

Results

a) Just as in other analogous cases verified on other species, ionization caused great abortion of seeds; further reproduction was scarce and without any apparent cause, many plants died, after having lived through the winter, during the course of development. Judging by appearance, and in accordance with all reactional probabilities, the plants that died which were morphologically more mutated than others, could not remain alive because they lacked that minimum specific directive necessary to the unceasing physiological metamorphosis of vital evolution. Their limp, irregular appearance, the asymmetry of the leaf design, the irregularity of the insertion of leaves on the stalk which was abnormally shortened and exaggeratedly swollen, as in all plants of this group, are the outer signs of the immense upheaval provoked in male plasma by ray ionization.

Nevertheless, despite these drawbacks, which accompany necessarily the powerful forcing of normal development in the laws of Nature, this experiment had the most conspicuous results and best homogeneous outcome among the individual plants of the group.

Fig. 40 shows one plant only, the extreme instance in this group, in which the enormous stalk, swollen beyond all measure, fills the entire area of the vase, (7 cm.) in which it stands to be photographed at the customary distance.

The most noticeable feature about it is the strong curve of the stems, the swollen aspect of the stalk and the greenish color of the flowers; in many individual plants a tendency to reflower was verified; in these instances, the second flowering was white or almost white, even though the first blossoms were distinctly greenish.

The flaccidity is not restricted, as occurs in many instances of magnetic ionolysis, to the flower stems, but extends to the branches, as well; and this both in the central axis and the lateral off-shoots (which abound in each individual plant in this group). The contortion which stems from this begins very early, far sooner than the buds have emerged from the leaves.

Although the season was extremely dry, the plants developed considerably, far more so than in the comparative examples of plants, both in height and ramifications. The weight of the plants undergoing mutation in comparison to the others, was at least double, and even went so far as to be almost four times as heavy.

On the curves in the primary stems and the secondary stems, each of which bears a double flower, compact and greenish, other thin, very short and straight stems sprout, which, in their turn, blossom about a month and a half later, with blossoms of a white-greenish tint, far paler than the May flowers.

The photograph here reproduced was taken at the end of June and shows specifically the reflowering, while the seed-vessels, produced under normal flowering, are already almost withered.

As occurs in extreme instances of all monstrosities, the flowers in this group are almost completely sterile, and their seed-vessels are very reduced in size, being at times, hardly any bigger than the stem supporting them.

b) The simultaneous action of two artifices, each of them revealed as capable of specific genetic action, offers, in this experiment, an irrefutable proof of the necessity of experimental research, repeated for each single case, system, or combination of systems, and for each species. The specific contemporary actions produced by ionolysis and ionization by rays *cannot be amalgamated,* because their form of vibratility is so extremely diverse. Nor can they influence one another, and produce intermediate results half-way between the single deformations produced by each ionizing system.

This experiment offered the most important results and best homogeneity among the individual plants of the group. Fig. 41 reproduces a portion of the flower bed in full bloom. By comparing it with the plants situated in the background, which belong to another group, the reader can form an idea of the dwarfism induced by the simultaneous action of the two factors of ionization which, when isolated, produce far better developed plants which blossom much later.

Despite their lower stature, the plants of this group are well constructed, squat, and have strong, straight and rigid stems, very large and compactly double blossoms, which live long, are well fringed and all of a more or less conspicuous greenish tint. The photograph does not give the impression of this delicate pigmentation, but in E a plant with three blossoms, an extreme sample of virescence, is plainly discernible.

Besides regular stature, tint, and time of blossoming, these plants also have perfect homogeneous morphological structure of seed-vessels, which are strong, flattened, regularly undulated, while the equivalent electro-magnetic treatment alone, causes pointed or pear-shaped seed-vessels in the adjoining flower-bed (Fig. 37), and ionization (Fig. 40) with ultra-violet rays, alone, produces stunted and twisted seed vessels with atrophied opercula and flaccid, twisted stems.

The compact double quality of the flowers is so perfect in this group that almost all the anthers are transformed into petals, and the few stunted ones which are hidden by the others in their thick compactness, do not mature at the same time as the stigma, so that not many seeds are obtained from this species.

When the ultra-violet light acts alone on the pollen, it causes a very grave relaxation in progeny. But when its action is accompanied by pulsating magnetic ionolysis, which provokes remarkable monstrosities (Section 63) when it acts on its own, the biologic deficiency is parried, and a species is obtained which can vie with the original type of comparison in strength, even though it is dwarfed and regularly endowed with curious greenish pigmentation.

65.

Mutation by the Application of Radium

It was to be foreseen that radium action would give very much the same result as treatment with ultra-violet rays; but it would seem that the results are much closer to those obtained by frequent cycle electro-magnetic ionolysis. The following experiments were made:

R^1. Fecundation with pollen radiolized in the apparatus seen in Fig. 6, without screen excluding α-rays for 24 hours.

R^2. As above for 48 hours.

R^V. Analogous treatment as in the foregoing, but on plants with greenish blossoms, in consequence of previous ionolytic origin.

R^N. Fecundation with pollen of flower radiolized in bud, commencing 10 days prior to blooming. Average distance from radio-active salt: 2 cm.

NB. The quantity of radio-active salt in the first three experiments, was 1.42 mg, and the distance of the pollen from the radio-active salt 6 millimeters.

Results

R^1. Little evidence of effect in seed-vessels; seeds miscarried for the most part. Birth fairly good. This group, rather dwarfed, resembled that in Experiment B (Section 62). No samples of greenish flowers or peony-like flowers.

R^2. As in the foregoing little evidence from seeds. The entire group notably dwarfed. Unlike Groups B and C (Section 62) the flowers are few, large, completely white, and although the plants are dwarfish, they do not show any deformation in stalk. As seen in Fig. 42 the plants bloom again very late, in July, giving a good quantity of seeds, contrary to what occurs under action of ultra-violet rays and in the extreme cases of virescence induced by electro-magnetic treatment.

R^V. The low birth among this group does not allow any definitive judgment. The four surviving examples are dwarfs, but have lost their green pigmentation completely, though this is manifest with permanent hereditary features in the iono-born sub-species.

R^N. This fecundation did not yield even one vital seed.

66.

Magnetic Ionolysis in Cucurbita Maxima

The Cucurbita species, with its very coarse pollen, was one of the the first to respond to slow cycle magnetic ionolysis, applied in the early experiments, while it was slow in showing any of the genetic modifications attempted by radiation and rapid cycle magnetic ionolysis which acted promptly, but generally with disastrous results.

Pumpkins are monoecious plants (Section 16), extremely easy to fecundate. They do not need castration, and when the necessary precautions are taken in good time to isolate the female flowers before they open, they easily offer the best guarantee for a successful experiment.

The imminence of flowering is indicated by the enlargement of the buds and by their color which changes from greenish to orange-yellow, as well as by the swelling of the ovary beneath the cup, which loses its pubescence.

To ensure the female flowers against the all-too probable danger of extraneous fecundation (bees pay calls on them in the very early hours of the morning), the small isolating sacks must be put into place the evening before.

The pollen is easily gathered, and this should be done early in the morning; it retains its vitality until the following morning, if the necessary precautions are taken (Section 61).

Marucca Pumpkin with green, knotted skin
(*Cucurbita Maxima, verrucosa* variety)

Experiments were made on two different varieties of the marucca pumpkin in the following manner:

A. Test fecundation.

B. Fecundation with pollen placed between the poles of the rectilineal electro-magnet (Fig. 11), excited by alternate 42 cycle current. Maximum intensity of field, 5600 gauss. Duration of treatment 3 hours.

C. Fecundation with pollen placed between the poles of the same electro-magnet excited by *direct current,* producing an intensity of field of 7600 gauss. Duration of treatment, 1 hour and 30 minutes.

Results

A. The plants born from the test fecundation were similar in everything to the green Marucca Pumpkin. The cortex was somewhat more bronze in appearance, and in a few of them, the fruit was lightly streaked with red.[1] The shape of the globose was as in the original species.

B. Regular birth and development, as described in the comparison above, the flowers being prevalently smaller, and twisted on one of the plants; the petal section slanting obliquely in respect to the symmetry of the axis; this type was slightly narrower and thicker than usual.

All the fruits had a homogeneously flattened appearance, in respect to the archetype of the variety. The color of the skin varied from greenish white to silvery grey and even to bronze, and a vivid scarlet. In each sample, pigmentation was unified in color, without stripes.

The most remarkable modification obtained was the scarlet variety of flower with narrow cup and the obliquely reversed petals, as described above.

In all plants of this group the seeds were normal, except for those in the scarlet fruit, which had somewhat smaller seeds of a brownish-yellow color.

The pulp was firm and tasty in all fruit, even the scarlet variety.

Among many others there are varieties in the Marucca Pumpkin species which have an orange- or red-tinted rind, but the scarlet color was completely novel; and since I had had the good fortune to obtain it, I took good care to test its genetic constancy. If one wishes to reproduce with certainty a monoecious plant like the

---

[1] Probably because the pollen was from a different soil than that in which the seed-vessel had grown.

pumpkin, it has to be isolated, kept far away from all similar varieties, fecundating the female flowers, after protecting them against the visits of 'nuptial happy' insects, with its own pollen. I was unable to comply with these rules, because the individual plant with the scarlet fruit was situated right in the middle of its own group, nor did I suspect when it was in flower, the curious pigmentation which made its fruit so attractive.

At any rate, even though they were not entirely of homozygous conception, all the seeds obtained from the scarlet variety were sown again and, in 1918, about one third of the plants they produced had red fruit and relative hazel-colored seeds. So duly making allowances for their undeniably hybrid origin, their reproductive constancy was, so to speak, attained. The remaining two thirds of the plants reproduced and had more or less distinct and broad streaks of red in their fruit.

The vicissitudes of war unfortunately destroyed the lively interest aroused, and it was impossible to rekindle it later with the same colorful intensity.

C. Plants in this group did not show any change from those used as comparison. Already in sections 39 and 44, reference was made to the cause of ineffectiveness of magnetism with polar constancy; but like other experiments of the kind, this attempts only to establish whether or not an intense magnetic field alone may, of itself, exercise any influence on atoms of paramagnetic and diamagnetic substance such as genital plasma contains, albeit in minimum quantity. If the effect of magnetism could displace such atoms, then the hereditary units would be more or less modified; but this experiment, just like others carried out later, would seem to belie this supposition.

In experiment B there was only one constant characteristic peculiar to pollen ionolysis: the flattened shape of the fruit; but in regard to polychromy, a doubt, which perhaps was not completely justified, persisted; namely that some unknown and distant relative of the original variety had influenced the determination of the varying chromatic tonality in some atavistic way.

As a precaution against any eventual cause for error, I repeated the experiment, prolonging the period of exposure, on a regularly constant species, which was perfectly homozygous, with very long, ashy-grey colored fruit, which reproduced itself with utter fidelity, as I had had occasion to observe in person for a number of years. The experimental tests described below were the only ones which succeeded out of a dozen and more fecundations with pollen subjected to various methods of ionolysis.

Fecundation of the wart-covered pumpkin is especially difficult, and often the fruit will not set at all, or sets badly, breaking off after a few days.

Long ash-grey Marucca Pumpkin, with knotted skin.
(*Cucurbita maxima*, ash-grey variety)

D. Fecundation with pollen exposed for 4 hours between the poles of the curved electro-magnet (Fig. 15), excited by alternating 42 cycle current. Maximum field intensity, 5800 gauss.

E. As above. Fecundation with pollen exposed for one hour and 30 minutes in the interpolar area of the lineal electro-magnet (Fig. 13), complementary polarity. Exciting alternating 40-volt current, 42 cycle, interrupted by Wenhelt apparatus. Maximum intensity of field, 2640 gauss.

Results

D. The plants in this group bore fruit late, and were enormously enlarged. The characteristics of the fruit were generally attuned to those in experiment B. Perhaps by reason of relativity, since the prototype of the species has very long fruit, (Fig. 43) no flattened shapes were found here, as in Group B; nevertheless, as the illustration shows clearly, the experiment did produce a considerable deformation in the fruit. Polychromy was not so extensive as in the experiment described above; but here again were many reddish fruits and one completely red, but not shining scarlet as that described under B. The more flattened shapes had a distinctive feature which had not been observed previously, a very thick peduncle without any knots.

Fig. 43 shows us the fruit of the species used as comparison;

beside it, (Fig. 44) are two flattened fruits, with enormous, fleshy peduncles and a scarlet fruit on the right.

E. Very limited production. The few plants born are strong, satisfactorily fertile, and do not differ from the prototype except in the color of the rind, which is yellowish-white, instead of greenish-grey. Fruit retains a strange milk-white tint until ripe.

67.

Ionolysis in Cucurbita Pepo, Var. Melopepo ("Pasticina" Pumpkin)

Experiments carried out on this variety of Cucurbita pepo, were slow cycle, and although they produced good seeds, they were unsuccessful on account of the bad climatic conditions which destroyed the young plants, while the rapid-cycle experiments did not set after fecundation.

Only the plant described below was an exception, and produced some fifty samples.

P. Fecundation with pollen exposed for half an hour to pulsating magnetic field produced by Wenhelt switch with exciting 80-volt current. Maximum intensity of field 5270 gauss.

Results

P. Most of the plants forming this group faithfully reproduce their variety; but in at least one third of them there are traces of mutation. The varieties observed concern the fruit almost exclusively, and may be divided into two categories.

In the former, the fruit tends to be globose in shape; the crown is smaller, and even disappears completely in two samples. The characteristic apophysis is only slightly protuberant and tend to converge on the tip of the pistil (Fig. 45). The skin is ash-grey and smooth.

The latter has both variegated and green streaked fruit (a new color in this species, which normally does not vary at all).

68.

The Most Conspicuous Achievement: Dioecious and Monoclinous Cucurbita Pepo

Long green Italian Vegetable Marrow. (*Cucurbita pepo, var. cucurbitella*).

I preferred this for genetic experiments to many other varieties, because of its more stable characteristics than other similar species with which I am acquainted.

Fig. 46 shows us a group of these Italian vegetable marrow fruits with their finely cut, characteristic foliage.

To protect myself against any eventual appearance of spontaneous variations on the scene, I planted a flower-bed with seeds of the prototype of the variety, obtained by careful artificial fecundation, and taking all due precautions to protect the stigma against extraneous fecundation, at the same time that I sowed seeds in another flower-bed for my various seminal experiments. Each flower-bed contained about 40 to 50 plants, well spaced out. Here are the experiments:

1. Control test fecundation with fresh pollen.

2. Fecundation with pollen exposed to fluctuating magnetic field, 42 cycle, for 30 minutes. Maximum intensity of magnetic field, 4750 gauss.

3. As above for 90 minutes.

4. Fecundation with pollen exposed to fluctuating magnetic field, 600 cycles, for 30 minutes. Maximum field intensity 3250 gauss.

5. As above, for 60 minutes.

6. Fecundation with pollen exposed to pulsating magnetic field produced by Wenhelt switch on alternate 80-volt current for half an hour. Opposite polarity. Maximum intensity of field approximately 2000 gauss.

7. Fecundation with pollen in identical conditions as the foregoing, illuminated by ultra-violet ray produced by the spintherometer of the apparatus seen in Fig. 17. Equal time exposure.

NB. The experiments with ultra-violet light, when used without magnetic field, and those carried out with various exposure for radiolization, were all unsuccessful.

166

Results

1. The group, or better, the control flower-bed, was perfectly analogous to the variety prototype, both in fruit and foliage. Fig. 46 shows us two coupled plants, each with two fruits. The fruit is green, and streaked with yellow.

2. Among about 40 plants forming this group, only two were particularly modified by the slow and relatively short process of ionolysis. One of them had long fruit of normal shape; but its rind was yellow, lightly streaked with a pale green, instead of the dark green with yellow ribbing characteristic of the ripe fruit of the species prototype. The other modified specimen had very squat fruit, with a slightly lighter colored rind than normal, with very long and thin peduncles. Later observations on fruit of this type in other groups, confirmed their monoclinous nature. Both in the one and the other variety, there was no modification in foliage.

3. This group presented poor development, compared to that of the control group and others which are described further on. The fruit was yellow, slightly streaked with green, and in almost all specimens, somewhat shorter than normal, and also extremely fertile. Some plants bear as many *as seven vegetable marrows* while the group used in comparison rarely bore 2 or 3 on each plant. There were no instances of an elongation of the peduncle. Fig. 47 shows a plant of this group which has one specimen, likewise with short fruit, of a yellow gold color, without streaks.

4. Cycle frequency produced two main anomalies in this group, which are worthy of detailed description. On the whole, this group does not deviate from the specific physiogonomy, but the fruit develops with considerable precocity. Three anomalous plants stand out by reason of their reduced stature and almost total lack of stalk and petioles. Fig. 48 shows us the more characteristic example of *diecious form,* of which there were three specimens in this group. These are extremely dwarf-like, with verticillated and very thick leaves. They bear only female flowers, with very short ovaries. The petals form a star, instead of being closed in a bell-shape, and open before the normal period of dehiscence, laying bare the still immature stigma. When it has attained ripeness, this becomes fecundated with pollen from the adjacent plants,

causing the ovary to swell. The extremely squat shaped fruit develops within a few days, then its development ceases when it has grown as large as a big pear; later it becomes yellow and shrivels without producing seeds.

Undoubtedly, this diecious form is the most conspicuous modification caused by ionolysis. All organs of these three plants are deformed—stem, petioles, leaves, flowers, fruit—and even the masculine sex has been completely suppressed.

Ionolysis produced yet another important variation: the *monoclinous sub-species,* verified in only one specimen in this group, and which produced male flowers only slightly different from normal, while the female flowers, borne on robust peduncles, had monstrous stigmas, strangely curved about twisted anthers, and producing gibbous, shrunken fruit, with a long, thin peduncle.

While one observes considerable homogeneity in the results of slow cycle ionolysis, the rapid variation of field has caused only a few but well characterized forms, differing widely from the species prototype of this variety.

It is important to recall that two seed sowings were effected in this experiment; the second, made *with the same seeds* taken from the same fruit, took place approximately two weeks after the first, which was somewhat unsuccessful, owing to the season, which was still cold. The highly important variations described above did not recur in the first sowing.

I have called the attention of the reader elsewhere to the importance of a well conducted sowing, when one has to protect individual plants which are far more delicate than their species generally is, particularly during the critical period of germination, owing to the constitutional derangement from which they originate.

5. Quite probably, this group should have contained a higher percentage of anomalous plants, but instead, owing to their precocious sowing, they did not evince any considerable modifications, despite the double time exposure to a fluctuating magnetic field treatment, as compared with the foregoing group.

6. The pulsating magnetic field produced a good third of plants with variations only in the fruit, which was short with long petioles. (Fig. 49). It should again be observed that these were

monoclinous plants, similar in every way to the specimen already described in Group 4. This group also had plants with broad, only slightly cut leaves, and preceded the ripening of fruit on the comparative specimen by 7-10 days. Another outstanding anomaly consists of the gemmation of fruits, likewise reproduced in Fig. 49; lastly, we observe an immense, semi-creeping plant which produces male flowers in abundance, while it is also rich in female flowers which, however, regularly fall when only half developed.

7. Ultra-violet rays caused considerable abortion in the seeds, and those sown in the soil were scarce in quantity when born. Perhaps a later sowing would have been considerably beneficial, in the interests of preserving vitality even in the less robust seeds. The group does not differ from its prototype comparative specimen, save in four specimens of enormous development, with less incision in the leaves than in the original prototype, and of which only one of them produced an enormous fruit of 1.18 meters in length, well proportioned, but weighing about three times the usual weight.

* * *

Beside the extremely important mutations offering particular scientific interest in Group No. 4, and which would doubtlessly have been numerous also in Group No. 5 and in the other groups, if the sowing had been more carefully carried out, this series of experiments produced extraordinarily fertile and precocious types in Group No. 3 and partially in Group No. 6, such as were undeniably useful and which deserve both attention and closer examination from a speculative viewpoint. The lesser homogeneity in the results of these experiments, and in other species with coarse pollen, as compared to those carried out on poppies, may be justified by the fact that the smooth fine pollen can easily be spread out in a thin layer and thus benefit from an almost uniform magnetic field, while the coarse and clotted pollen which forms large lumps, such as one finds with vegetable marrow, cannot form an even surface in the interpolar area, nor, in consequence, receive any homogeneous intensity of the magnetic field.

169

69.

Hibiscoid Althaea Obtained by Magnetic Ionolysis

Althaea rosea (Hollyhock) (cultivated in very barren soil).

Althaeas, or hollyhocks, like all malvaceous plants, have a relatively coarse pollen which is highly sensitive to ionolysis but which does not tolerate ionization by rays, and most decidedly not by ultra-violet or β-rays of radium, unless later tests prove something to the contrary.

Their flowers are easily castrated, and this may be done as soon as the flower opens spontaneously, only showing its stigmas on the following day (until then, they are enclosed within the column supporting the stamen). It is also easy to isolate the castrated flowers, which is necessary in order to protect them from extraneous fecundation, with small sacks of transparent paper applied to each individual flower after the removal of the anthers, or else by one single wide tubular protective device which covers all the inflorescence on which one has to operate.

It is also extremely easy to gather the pollen.

This species always has seeds which are perfect in appearance, no matter to what kind of ionolytic treatment the pollen has been subjected; but when rapid cycle frequency is used, or the treatment is short, the seeds either do not germinate, or do so imperfectly.

The experiments listed below were made on hollyhocks, with simple wild-type flowers:

A. Fecundation of the comparative specimen, performed with pollen gathered 36 hours previously.

B. Fecundation with pollen exposed for 36 hours in the interpolar area of the electro-magnet seen in Fig. 16, excited by alternating, 42 cycle current. Maximum intensity of the magnetic field 3500 gauss.

C. Fecundation as above, with finely shredded iron mixed with the pollen.

D. Fecundation, as above, with finely shredded bismuth in place of iron.

NB. I made other experiments with ultra-violet rays, radium, etc., on this same species; but such treatments destroyed the germinative faculty of the pollen, so that fecundation did not take place, or there were no visible seeds when it did.

Results

A. The seed-vessel produced by normal fecundation contained perfect seeds, which ripened regularly, producing quite normal plants; the flowers were vivid pink and homogeneous in color. (Fig. 49).

B. The ionized pollen produced normal fruit and seeds, likewise well constituted. Sown in the soil at the same time and under the same condition as the comparative specimen A, they sprouted much later, and very sparingly; only three plants.

Just as occurred in other species, the plants produced by ionized pollen flowered later than their companions of the same genus. The delay is somewhat conspicuous in this malvacea too. The two surviving specimens which lived through the winter in which, like many others of the previous group, the remainder died, flowered ten days later than their comparative specimens, to which they were considerably inferior in stature. (Fig. 50).

Though retaining the form of the original plant, the flowers had far smaller corollas, less divergent and less opened and in many flowers had an excessive number of petals (6 in place of 5 petals). Instead of being pink, they were white in color, tinged slightly with lilac, and purplish streaks at the insertion of the cup. On the whole, they resembled the related genus of *Hibiscus syriacus* far more closely than they did the hollyhock flowers from which this genus stems.

As is known, the althaea has two series of axillary flowers on both sides of the insertion of each petiole of the leaves adorning the floreal stem (Fig. 49). When the first series has blossomed, the second series flowers. In modified plants, which I term *hybiscoid,* three and sometimes four buds are grouped about each foliar axil, and these flower in succession, protracting their bloom almost until the fall.

171

The structure of all the plants induced by iono-treatment is considerably reduced, and consequently the compactness of the flowers and their buds, which are smaller than normal, is more apparent.

The hibiscoid althaea produces a great quantity of perfect seeds, just like the originating wild genus; but in diameter and in weight, it is little more than half of that produced by the comparative specimen plants.

The accessory production of flowers has been found also in other analogous experiments on other species, and without going much afield, it is enough to cite the examples of poppies in groups C (section 62) and a (section 4) which flowered anew in the summer.

C. The addition of iron to such delicate pollen gave rise to the suspicion that the pollen grains must have been damaged by the derangement produced unfailingly by the exciting action of the electro-magnet. Although extremely fine, the iron particles have a certain sharpness which might graze the pollen when the magnetism, on entering action, forces the grains to range themselves along the lines of force. But experience has shown that a good part of the pollen is not damaged at all, and retains its fecundating properties. So again in this instance too, fecundation proved effective, as was the case with the poppies, and yielded good seeds. The fact that these seeds did not germinate later, might also depend on the fact that the seed-vessel was taken when still immature. In Chapter VIII other experiments on the Althaea genus, executed with pollen mixed with powdered iron, and which yielded good and vital seeds, with the same system of excitation, will be described, although the treatment was of lesser duration.

D. This fecundation too, produced good seeds, though the presence of bismuth in the midst of the pollen, prevented the latter from benefiting by the maximum variation in the field, because of the reactionary currents produced among the fragments of bismuth; but they did not germinate, probably for the same reason cited in the previous instance.

The hibiscoid althaea is *reproduced exactly by seed;* but the spring sowings produce plants which flower at the beginning of July *of the same year,* instead of in June of the following year, as occurs with the prototype species, which is biennial.

This is an important and by no means negligible factor, although this species does not carry any great weight in the interests of horti-culture.

The suitability of using the definition '*mutation*' in preference to the more general term of '*variation*' is once again confirmed, in re-gard to the ionized progeny of the poppy, the althaea and other species.

A regular upheaval in genital plasma is involved which, com-mencing with ionolysis, continues to transmit the effects of it to the progeny it helps to produce with an anomalous arrangement, with a characteristic all its own, which is renewed from generation to generation through the organs of reproduction, never more to be extinguished.

70.

Modifications of Lunaria Biennis

Lunaria biennis (*Pope's Shield*–Italian term) (In English: Hon-esty, or satinpod).

Several experiments which were partially beneficial, which I had made a year previously on two species of hybrid cabbages, induced me to operate in the same way on this cruciferous plant, too, to test its sensitivity to ionolysis.

Although a biennial species, the Lunaria may flower during the year following fecundation, providing that the seeds are put in the ground very soon. So it can be regarded as an annual species and like the Althaea, can be enumerated among plants suitable for genetic experiments of which one is anxious to see the results quickly.

The ablation of the anthers from the flowers destined for artificial fecundation is extremely easy. As soon as the bud is about to open, it is delicately unclosed, two petals on one side being turned aside, and two on the other, until the opening thus pro-duced in the cup reaches its insertion on the pedicle. Now the anthers attached to the inner wall of the cup itself are taken be-tween small pincers and removed. Then, when the anthers, which are still closed in this initial phase of flowering, are removed, the entire castrated inflorescence is enveloped in one large sack of strong paper.

Within a very short time, the petals which have been forcefully parted in order to remove the anthers, again close spontaneously, protecting the stigma from the rays of the sun.

The pollen is easy to gather and to handle during fecundation, which is achieved by the hair of a feather instead of by a brush, and may be preserved at length, without losing any of its fecundating properties, nor suffering any debilitation of its specific characteristics, as occurs with poppies, vines, etc.

The experiments were as follows:

1. Fecundation control test with pollen of 5 days standing, as in all experiments described below.

2. Fecundation with pollen exposed in the interpolar area of the electromagnetic apparatus seen in Fig. 11, excited by alternating, 42 cycle current for 5 days. Maximum intensity of field, 5500 gauss.

3. Identical conditions as the foregoing, with an addition of pulverized iron mixed with the pollen.

4. Fecundation with pollen exposed in the interpolar area of the electromagnet seen in Fig. 16, excited by 42 cycle alternating current for 60 hours. Maximum intensity of field, 4750 gauss.

5. Similar to the foregoing, but with powdered bismuth mixed with the pollen in the proportion of one-third.

6. Fecundation with pollen exposed to pulsating magnetic field excited by alternating, 42 cycle current, 80-volt, interrupted by Wenhelt apparatus (not well attuned to the electro-magnet). Intensity of field approximately 5000 gauss, for half an hour.

7. As above, the pollen being mixed with one-third bismuth.

8. As above, with rectilineal electro-magnet (Fig 11), excited by alternating, 42 cycle, 50 volt current, interrupted by Wenhelt apparatus, for 6 hours. Maximum intensity of magnetic field, 6000 gauss.

9. Fecundation in identical conditions as the foregoing, with pollen mixed with powdered iron in the proportion of approximately one-third, which increased the intensity of field to an undeterminable degree (Section 66).

10. Fecundation with pollen exposed in the interpolar area of the electro-magnet (Fig. 15), excited by 500 cycle alternating current for 1 hour. Maximum intensity of field, 3250 gauss.

11. Fecundation as above, with pollen mixed with powdered iron, as in No. 9.

12. Fecundation as in No. 10. Duration of treatment 3 hours.

NB. Radium experimentation produced plants affected by extreme nanism, which have not yet flowered.

Results

1. The comparative specimen plants faithfully reproduce the species type (Fig. 51-A).

2. No appreciable difference from the comparative group.

3. Somewhat dwarfish plants, with a few traces of yellowish variation, in one specimen.

4. A small, but properly homogeneous group of plants with tardy development which flower 10-12 days after their congeneric kin; in height they measure about one-fifth more than the comparative specimens. A proportional expansion of the inflorescence corresponds to the development in height. No specific morphological characteristic differentiates flowers or seeds.

5. Does not differ from the previous group.

6. Utterly similar to the comparative specimen; several specimens slightly more dwarfish.

7. The same as 6.

8. Homogeneous group of plants somewhat smaller in stature than the comparative specimen, flowering about a week later (Fig. 51-B).

9. Same as 8.

10. Group consists entirely of dwarf plants of squat appearance, late in blossoming, defective seed-vessels due to some unknown anomaly, which is not understood, in their sexual organs.

11. Less tall and less homogeneous than the above.

12. This group is still smaller than No. 10, although it shares the already listed prerogatives of it. The fruit-bearing pods are shrivelled in proportion (Fig. 51-C).

NB. In about 400 specimens comprising the above groups, no modification in the color of petals was obtained.

71.

Pulsating Ionolysis in Wallflowers

Pink Wallflowers (*Cheiranthus annus*).

The premises and details supplied by experience in fecundating the lunaria genus, may apply also to wallflowers which belong to the same botanic family.

The type used in these experiments was the single flower variety. Wallflowers belong to the phanerogamian group which De Vries described as "always variable," on account of the complete transformation of stamen and pistil into petals in the flowers they duplicate; this tendency makes it impossible to obtain seeds of the double variety, precisely because of their perfect duplication.

The simple variety does possess however (when properly cultivated and assisted by some artifice) the property of procuring perfect duplication in a large percentage (50-70%) of the individual plants born from its seeds.

The cultivators of wallflower seeds stimulate duplication of the seed-vessels in the plants by facile artificial cultivation means (pruning, rich manure). The hypernutrition of the genital organs induces tendency in the sexual cells to form supernumerary organs. The wallflower inclines to petalomania, and exploits avidly the stimulation supplied for this purpose. But no matter how great the tendency to petalomania may be, one should not expect that ionolytic treatment might further it, since it has a generally debilitating and wearing effect, never an invigorating one, still less so on account of the high frequency or strong variations and abrupt modifications in the magnetic field.

The following were the most interesting experiments:

A. Fecundation of simple pink wallflower with its own pollen in quite mediocre soil (this applies also to the following experiments).

B. Fecundation with pollen exposed for 6 hours to the electromagnet seen in Fig. 11, excited by 42 cycle, 50-volt, alternating current, interrupted by Wenhelt apparatus. Maximum intensity of field about 3000 gauss.

C. Fecundation with pollen mixed with powdered iron in the

176

proportion of one-third in the conditions identical to the above experiment.

D. Fecundation with radiolized pollen in the apparatus seen in Fig. 6 for 24 hours. The radium was 5 millimeters distant from the pollen, as usual.

E. Fecundation as above; duration of exposure to radium 48 hours.

Results

A. The comparative specimen group consisted of simple-flower plants, absolutely identical with the prototype of the variety.

B. The development of the plants in this group varied exceedingly in regard to stature, which was prevalently much shorter than the comparative specimen. At least half of the plants were dwarfed, bush-like in appearance, with the flower shoots shorter and thicker than the comparative specimen. But the overall character distinguishing this group was the retarded blossoming (from one week to a month later than the control specimen). The size of the flower did not undergo any appreciable diminution, not even in the smaller specimens. Nor did even the most weak and extremely retarded plants show any variation in the pigment of their corollas, which was however slightly darker, though not having any substantial difference in tint.

The shorter and more retarded the plant, the less seeds it yields.

C. It does not differ substantially from the foregoing group, nor would it be logical to make any thorough comparison, since it consisted only of 6 specimens surviving in a larger group of dwarfed plants. *Seeds in this group, as in those of group B, faithfully reproduce the nanism acquired,* confirming what was already said about althaea and poppies deformed by ionolysis.

D. A distinctly dwarfish group, absolutely homogeneous, with a slightly more compact flower, and more vivid than the specimen group, over which its blossoming has a few days' advantage.

E. Identical to the above.

NB. Lack of space obliges me to omit the inconclusive experiments of slow cycle ionolysis which proved ineffective, the same as did those with pulsating 80-volt current and alternate 500 cycle current, which yielded no significant results. In Chapter VIII the reader will find hybrid forms obtained in certain varieties of cabbage in which the results coincide with these experiments. It seems that only a pulsating magnetic field of *moderate intensity* and frequency proves effective in causing magnetic ionolysis in cruciferous plants. This would furnish yet another proof of the necessity of harmony stressed several times already, in the interests of achieving the distinction of determined molecular groups in the chromosomes.

At the same time I was making the aforesaid experiments, I carried out as many other experiments on blue wallflowers *in good soil*. The results did not differ except in the greater percentage of double-flowered plants.

72.

Iono-Induced Mutations in Sunflowers

Giant Russian Sunflower (*Helianthus uniflorus*).

Both the sunflower and the dahlia (I worked only on this species of composites, lending itself easily to artificial fecundation) and perhaps all composites in general seem but little susceptible to ionolytic modification of their pollen. Composites, especially in those species which, like the sunflower, have coarse pollen, evince instead excellent genetic modifications in hybridization. This will be dealt with extensively in Chapter VIII.

At first glance the castration of the small flowers in composites would seem to be difficult, both because of their minute size, and because the style is sheathed between the anthers which close about it like a tube. The friction of the stigmal papillas against the interior wall of the staminiferous tube in which the pollen abounds, gives the impression that the stigmas become imbued with it, thus assuring fecundation; but this does not occur because the receiving stigmas are situated in the interior of the two dilatations at the top of the style; these dilatations are folded back during the passage through the staminal tube. Only insects can effect fecundation of composites. But it is not enough that a flower be protected from their visitation, in order to guarantee the absolute virginity of the stigmas; one has to remove the staminal tubes from the capitula when they are still somewhat immature.

This is easily done in the very early hours of the morning, and succeeds far more rapidly than in many other species. With a properly sized pincer and a little practice, 100 and more small flowers may be castrated in the capitulum of a sunflower in 12-15 minutes. Only the outer branches near to the ligules should be used for genetic experiments, because the seeds in the interior ones are of inferior quality. Preservation of the castrated flowers is assured by wide sacks of oil-paper, or by a very fine, flexible fabric of metal threads; this later method is particularly suitable on sultry days, when the excessive heat produced by the paper bags might harm the stigmas.

The following experiments were made:

1. Control fecundation with pollen gathered 8 days previously.

2. Fecundation with pollen exposed on one single magnetic pole for 18 hours in the electro-magnet seen in Fig. 11, excited by 42 cycle alternating current. Maximum intensity of magnetic field, 4000 gauss.

3. Fecundation of pollen exposed between the poles of the electro-magnet mentioned above, for an equal length of time. Maximum magnitude of field, 5580 gauss.

4. Fecundation of pollen exposed between the poles of electro-magnet (Fig. 16), for 4 days, excited by 42 cycle alternating current. Maximum intensity of field, 4750 gauss.

5. Fecundation under the same conditions, but with excitation at 500 cycles for a period of 4 hours. Maximum intensity of field, 3250 gauss.

6. Fecundation of pollen exposed to pulsating magnetic field produced by 42 cycle, 40-volt alternating current, interrupted by Wenhelt apparatus, for 16 hours. Maximum intensity of field, 6000 gauss.

7. Fecundation with pollen exposed in the polar area of the same electro-magnet excited by *direct current* for 2 hours. Intensity of field, 7000 gauss.

8. Fecundation with a radium-treated pollen exposed for 8 hours.

9. Idem for 16 hours.

10. Idem for 32 hours.

11. Fecundation with pollen exposed to ultra-violet spark light at about 3 cm. from the spintherometer of the apparatus (Fig. 13) for 2 hours.

Results

1. Tall, straight plants, with big, drooping capitula (Fig. 52-A); seeds prevalently white, with more or less broad black streaks.

2. Group fully similar to the foregoing. But one observes one plant with weak and contorted stalk, as though hardly able to support its flower of meagre size. The deformation of this single plant might be analogous to that induced by the same cause on the poppies; but since it was limited to one single plant, the anomaly cannot be taken into consideration. The seeds are identical to those in the prototype specimen.

3. Plants in this group were somewhat dwarfed, that is, a good third lower than in the comparative specimen. But their stalk was very straight; flowers and fruit average, seeds as above.

4. Strong group consisting of straight plants bearing loaded disks of good seeds. Only one single plant with stalk contorted at the top, and tardy blossoms, similar to that observed in Group 2.

5. The specimens in this group were considerably weaker than in the previous ones, and their structure was prevalently ramified, instead of being one single stalk, and they blossomed later, while the seeds were somewhat darker.

6. In this experiment which was carried out in several stages and protracted in duration, so as to allow the electrolytic switch to cool, and also because it was not possible to attend the experiment straight through, as would have been desirable, the pollen had been gathered 10 days previously.

Without trying to find, for the moment, any cause, since there are no reliable comparisons to work on, one did observe a considerable miscarriage of seeds (about 70%) yet the few plants born from the perfect seeds surviving, did not show that the lengthy treatment had caused any noticeable modification in this species.

Of the few plants (8 in all) comprising this group, only two had a new characteristic, that is, their concave surface (instead of a convex one) in the floral capitula and fruit. The other six plants were similar to Group 5 and blossomed late.

7. This group consists of strong plants with robust stalks, enormous leaves, and enormous fruit which exceed the positive qualities of the comparative specimen taken as a whole.

8. Radiolization caused strong miscarriage of seeds, of which only a few germinated. The survivors are easily recognized, when compared with the other experimental groups, by their extremely tardy flowering. Fig. 52 shows, in A, one of the later specimens of comparison, in C, a similar specimen of this group in which all the individual plants have their floral peduncle and the reverse side of the disk covered thickly with strangely folded-back leaves. There is nothing abnormal in the flower, except for the reduction in the length of the ligule, which, in several specimens, is half the normal size. The disk is much smaller and convex, as seen in the illustration. The better characterized plants, shown at the beginning of their flowering, look like enormous dragon necks with large scales.

9. No viable seed.

10. As above.

11. Fig. 52 shows us, in B, a flowering top in this homogeneous, though slender group. All components of it have stalks and the rear of the flowers bristling with small, clustering leaves, as in No. 8, which flutter ornamentally in the twisted tops. The reblossoming in this group occurs much less late than in the previous group 8.

73.

A General Survey of Ionolysis in the Species

The various series of experiments hitherto described are those which were not entirely unsuccessful when attempted on other species, but the same artifices were applied also to others, such as horse chestnut, portulaca, petunia, dahlia, cucumis, hypomaea, iris, the vitis and the pyrus in which seeds are easily obtained; but these germinate with difficulty, or do not manifest any variation worthy of note.

But one should not imagine, because of this, that only a few species are sensitive to electro-magnetic action in a variable field, or to ionolization by ray treatment. As I have said, the possibility of mutation is caused by the harmony of the activating system with the mysterious intimate composition of the genital plasm (or perhaps I had better say of the chromosomes), in which the partial disintegration of their structure is to be accomplished. One must retain harmony and dosage which allow for the disruption of the characteristic outlines of the specific molecular structure without depriving it of that undeterminable quality, fusion and necessary stability for maintaining not only life in the embryo and seed, but also rendering this strong enough to overcome the critical phase of germination, which unfortunately is fatal to a great part of the seeds formed with pollen which has suffered violation (Section 69).

The most conspicuous variations undoubtedly correspond to treatments which verge on death itself during operations on the plasma (Section 64).

In order to obtain the best possible results, the physicist must conduct his experiments with the cooperation and assistance of an expert sower, able to evaluate them, and save the life of part of those seeds which, on account of their abnormal constitution, are less likely to survive the difficulties of the phase of germination, since from a teratological point of view, these anomalies hold out the best promise. Among them we find monstrous, macrocarpous and gigantic types, in the majority of the weaker specimens (sections 96 and 92).

A glance at the foregoing notes and at Figs. 40, 41, 43 and 44 will suffice to convince even the greatest sceptic how advisable it is to attempt the different possibilities offered by ionization methods, because somewhere among them we may find those which will lead to improvements in a horticultural sense.

Any mutation or variation of the species (not excluding gigantism) is biologically imperfect in respect to the wild species; no one can emulate Nature insofar as biological harmony in maintaining vitality intact, even under the harshest tests, is concerned; everyone agrees on that, but in cultivation, vital energy may not weigh excessively in the balance of production, color, new form, or general morphological gigantism, whether this is limited to certain organs or to the reblossoming property; modification may be unnatural, yes, but it is well received, and even sought after in the market and by the connoisseur.

Certainly the experiments that were carried out so far, and to which it was impossible to dedicate the necessary attention, since they were done during brief pauses in daily occupation (many groups were completely ruined because of climatic conditions, or unfortunately partially ruined by accidents of all description), cannot be considered as outstanding exponents of the artifice practiced. It is only among poppies, on which I have been working, and continue to work, for some time, by preference, that after a series of failures, I have obtained a series *less deficient* in experimental data, even though it is far from being well ordered and extensive in regard to each category of the five principal means of ionization as it should be.

In regard to poppies, there is one very important thing that should be stressed. It must not be believed that the opium poppy is a species which may be easily or extensively deformed, in a numerical sense. Together with my experiments on the *double* opium poppy, I have carried out experiments on the *simple* opium poppy; these experiments were analogous but consistently negative, so 1 have not referred to them. Even the most effective artifices to which the double poppy responds excellently, do not affect the simple species at all. Therefore, even the selection of a certain variety may favor the manifestation of ionization-induced mutations considerably, and it is intuitive thinking that tells us that the variety which is most dissimilar from the wild species, will be more suitable to experimental work, since it is already more imperfect congenitally than the original wild species[1].

[1] H. De Vries, *Species and variety*. R. Sandron, Palermo, Vol. II, pp. 487--515 *et passim*.

CHAPTER VII

Hybridization

74.

Outline of Hybridological Technique

THE TWO definitions *hybridization* and *crossing* might be regarded as synonymous; they signify gamic coupling of two different species or varieties.

Technically, the former is used in connection with the mating of species, the latter to indicate mating between varieties, or kinds, of one and the same species.

The hybrid *kind* or *population* is constituted by a complex of individuals born of hybrid semination. The term 'kind' is generally used for hybrid progeny, which careful selection has induced to reproduce its own kind within restricted limits of variability.

Agriculture in general, and horticulture in particular, do not avail themselves of pure and simple improvements in any botanic species (Section 23); the majority of new horticultural varieties, especially those obtained in recent years, originate from another important operation, artificial fertilization or *hybridization*. When ameliorative compulsion, to which there is reference in Chapter II, acts in conjunction with hybridization, the probability of obtaining genetic improvements is greatly increased.

Widely practiced in grape-growing, horticulture, and, recently, cereal-growing, hybridization strives to produce new varieties which offer improvements in respect to the parent species.

To hybridize means to *mix*, by the natural channel of fecundation, two different species or varieties; to mix the characteristics of one series of individuals, and to select with vigilant care only those which best correspond to the determined goal.

Through hybridization, the extremely difficult problem of reconstituting the vine on grape stock refractory to phylloxera in calcareous soil was solved, thanks to hybrids of *Vitis berlandieri*, a species which tolerates chalky soil, but which rarely takes root by scion.

Analogous procedure has produced vines which are relatively refractory to both phylloxera and cryptogamic diseases, *direct producers*, as they are improperly called. Various improvements have been obtained, too, in fruit, vegetables and, quite recently, in cereals.

Vegetables and flowers, which are generally annuals, are plants which have derived the greatest benefit from hybridization, when wisely linked with the stimulus of cultivation, carried to its maximum degree.

There has been wonderful progress during the last few years in several species, and particularly in the genera: violet, dahlia, gladiolus, begonia, carnation, chrysanthemum, amaryllis, geranium, petunia, etc.

The operational process of hybridization is extremely simple. But the preparatory phase is not so easy for several species which have genital organs involuted, such as wheat, oats, rye, etc., or the very small, fragile, or hooded flowers (Vitis) with an extremely delicate stigma.

In the first place, one has to prevent fecundation of the flower, or flower group, of the chosen species which is to act as mother (seed-bearer) by its own pollen, or that of neighbor plants. In the previous chapter, it was explained how the removal of the anther is performed, and isolation, that is to say, preservation of the virginity, of the female organs is assured. The preparatory process is analogous in every way, even when hybridization is our purpose.

The sole difference consists in this, that instead of fecundating the stigmas with pollen of their own species, pollen of another species or variety is used. When the flower, from which the anthers were removed when still immature, shows that it has attained full maturity, which may be detected in the majority of cases, by the viscous appearance of the stigma, fecundation should take place without delay, and this consists in the pure and simple depositing of pollen on the stigma. If this is extremely delicate, it will be blown on to it, which does not alter anything in respect to the ultimate objective, that of putting pollen into contact with the stigma.

If the pollen was taken from a species of the same genus of seed-bearer, or even from a species merely botanically affinitive to it, it will be observed that the ovary swells, and the formation of the seed, or seeds takes place, as though it were just an ordinary fecundation.

The seeds, berries, stone fruits and even, externally, fruits obtained by hybrid fecundation are always analogous to the species which bore them; and nothing, save for rare exceptions, will betray their bastard origin.

Yet they are hybrid seeds which give origin to hybrid plants; that is to say, they unite, in a more or less evident way, both characteristics of the different species which have cooperated in producing them.

As soon as hybrid fecundation has been effected, the ovule develops with the present participation of the extraneous fecundating male element which, right from the beginning, appropriates *part* of the nutritious elements transmitted to the ovule, *converting them according to its own specific structure.* So the hybrid individual is distinguished *by two blended physiognomies.*

It is not possible to carry out a corroborative and tangibly differentiative investigation of the intimate composition of hybridized seeds, *id est,* produced by hybridization. If this were possible, it would enable us to establish how, already from the commencement of its development, the hybridized seed consists of two different plasmas each of which works independently, blending their structures, cell upon cell, little by little as the elements are fashioned.

75.

Xenia

Rarely do seeds obtained from hybridization bear exterior traces of the nature which the different pollen, by which they were conceived, has intimately instilled into them. There are, however, a few cases in which the effect induced by fecundation with extraneous pollen is immediately manifest. This is verified in seeds with strong and very definite pigmentation. At times, not only the seed will show visible signs of the pollen influence, but even in the pulp and rind one will find slight modifications in pigmentation, which prove the existence of the modifying effect on the plasma surrounding the embryo of the seed of hybrid origin.

These exterior, *direct and immediate* manifestations due to fecundation by extraneous pollen other than that of the seed-bearer species, are phenomena of *xenia.* Among plants that are well known to everyone, the *Zea mais,* or corn, is most particularly subject to this. It is also well visible in wallflower seeds. Xenia phenomena were found less often by Gallesio, in lemons fecundated with orange pollen. Bouschet, Viala, Ravaz and Mendola observed the change in the color of the juice and even in the skin of white grapes fecundated with pollen of a grape with much darker pigment.

Xenia is not perpetuated; but disappears with the same fruit in which it was first observed. It is, at any rate, extremely rare in vegetables. The participation of extraneous pollen forming the seed is hardly ever apparent, both because the seed is generally covered by several membranes and teguments which protect it, and because it generally is lacking in any distinctive pigmentation which might differentiate specific elements, so that identification is not possible. If every species had cotyledons with specific characteristic pigmentation, and if the teguments were properly transparent, the xenia, observed in corn, might well be quite a common phenomenon; it would reveal the hybridative process in every vegetable, and would permit us to follow the elementary propagines, and respective structure of the two factors.

76.

Compatibility in Collaboration of Different Plasmas, and the Possibility of Interbreeding

Mating of genera of the same family of phanerogamic plants is hardly ever possible; in the rare instances in which fecundation did take place effectively, *bigeneric crosses* were produced which, as a rule, are absolutely sterile, even though they produce flowers which are apparently normal.

Fecundation between two different species of one genus produces the *hybrid,* or *bastard,* and it is always possible, save for a few very rare exceptions. Progeny among hybrids is generally fertile; but there is not lack of *sterile,* or *mule hybrids,* when there is an appreciable botanic distance between the species mated. The sterility of mule crosses is due to imperfection of the organs of reproduction and is quite independent of the major or minor robustness and physiological fitness of the plant.

The *half-breed* or *cross* produced by cross fecundation of two varieties of the same species, always produces fertile progeny.

Both these and the progeny of hybrids are subject to continuous variations, to uncoupling, at times definite, at times very slight, and often confusing, of the characteristics of one of its two parent origins; according to the different mating of characteristics, each of which will blend in a more or less complex manner with the others, the greater will be the number of chromosomes (Section 17) distinguishing the species mated.

Renewal of blood, which in botany would be better described as "genetic perfection process," must not be confused with hybridization or cross-breeding, for this consists in the cross-fecundation of flowers of a given species or variety, with pollen of the identical variety, cultivated in different soil or climate, or at a different altitude.

Summing up the results of *possible* fecundations, they may be grouped as follows:

Hybrids
- among genera of the same botanic family; rarely obtained; always sterile; generally weak.
- among species of the same botanic genus
  - Sterile
  - Fertile — with apparently unequal characteristics or intermediary ones among parent species

Cross-breeding among varieties of the same species: Always fertile as above.

The compatibility in mating, for purposes of hybridization, is not exactly to be gauged. It has no connection with ancient or modern taxonomic systems, nor with morphologic features which may frequently be misleading, inasmuch as the exterior appearance cannot, and must not be taken as a valid exponent, for it does not reveal certain substantial internal somatic differences.[1] For example, the inuline species of the Cichoriaceae cannot be hybridized nor grafted on the amylose species. Likewise in the Solanaceae family, hybridization is unsuccessful between the different genera, despite the strong analogy in the structure of the flowers.

Armand Gauthier advanced the hypothesis of *plasma coalescence*[2] that is to say, the possibility of simultaneous aggregation and development of the propagines coupled in parallel, and mated in such a manner, as would allow mutual continuation in life, in a masterly synthesis which summed up into one sole biological factor the various experimental results of hybridization and grafting, as well

---

[1] Armand Gauthier, "Revue de Viticulture," Vol. XV, p. 588, Paris, 1901.
[2] *Ibid.,* p. 560.

as the mutative phenomena caused by trauma and parisitary reasons.

The possibility of coalescence is amazingly vast and could be divided into two main categories: *coalescence of botanic affinity* and *coalescence of bio-chemical affinity*.

If the former concerns grafting and hybridization only, the latter is by no means secondary in the general interests of this present volume; the electric mutation of the species is very closely connected with it.

Gauthier demonstrates, with supporting facts, how plants and plant organs are frequently modified entirely, or in part, when a parasite is concealed in them.

If stung by their natural parasite, the stalks of peppermint will become deformed; they lose their pubescence, shape, fragrance, and the essential oil extracted from it is dextrose, rather than levulose.

When parasites prick the leaves of roses or American vines when they deposit their eggs, they induce the characteristics of aculeolate gall all around them. The gallicole phylloxera of the vine plant is known to everyone. From the progeny of the first moss rose which appeared on a bush covered with galls in the Luxembourg Gardens, it is evident that the tendency of the leaves, which alone are affected, to form anomalous organs had migrated to influence a bud which, in the course of development, reproduced the anomalous polyvalence which characterized the stalk, cup and sepals of the moss rose. The characteristic thus acquired was perpetuated through grafting, and is partially transmittable by seed.

A relationship of mutual influence between the guest and the plant which nourishes it, is necessary. Whence does the infected plant receive the stimulus which deforms its organs? From the continued substraction of chemical elements, or from the secretions of the parasite which, injected into its plasma, influence it in deviating from its inherent constructive task?

It is probable that the deforming stimulus could not be acquired by the vegetable by just any cause or matter, but only by one attuned to it, a highly special combination of bio-chemical elements peculiar to that parasite, and which, when in contact with those of the host species, have the power to *inoculate* it, and disarrange the order of the providential design of Nature, while yet not causing death.

In whatever section, organ or branch the parasite may act, the vegetable plasma reacts like a most anomalous hybrid restricted to that area, creating completely new cellular systems with no relationship at all to the normal characteristics of its species. Probably the insect, when settling in the vegetable tissue, injects secretions which are not only stimulating, but endowed with a mysterious faculty of collaboration; powers which are susceptible to fusion and control, in a state of progressive symbiosis with the vegetable plasma, so as to deform its cellular structure to the benefit of the parasite. The propagines of the respective tissues thus deformed, may extend quite far, under certain circumstances; if they succeed in invading a bud, one may find a mutated branch.

The moss rose originated from a similar invasion, and is one of the most remarkable organic mutations existing, which was induced by parasitic symbiosis.

In gamic hybridization there is a certain analogy with the phenomena of the above described coalescence, insofar as cooperation with plasma is concerned.

But while bio-chemical, affinitive coalescence is extremely rare and involves the participation of two kingdoms (vegetable-animal), the widely extended botanically affinitive coalescence cannot take place except between the symbionts, that is to say, the species or varieties mated by hybridization, having close relationship one with the other.

Just as in any device in which two different gears, possibly even unequal in diameter, stand face to face, it is necessary that in order to function, they both have the *same connection angle*, so must the two wedded plasmas in a hybrid, satisfy rigid laws of *affinity* in order to persevere in their vital mechanical function. I say mechanical in the sense that development cannot be conceived as independent from a continued aggregative action, with constant control and direction.

Fecundation becomes possible only in the case that there is *possibility of union and mutual substitution in formation of the tissues of the propagines developed by one element with those of the other element in conjunction with which it is working.*

From this we have the reason for the impossibility of executing positive fecundation between other than very affinitive species, kinds or varieties.

In this connection, grafting is less complicated than gamic matings because it may also succeed between widely differing genera: for example lilac (*Syringa vulgaris*) may be grafted successfully on the oak (*Quercus robur*), the fruit-bearing Rosaceae on the quince-tree, the Myrobalan, the hawthorn, etc.

Recently hybridization was carried out among plants belonging to different botanic genera, with particularly conspicuous results among fruit-bearing Rosaceae, that is to say, among bigeneric hybrids, Plum-Apricot (Prunus x Armeniaca), Peach-Apricot (Amygdalis x Armeniaca), Plum-Peach (Prunus x Amygdalis); these last hybridizations were achieved by my good friend Dr. Ragionieri, who has worked on them for years with the intelligence of true devotion. It was this same famous hybridator who obtained the crinadonna, or amaryllis lily (Crinum x Amaryllis), as well as other extremely interesting horticultural hybrids.

There are very many bigeneric hybrids among orchids, which were obtained in England, France, Belgium, etc.

If *fertile* mating is somewhat difficult, however, and possible only in certain species, one finds even more rarely fertile plants among bigeneric hybrids. One finds sterile hybrids even among some hybrids of botanically-distinct species. Thus I was never able to obtain fertile plants in the hybridization experiments listed below, and to which I have limited my stock of examples, having extensive knowledge of them:[1] Blue-passion-flower x Sweet Passion-flower; turban squash (*Cucurbita maxima*) x Jerusalem cucumber

---

[1] Among experiments of note made by others there are those of Millardet on the vine. Pollen of viniferous vine does not fecundate the American Scuppernong variety, belonging to the Vulpine Vine, although there does not seem to be any substantial difference between them. Not even the pollen of the Labruscae Vine is effective on the Scuppernong, although they are fairly affinitive. On the contrary, varieties of the Viniferous Vine, can be fecundated satisfactorily with Scuppernong pollen, which does not, however, pass on any of its characteristics to its progeny.

(*Cucurbita moschata*); common raspberry with red fruit (*Rubus idaeus var. hortensis*) x wild black raspberry (*Rubus idaeus*); white opium poppy, both single and double (*Papaver somniferum*) x Oriental poppy (*Papaver bracteatum*).

All the plants born from these hybridizations were of normal constitution, good health, with flowers complete in all their parts; but careful examination of their anthers and carpels showed their imperfection (cause of sterility) even to the naked eye.

77.

Constitution of the Hybrid

I repeat that the individual hybrid *is only apparently a fusion of two species*, while in reality it is an aggregation in which all the cells forming its tissues and organs, not excluding the sexual ones (Gamete), are *singular in species and pure* (Section 84); this makes it seem more paradoxical that fecundation, which has been established as possible, in the primary instance, between the two originating species, is found lacking in the reproductive elements in the hybrid.

Sterility is justifiably more extensive in hybrid animals, and especially among the superior category of animal, because of somatic reasons, since here the blood in its circulation, converges entirely on one given point, as to a central treasure house, from which it is sent forth once more to every organ and limb, and consequently, to the sexual organs, as well.

The act of fecundation in zoological species, has both somatic and nervous connections. In the vegetable world, where sap has a very slow and sectional circulation, (Section 5) and each element in the plasma, and therefore in the vegetative tissues, is far more independent, since it is, so to speak, *grafted onto the vegetative axil,* there is a far more extensive possibility of mating and of fertility.

Although rare, sterile hybrids among botanic species are caused by imperfection or atrophy of the reproductive organs, and *prevalently of the anthers.*

78.

Bio-Coenotic Cause of Sterility in the Hybrid

One, if not the only, possible cause of sterility in certain hybrids (and one which does not prejudice the blended unispecific constitution[1] of it), which has been indisputably proven among all types of hybrid, is the diversity in the blossom time of the two generating species.

An example will be more explicit than any general demonstration, and better able to concentrate the attention of the reader on the cause of the dehiscence lacking in apparently normal anthers.

The common red raspberry (*Rubus hortensis*) and the black raspberry (*Rubus idaeus*) have strong affinity in all their organs. Their hybridization suceeds very well indeed, and produces a large number of perfect seeds; the individual plant is strong, with intermediary characteristics of both species. The hybrids flower abundantly during the second year after insemination; but one would look in vain for any fruit on them. Among hundreds of specimens, born from this hybridization, I was unable to find even one. As soon as they open, the flowers would appear to be perfect; but after a few hours, they reveal their yellowish anthers; toward evening they became brownish in color and are withered the following day. And they have not opened. The time of flower of the two species, although so affinitive and native to the soil, is at one month's distance from each other.

Now there are grains of pollen and their relative connective tissues, and coverings etc., of the precocious species bearing red fruit, and an analogous number of black fruit species pollen grains with equal number of subsidiary organs in each organ of the hybrid

[1] A. Naudin, Nouvelles recherches sur l'hibridation des végétaux. Mémoire couronnée par l'Institut, Paris, 1862. M. Ganzin, "Revue scientifique," July 30, 1881, Paris.

plant, not excluding the anthers, to which I am limiting my investigation, and this by virtue of the aforesaid mosaic composition.

The stalks grow under the influence of heat; after accumulating a determined amount of calories, more or less intermediate between the amounts required by the original generating species, the buds unclose their white corollas. The genital organs mature, together ~with stamen and pistil at an equal rhythm. *But there is no dehiscence of the anthers.* Probably *half the pollen* stemming from the red raspberry was already mature *before the flower opened.* This half on its own would have caused the anthers to open very prematurely; but it is prevented from doing so by the connection with the other half, belonging to the tardier species, *which keeps the pollen lattice cells closed.* In its turn, when the tardy pollen is ripe, it does not cause the opening, because the precocious pollen has lost its vitality, with which it is closely intermixed, and with it the *motive power* which one presumes is possessed by the pollen lattice cells.

Hybridization between the opium poppy and the bracted poppy also confirms the absolute necessity of synchronization and concomitance between the stimuli of propulsion, determining the opening of the anthers, in my opinion.

These two species, both cultivated in the same environment, flower at a distance of about twelve days from one another; the bracted poppy is the first to bloom.

Since both plasmas constituting the hybrid tend to form the cells after their own specific characteristics, and independently from one another, the hybrid should blossom six days later than the bracted poppy species. In fact, the hybrid flowers between eight and nine days later.

In appearance, the anthers are normal, utterly similar to the immature anthers of the above named species, which are a handsome, glossy violet in color. One awaits their opening in vain. I believe that the cause of this must be attributed to the asynchronism of the stimuli attending the staminal dehiscence. While the elements representing the bracted poppy species strive to provoke it, the still immature organs of the opium poppy species prevent it.

In the previous hybrid raspberry specimen, the stigmas are

normal, and when artificially fecundated, bear fruit, utilizing both the maternal and paternal species pollen. This is not the case with the poppy, in which the ovaries, similar in every way to those of the poppy plant, are sterile.

79.

Justifiable Fertility of Inbreeding Among Affinitive Varieties

Fertility of progeny knows fear of neither exceptions nor limitation in inbreeding, not only because there is greater somatic affinity, but because the varieties of one and the same species flower more or less about the same time. Nor is the different period for blossoming always the only cause, and still less is it the absolute and general cause, of sterility in hybrids. Hybrids among the American species of vines are liable to be fertile, and are indeed fertile, constantly, Riparian, Rupestrine, etc., with varieties of the viniferous vine which flower as much as three weeks later.

This exception is however justified, for the American species, when mated with the European ones, cause such precocity in flowering that they equal that of the above listed species in the hybrid (and there are hundreds of hybrid producers who can prove it). This constitutes a confirmation, instead of an exception, of the rule; a justification which confirms the mechanical concept, if I may say so, of the inhibitive cause determining sterility.

Another fact corroborates the hypothesis of asynchronism of dehiscence as a cause of sterility, and this is it: that one never obtains two kinds of hybrid individuals from the same hybridization.

They are always either *all fertile,* or *all sterile:* nor is it any good to invert either the sex of the parents, or the conditions of environment or culture.

The reader will have occasion to see, in the next chapter, how ionolysis of the pollen may be of assistance in this case; how with such help an immense new horizon opens out before hybridization; how the more obstinately refractory sexual matings may, in regard to fertility, be enabled to give seed, by attenuation of the virulence of the genital plasma of one of the factors.

80.

The Hybrid As a Living Mosaic

The hybrid was rightfully defined by Naudin[1] as a *living mosaic*. Already at conception, the two plasmas, united in the egg-cell, *imbibe in common the nourishment provided,* and derive their building materials from that which the sap brings to them constantly, influencing it according to their own propensities, and blending their single structure little by little as they fashion the embryo in concert.

The elements of construction are so intimately blended that they cannot possibly be discerned in the vast majority of instances, not even when they have a well differentiated pigmentation of cellular structure.

Some modern authors, as far as I have been able to gather in the volumes known to me, are in the habit of admitting that the specific cellular elements are blended or combined, as one prefers, in the hybrid, and separate in the flowers only at the moment of forming the sexual organs. I think that this is a superflously complicated hypothesis, and that it does not correspond to fact.

In some instances, and especially *in the early stages* of hybrid symbiosis, it seems that the two plasmas, their propagines and hence the tissues formed by them, are only *loosely blended.* The hybrid form is only definitively established after some length of time.[2]

Perhaps the vine offers the most conspicuous example. Fig. 53 shows several leaves of *young* hybrid vines, photographed in the late fall.

During the summer there is no noticeable difference in pigment in them; but toward the time of defoliation, the disappearance of chlorophyll permits one to observe the location of the two different colorings characteristic of the generating parent species. It must be pointed out that this phenomenon is observed only in cases where two varieties were used to form the hybrid, only one of them being rich in oenocyanine.

[1] P. Pacottet: "Revue de Viticulture." Vol. XVI, p. 708.
[2] H. De Vries, *op. cit.* Vol. II, p. 769 et passim.

I have observed a patchy coloration in the leaves of several young inbred vines; in many specimens of crossing between Chasselas with indented leaves (white) and the melon grape (black, with grey flecks); in a complex hybrid of Labrusca vine x viniferous vine with white Chasselas; in a specimen of crossing between muscatel vine of Mandresfield (dark red) with black Olivetta (very black, with blue flowers)[1]; and in a few specimens of another crossing between extremely precocious comestible grapes,[2] derived from the Arcetri Greek grape (white) with Ischia grapes (precocious, black); in a cross between Caprizzise with Regina grapes; in various plants of a complicated hybrid between white varieties and black, as well as a cross between Malaga muscatel and yellow muscatel; and lastly, in many plants of the hybrid (black Carignan x Riparian) of which the leaf may be seen low down on the left in the illustration below.

The anomalous mottled aspect disappears even in the most conspicuously characterized specimens, with age.

The leaves would seem to indicate that the fruit, too, should bear some evidence of the loose aggregation of the fibrovascular fasciae influenced by both the parent varieties, but the phenomenon is hardly ever observed in adult vines. When it is, and especially when these stem from seeds, they do not bear grapes.

Only in a few specimens of inbreeding of transparent[3] rose grapes which seem to be homogeneous in tint when looked at directly, does one observe when looking at them against the light, how the rosy tint is conferred on them by a fine *network* of dark rose color apparent on the surface of the skin.

Another proof of the inequality or imperfect homogeneity of vegetative cellular fusion in hybrids, is presented by the variations produced by bud, or *sports*. These originate from buds of hybrid plants in which, for reasons not yet well understood, the influence of one of the generating species is prevalently localized in one section.

[1] Pirovano cross No. 83
[2] Pirovano cross No. 17.
[3] Noticeably in the Pirovano cross No. 74, but also found in many uncatalogued specimens.

198

81.

Fluctuations in Rearrangements

The phenomenon of *rearrangement*, or *postmutation*,[1] by which the first flowers and fruit-bearing in the hybrid plants are subjected to fluctuations in the apparent characteristics, should be attributed to an incomplete rearrangement of the elements in a young hybrid. The first fructifications are frequently very different from those which the same plant may have ten or twenty years later. In the vine, which I have observed with particular interest, the first fruits are generally larger in the individual grape, though the bunch is less prolific; many varieties lose or transform the aroma of muscat,[2] others which, at the first fructification[3] are bitter, coriaceous, improve, in regard to sweetness, modifying the original characteristic. A large number of crossings with slightly rose grapes[4] have turned white, and even colorless, as I have seen several series of crossings between muscat Chasselas and white Sultana do, though with their first fructification, their grapes were finely striped with violet.[5]

At times this fluctuation in rearrangement is so extensive that it influences all the organs in the plant. Among many multiplications of the vine IP-33[6] (Luglienga x Ferdinand de Lesseps), one extreme specimen of precocity did not only show outstanding differences in the design of the leaf, but had a parallel range of modifications in its fruit, which resulted in a specimen of larger grape, which ripened a month and more later than its type.

The mosaic composition of the hybrid is easily discernible in certain hybrids of golden cattleya with the rosy species of *Cattleya Laelia;* their translucid petals permit one to glimpse the magic cellular division of their strange and aristocratic corollas.

---

[1] G. Molon, *Horticultural Re-awakening (Risveglio Orticolo)*, A. Koschitz & Co. Milan, 1919.

[2] Cross Nos. 5, 8, 9, 26, 34, and 64.

[3] Cross Nos. 2, 47, 54.

[4] Cross No. 45 and many uncatalogued and abandoned specimens.

[5] All uncatalogued; abandoned.

[6] Pirovano cross 33.

82.

Advantages of Hybridization and Individual Hereditary Capacity

Hybridization has the advantage over ameliorative induction (Section 20), obtainable from one species just by repetitious selection or by hypernourishment, of giving instantly, and surely, origin to new varieties, new species and even to new botanic genera. Genera and species which have absolutely no stable characteristics, and which are incapable of transmitting them.

Without discussing the value of these for the time being, one should stress how the majority of cultivators, and particularly the genetic neophytes expect far more from the hybrid than it can possibly give. On the other hand, there is no lack of denigrators of hybridization. It is sure, on the contrary, that it gives vigor to plants.

The two sexual particles which form the hybrid do not *amalgamate*, but *complete* one another, to form a unit, the hybrid *unit*. No hybrid can possess all the good qualities of *both* the parent species. Among the many which are born from one cross-breeding or one hybridization, the characteristic of the variety or species may prevail or be lacking in different manner and proportion from individual to individual, but always in a *compensating sense*. That is to say, there are specimens in which the characteristics of one parent will prevail, others which reveal the characteristics of the other parent in a preponderant measure, and there will be others which are morphologically well balanced.

If an exact evaluation of the positive characteristics of any hybrid of two species of which one was cultivated for its product, the other for its parasitary resistance, as occurs in vine hybrids, could be impartially expressed in fractions of its unity, it would be seen that the sum total of its positive points would be more or less unvaried in specimens of the same hybrid population.

The hybrid being is a biological exception, not a miracle, but simply a *mixture* of two affinitive vital elements which, as a rule, *despite their exterior appearance*, are present in the individual hybrid ($= 1$) in equal proportions ($\frac{1}{2}+\frac{1}{2}$) (Section 85).

Such proportions become complicated in recrossings of hybrids with other hybrids, because the single characteristics, mating variedly among themselves, give origin to an extensive polymorphism. But there is no *increase of hereditary capacity*, even in secondary hybrids, although there is *complication* in the amalgamation and disposition of the ancestral characteristics.

Like every other living, normal being, the hybrid inherits specific characteristics in a pre-determined measure; this measure is sometimes stable, at other times fluctuating.

But hereditary capacity, that is, the individual tendency to take on characteristics of the ancestral species, is always steadfast, that is, *inextensible and irreducible.* Hereditary capacity might be compared to any capacity among the many customary to us; the more there is of one element, the less space will remain for another.

The person carrying out the process of hybridization is not the direct author of the hybrid mixture. He must content himself with selecting, among the natural range of variations produced by Nature. For it is in this precisely that the selection of hybrid issue consists.

In an extraordinary way, and solely from an agrarian point of view, the biologic capacity of a hybrid may be superior to normal, that is to say, superior to ordinary capacity, already balanced in 1, with perfect analogy to that which occurs in the ameliorated species (section 20 and 21). But it has been proved that *the selfsame ameliorative stimuli have greater effectiveness in hybridization* than they have in pedigree cultivation, in promoting positive ameliorations.

The plants which agriculture destines for amelioration, so that they may respond better to their cultural environment (profitable objective), are never physiologically perfect, in a naturalistic sense.

Guided by their exterior appearance, the author of hybridization chooses those specimens among hybrid progeny which vary often in form, stature and pigment (often very deceptively in the early vital phases (section 81) of their first flowering and fructification), which total the positive characteristics suitable to the soil and environment in which he is active. For this reason, his choice will fall on specimens which are *generally good*, superlatively good only there where the selection occurs, or perhaps elsewhere, providing that there are *equal conditions* of climate and soil.

The discrepancies in judgment on certain hybrids, and particularly among the direct producers of vines (the vine is the plant on which most hybridization work has been performed), are due to the different conditions in which they are placed.

As direct product, the vine should respond ideally to four main requisites: refractory capacity to phylloxera and cryptogamic diseases, good production, abundant fructification and extensive adaptability. These requisites conflict one with the other, for a hybrid is all the more refractory inasmuch as it is closer to the wild American species; all the better in an oenological sense, inasmuch as it contains, as one says, the blood of the viniferous vine; and it will be all the sweeter, the fewer grapes it has. Nevertheless, a satisfactory harmony is obtained in certain specimens, (particularly in secondary hybrids), chosen from among thousands of unsuitable and mediocre sibs; in these specimens their radical structure inherits the characteristics of the American species in prevalence, and the fruit is that of our own vines.[1]

But when the cultural environment varies, the *miraculous* balance of distribution, by which the hybrid specimen *satisfied antagonistic requirements*, will be disturbed to the detriment now of its resistance, now of its productiveness, according to the cultural conditions.

The example of the hybrid vines is an extreme case of the difficulties involved with so many essential requisites. The problem of adaptability is of secondary importance in other cultivations.

83.

The Drawbacks of Hybridization

One finds excellent form, robust specimens which represent genuine ameliorations in respect to the original species, both for the size of the flower or the fruit, fertility, etc., in some hybrid progeny. Generally, cultivated hybrids also yield good seeds; but these *never reproduce* exactly the characteristics of the plant which

---

[1] Coudere, 82-32, 198-21, 199-88; Castel, 13317; Grimaldi, 935 and 953.

bore them. Unlike the pure species, the hybrid is extremely unstable; it inclines to split its personality, reverting to one or other of the two species from which it originated, either spontaneously or by artificial fecundation.

In the light of genetics, the hybrid is a *temporary* species, which contains the property of self-division; this property will endure through the successive seminations, until heterozygous forms are conceived. (Sections 84, 85).

When a good form, a good hybrid variety, is obtained, it is easy to multiply, if perennial or dicotyledonous plants are involved, by scion, layer, grafting or some other agamic process; the seed can never be called upon, without running the risk of having new types.

Annual or biennial plants, or monocotyledonous plants, among which there are only a few species which can be multiplied by division of the trunk, cannot, however, be subjected to any means of agamic multiplication. Here one can only rely on the seed, with the disadvantage stressed above.

In annual and biennial plants, the multitude of hybrid specimens obtained through artificial fecundation must be subjected to a special process of selection, with a view to eliminating, in the first place, the more imperfect specimens. Seed producers use special selection of horticultural varieties to contain the kind within the restricted limits of variability.

Since this is not profitably applicable to any great number of species, the selection of hybrid specimens consists in reiterated suppression of all specimens showing tendency to revert to atavic characteristics. Repeated over a number of years, such a discerning selection will lead to *established relativity;* the *kind* will then be practically permanent.[1]

But it should be repeated that the majority of botanic genera are refractory in this direction, and the species subject to the first law of Mendel (Section 84) are particularly so.

Cereal-growing runs into this difficulty; for the grain bearing plants stand under the genetic rule of this law. The selective

---

[1] A. A. Gauthier, Le mécanisme de l'hibridation, "Revue de Viticulture." Vol. XVI, p. 589.

process on hybrid kinds of wheat, barley, oats, etc., is based on another directive: the search for the *homozygous specimen*. Only this could yield seed which would reproduce it faithfully. In section 85 this will be dealt with at greater length, in discussion of the mechanism of hybrid scission in spontaneous reproduction (that is, autogamic) in the primitive hybrid.

It will be seen how an infinity of secondary types can be obtained herefrom, all the more numerous in proportion to the greater number of characteristics involved. These will mate in the most varied ways, but always *unstably*. In the course of several generations, the practiced eye of the hybridizer will know how to select among specimens of various *rows* (the seeds of each specimen being planted in parallel *rows*) those which presumably do not vary. After obtaining proof of their stability, after various extensive eliminations, one can be sure of having a kind which will behave like a pure species.

It is indeed true that hybrid cereals which one finds in commerce, could be regarded as species which have reverted to purity, *through hybrid combination*. It seems to have been proven that this can be beneficial, especially insofar as the robustness of the kind is concerned. Likewise, one may observe the acquisition of some residual and positive characteristics left over from the temporary amalgamation with different species or variety.

However, the strengthening and amelioration may be conferred with equal success to any kind of so-called pedigree cultivation, if based on reiterated selection among the best specimens of one variety.

The matter of whether amelioration in the varieties of cereal should sooner be attempted by *pedigree* cultivation rather than hybridization is still under eager debate, precisely because of the fact that as long as some visible or latent characteristic acquired through hybridization exists in any given specimen, it will be impossible to reckon on an unchanging type.

Hybridization cannot bring any real, genuine benefits to annual plants on the whole; nothing at all which might be compared, in fact, to what has been achieved by it in horticulture and viticulture on perennial species.

84.

The Rules of Mendel

Under section 80, reference was made to the mosaic composition of the hybrid vegetable, and the reader was offered instances of evident confirmation and biological corollaries of this assertion, but without opportunity to form any extensive concept of this fact in a measure which might permit generalization.

Direct investigation has been able to establish but little on the constitution of the hybrid; but in studying the genetic behavior of the progeny with diligent perseverance, it has been able to cast much more light than all the microscopic, chemical and polarimetric research has been able to do.

The first to observe and confirm the disjunctive mechanism of gametes in the hybrid was a learned monk, teacher of physics in Brünn in Austrian Moravia, the abbot, Gregory Mendel.

He formulated the well-known laws to which the sexual heredity of all hybrid beings, including vegetable and animal cross-breeds, are subordinated. The discovery of the great forerunner of modern Genetics was ignored for a long time, and after thirty years of oblivion, the analogous studies of De Vries, then those of Bateson, Correns, Tschermak, etc., again brought it to the light. Here in our country the same principles were advantageously applied by various hybridizers, already mentioned.

The laws of Mendel gave an entirely new impulse to Genetics, a sure sense of direction, a concrete foundation on which to build this section, which, thanks to them, has become an experimental one. The scission of characteristics which takes place with mathematical precision in successive hybrid generations is the most valid support of the divisionistic theory, (Section 80).

The reappearance of the specific characteristics which, mingling in the hybrid, return again quite pure in successive generations, confirms the hypothesis which attributes a severely identical composition and inviolable integrity, unassailable to collateral elements, to the sexual cells.

In hybridization one finds an even more valid confirmation of the concept, expressed in section 27, regarding the molecular composition of chromosomes, and the ratification of the arguments already advanced concerning combinations of the molecular elements compatible with vitality.

It has already been explained how the stable *composition* and the manner of molecular and atomic *arrangement* determine the occult nature of the species.

An exact awareness of this is extremely important, especially in regard to one's directives in rational selection of bastard plants obtained through hybridization.

Botanic species, or *biotypes,* may be distinguished from hybrids precisely because of their unvariability of seed. The *genetic test* of an unknown plant is based on this assertion. It is a pure species if its progeny is homogeneous; otherwise it is a hybrid.

In an indirect but irrefutable way, the laws of Mendel reveal the purity of *the gamete* in hybrid plants. They also reveal how *composite elements* of both the specimens forming the hybrid *cannot co-exist* in the sexual cells. Hence the logical deduction that the whole of the hybrid plant originates from the aggregation of sharply differentiated cells of one single species of both the biotypes.

Two heterogeneous species mated in hybridization *construct,* right from the moment of fecundation, the individual hybrid in *complementary mutuality;* each of them makes its own material contribution which bears, so to speak, a stamp of its own, and which is not influenced by the neighboring cells of another species.

Although this bio-coenotic process in the hybrid is not apparent, or at least not completely apparent, it may no longer be held in doubt, for the diminution of any factor in the genital plasma furnishes irrefutable proof of it in experiments on genetic ionolysis, which forms the subject matter of the next chapter.

The laws of Mendel and their logical corollaries have belied most formidably the theories of Lamarck, Darwin, and Jordan.

The phenomena which in pangenesis were attributed to hereditary variations, are today separately established and classified, and consist of polymorphism, hybridization and mutation.

The natural selection and slow, progressive metamorphosis of the species propounded by Darwin, according to which all living beings tend to unceasingly modify themselves, urged to do so by competition (the necessity of conquering in the battle for existence) have been positively and decisively denied by the doctrine of Mendel. The doctrine of heredity which was based on an insecure hypothesis, has become an experimental science, on equal footing with physical sciences.

According to the theory of Mendel, the sexual cells are not representative of one single hereditary principle, but are the *depositories of distinct and independent units,* each of them capable of determining a special *characteristic* in the progeny.

All the characteristics which, in manifesting themselves, confer an individual personal physiognomy on the plant, are occultly represented in the gamic unity, or gamete (Section 17) and are *precisely localized* in the masculine and feminine cellular nucleus.

Microscopic research has succeeded in distinguishing the composition and distribution of the *chromatophores,* or producers of color pigment, in an individual hybrid specimen, in cases where the specimen stemmed from the mating of two species of distinctly different color.

Undoubtedly, the molecular combinations representative of other characteristics too, but which, unlike the chromatophores, elude optical investigation, are all and constantly present in the gametic nucleus.

Every characteristic behaves like a *species in itself,* (this is proved by the composite separation of hybrid progeny); so, therefore, it has *life relationship* with the characteristic with which it is mated. It is *indivisible* from the species, but *independent in its ubication of connection.*

The conception of a composite structural gamete gives rise to several genetic features of *oblique transmission* in certain characteristics. (Section 86).

The inheritance of characteristics is subordinated to the *way* in which, by an uncontrollable but logical process, the chromosomes, representing the characteristics, join one another in the moment of fecundation.

The concept of embryonal conception must be absolutely distinguished and isolated from the mechanism of nourishment.

The formation, the characteristics and the vitality of any being depend on the chromosomes which participate in its conception; for a hybrid, it depends on the *manner of fusion* of the aforesaid chromosomes, which are present in the male and female sexual nuclei. *They alone are the authors* of the embryo, and therefore of the seed, and the plant. The nourishment they receive is put there at their disposal, and does not influence them at all.

Once the fecundation has taken place, the chromosomes are, so to speak, nested in the egg-cell; in this initial phase, the hybrid may virtually be regarded as a *double graft,* of two scions of different quality, which then blend their branches, their propagines (Section 86).

Just as in a graft operation, the branch fashions and then avails itself at pleasure of the sap placed there at its disposal by the tree, so is the sap which flows to the ovule in hybrid fecundation utilized in half-measure by the heterogeneous chromosomes which draw on it in cooperation with the chromosomes of the ovule, so as to construct the hybrid embryo.

There is one complication which may be deceptive and that is the occult aspect. The inheritance of characteristics is not *always,* nor *entirely,* apparent; some of them remain hidden in the beginning, and sometimes even in the second generation, to then manifest themselves either irregularly or definitively in successive seminations, whenever the hereditary hidden element of any zygote amalgamates with similar more recessive elements, or with elements which are able to evaluate it.

The laws of Mendel have helped to distinguish and confirm this behavior, which had deceived scholars in the past, who were misled by prejudicial error, their absence of method, and their imperfect ability to distinguish between the pure species, the variety and the hybrid.

The mosaic composition, which is generally very intricate, that is extremely subdivided, leads one to believe that the characteristics of the pure species are blended, or better still, combined in the hybrid; at times, certain parts of a characteristic in a bio-type are not apparent to the eye, or are extremely attenuated in respect to those of the companion species, and lastly there are instances in which no characteristic of the two mated species are retained at all.

Each of these manifestations is distinguished by the respective exterior exponents: *equality, incomplete dominion, absolute dominion,* and *mutation of characteristics.*

But the *specific effective constitution* of the hybrid does not correspond at all to the respective exterior exponents; in fact, the chemical analysis of any vegetable hybrid, even though subject to absolute dominion, will prove that its composition is always perfectly intermediary between that of the two parent species.[1]

What is deceptive is most certainly the visual impression, and among two discordant results, only the chemical or polarimetric ones should be taken into consideration. These show that the growth mechanism of the two plasmas in a hybrid is distinguished by *most severe equality,* in any species, no matter what exterior exponents there may be.

From this point of view, the laws of Mendel become a *simple distinctive classification of the different apparent manifestations,* which does not detract anything from the immense importance they have had so far in the field of Genetics. Here they are:

1st Law of Mendel. (*Law of domination*)

The bastards obtained from the first generation[2] have the characteristics of one parent, whether this played the male or female role in the process of hybridization.

In the second spontaneous generation, the bastard progeny produced consists of individuals of which ¾ manifest the dominant character and ¼ the recessive character, which remained latent in the first generation.

2nd Law. (*Equality or balance between characteristics*)

The products of the first generation of hybrid seeds have characteristics which are intermediary between the parent species. In the second spontaneous generation of these bastards with balanced characteristics, half of the plants still retain hybrid characteristics; ¼ pure characteristics of one parent, and ¼ pure characteristics of the other parent that cooperated in forming the hybrid specimen.

[1] L. Majocco, '*Mendel's laws and heredity.* F. Bocca, Milan, p. 43.
[2] That is, that the bastard progeny of seeds hybridized by artificial fecundation, are indicated as F[1], those of the second generation as F[2], etc.

3rd Law. (*Law of new characteristics*)

The bastards of two species or varieties present new characteristics which are peculiar to neither of their two parents.

(If one pays attention to the phenomenon of domination which, it should be repeated, is only apparent, the appearance of new characteristics is not surprising, because the externality often belies the true essence, concealing latent characteristics.)

If the seeds of hybrid plants subject to the 1st law are gathered and sown apart, one will obtain again in F^3 the dominating type; ¾ of the specimens of dominant character and ¼ recessive in character, while the recessive type does not vary; that is to say, it is faithful in reproduction, as though it were a pure species. Because *through hybridization* it has returned precisely to that.

By repeating separate semination of the three types obtained in instances of the 2nd law, it will be seen that the hybrid kind once again splits itself up in the same proportions: ½ hybrid, ¼ paternal, ¼ maternal, while the two pure kinds are also faithful and never again vary in reproduction.

85.

An Equal Law of Disjunction Controls Hybrid Progeny

Of these three laws, the first seems the strangest and most transcendent. But in reality it does not constitute any exception to natural laws. The intimate mechanism of reproduction operates in an identical manner in all three cases. The *apparent diversity in behavior* may be mentally conciliated, and everything reverts to normality, if one will admit that our senses deceive us, if we admit that the evaluation of phenomena must not be limited solely to a superficial and purely visual examination.

The reason for the apparent dominion in hybrids of the first law can be demonstrated by the following comparison, which is somewhat banal, it is true, but helps to interpret my thought effectively.

If two equal-sized, transparent bottles were filled, the one with strongly colored wine, the other half with the same wine and half with water, it would be difficult for anyone to distinguish between them by mere external examination. Whereas, if in the second bottle, instead of water and wine, there was a mixture half of wine and half of milk, the mixture would be at once apparent.

Water, that is the *transparency* in respect to the wine (dominant pigment) would be recessive to our senses (1st law). The milk, which has a *pigmentation all its own*, to balance the pigment in the wine would, in respect to the latter, be equilibrated (2nd law).

Now the words used in distinguishing liquid mixtures familiar to us, can aptly apply to those used in classifying those mixtures of species which are hybrids.

Chromatic domination and equilibrium are thereby justified; but the characteristics differentiating the species do not consist only in the color of some of their organs. One also has to consider morphologic characteristics. Among other features which may prevail or balance each other is that of *stature;* and the reasons advanced in justification of chromatic behavior do not apply, unless we are to take another adventurous step forward in the field of hypothesis, and suppose that the cellular elements of the dominant species are endowed with the power to *deform* the elements of the recessive species intersticed between them.

Since the factor of *"stature"* is nothing other than the sum total of the cellular whole, considered in dimension, the hybrid will in this case take on the dimension of the dominant species, among the cells of which the recessive elements are, so to speak, obliged to *force* themselves, driven by *the necessity of conjunctive balance.* When the parents of a hybrid consist of one tall species and another dwarfed species, one may suggest that the cells of the latter are obliged to stretch out among the compages of the surrounding heterogeneous cells, because wherever there might be an interruption in continuity, the circulation of sap could not be effected. So the reason for domination in the specific instance of stature (which is the most difficult to justify) would appear to be a physiological requirement, which exploits the *pliability* of the cells. This pliability is confirmed by the fact that in any cultivated area, plants which are very closely planted together, will stretch until they double their height and may even treble it over and above that usual in their fellows, in their need of the sun.

This argument will be resumed and developed more extensively in the discussion of genetic behavior of certain hybrids in which the invading species becomes recessive, under the effect of ionizing treatment of the pollen.

We have already mentioned how the proof of the mosaic composition of all organs in hybrids is inductively produced by the proven purity of the gametes. This purity is inferred by the results obtained from the second generation of hybrid specimens.

It is well that we specify that by second generation (F^2) we mean the product, that is to say the complex of specimens obtained from the seed of the original hybrid, created through artificial fecundation (F^1).

In vegetables subject to the 1st law, the entire group of F^1 resembles, as we have said, one of the two parents, that is to say, the dominant species. When the flowers are fecundated by their own pollen, as usually occurs, we have hybrid seeds which produce ¾ of the specimens similar to the dominant species (in the F^2) and ¼ similar to the pure recessive species.

This shows that in spontaneous mating both the male gametes and the egg cells of the F^1 are influenced in flowering in *equal proportion* by both parents, despite the exterior tendency in appearance to recall only one of the species in that phase of generation.

For by the rule of probability, there are four possible compositions between the male and female gametes of a hybrid.

Let us imagine that we are effecting a hybridization between a white flower species and a red flower species; this last is the dominant.

The hybridization will be thus expressed: species B x species R=BxR.

The appearance of the first generation (F^1) will be: R.

But by the above, the reproductive elements will in each specimen and each flower be: $B^n + R^n$, of which n is the number, equal for both types of sexual cells.

Each flower bears stamens and pistils; half of the pollen which the stamens are able to produce would reproduce the character of B *pure*, the other half the likewise pure character of R. The same applies to the pistils, or better, the egg cells.

Impartial probability will give us in F^2:

	Apparent	Real
1. Mating of a gamete R with an egg-cell R (will produce R progeny, which will no longer vary because it will be homozygous)	R	R
2. Mating between a gamete R with an egg-cell B (under effect of domination will produce R progeny, but will vary later because heterozygous, that is, hybrid)	R	R + B
3. Mating between a gamete B with egg-cell R under effect of domination will produce R progeny, but will continue for the above reasons)	R	B + R
4. Mating of a gamete B with egg-cell B (will produce B progeny which will no longer vary, because it will be homozygous)	B	B

The total of the four *apparent* combinations will yield precisely 3R+1B, that is to say, ¾ dominant characteristics and ¼ recessive.

But of the three R groups, the first is of pure character and is comparable to the other group, B. The other remaining two groups R are hybrids, *despite their appearance*. So we have 1R+2 (B+R) + 1B, which *in reality is equivalent to the equality formula*, i.e. the second law.

Often the dominant character is striking; in a superficial investigation it is impossible to discern which are the homozygous R specimens, and which the still hybrid R specimens. But the trained eye is able to separate the dominant progeny of F^2, the R specimens having reverted to the pure type. On the other hand, we find the imperfect dominant type side-by-side with *absolute* dominance, the former being already mentioned previously; a gradual scale of connection exists between the two forms of dominance.

In hybrids subject to Mendel's second law, if we are still imagining that we are observing a hybrid between one species or variety of white flower with another species or variety of red flower,[1] we will find equilibrium between the characteristics. The indicative manifestation of the cross-breeding will still be BxR.

---

[1] I am limiting my reflections for the sake of brevity, to one single, constant characteristic; but it frequently happens that one characteristic in hybridization will behave differently from another in respect to dominance.

The appearance of the first flowering in F^1 will be BR, i.e., pink.

The reproductive elements of each flower consist in an equal number of cells, which conform respectively to the two parent species that is to say $B^n + R^n$, as in the first law.

The possible compositions which will fashion the new progeny are still four, as follows:

	Appearance	Reality
1. Mating of a B gamete with a B egg-cell which will produce homozygous B progeny (which will not vary again).	B	B
2. Mating between a B gamete with an R egg-cell, which will again split (being heterozygous)	B + R	B + R
3. Mating between an R gamete with a B egg-cell it will behave like No. 2, because the sexes are inverted)	R + B	R + B
4. Mating between an R gamete with an R egg-cell (which will produce stable homozygous R progeny)	R	R

Therefore *both in appearance and in reality* 1R+2 (R+B)+1B.

In comparing the two tables, the reader will be persuaded that the biological mechanism and the numerical proportion *between hybrid individuals and homozygous ones are perfectly equal* for both the laws. The sole difference lies in the *exterior* exponent, which in the 1st law does not correspond to the essential factual state.

Mendel certainly understood intuitively the purity of the gametes and had attributed importance to the proportion by quarter in hybrid progeny; but it was Bateson who first showed the reason for the above mentioned mathematical relationship encountered in spontaneous generation of bastards, with his hypothesis, which is now generally accepted, of the purity of the gamete.

This would never have been attained, if the diligent observations of the reverend abbot, corroborated by the later identical results obtained by other experiments, had not first supplied the foundations; the logical coordination of constant proportion in specific dualism in hybrid progeny is nothing else than the rational outcome.

According to De Vries, the characteristic closest to the species prototype, which is physiologically the stronger, prevails in matings between varieties. In other words, the characteristic of the species dominates the characteristic of the variety, which is nothing else than a derivative form of the same species prototype, but lacking in a characteristic, and therefore, in a natu..listic sense, less perfect.

Dominance may manifest itself among hybrids of pure species; indeed, it is most conspicious, as for example, the cases of hybridization between opium poppies and bracted poppies, to which the reader's attention was already called in section 78.

De Vries too, points to cases of dominance in hybrids of such species as Datura, Hyoscyamus, Lychnis; so it is not the systematic relationship between the two gametes of a hybrid which determines dominance.

86.

Independent Fusion of Characteristics in Couples and Oblique Rearrangement

The laws of Mendel are corroborated precisely and with greater clarity in the progeny stemming from mating between species and varieties which are pure and homozygous, and sharply differentiated in *one single characteristic.*

Horticultural varieties are hardly ever the progeny of pure species, but the product of cross-breeding, often complex, and more or less remote in time. With operation on these, no sharply distinct results will be obtained, comparable to those obtained by Mendel.

By supernatural intuition, he took the precaution of selecting, for his immortal experiments, varieties or species which remain pure without any special artifice, such as peas, which fecundate their ovules before unclosing their flowers.

The modest priest succeeded, for the good fortune of science, in obtaining during his initial experiments on this species of autogamic fecundation, F_2 progeny with well differentiated characteristics, which were easy to recognize and reproduce.

If he had worked on other species or genera, he would have encountered greater difficulties; especially if he had chosen anemophilous species, in which extraneous fecundations, which complicate the phenomenon and mislead the observer, occur.

The selection by classification, too, is difficult when the parents are differentiated in two or more characteristics. Each of these will *act independently,* and may succeed (in appearance, let it be understood) in being dominant, equilibrated, or recessive in respect to the corresponding characteristic in the organ in which this is detected. In other terms, *every pair of characteristics* acts independently from the others.

Therefore hybridization between species A (tall, hairy, blue) crossbred, let us say, with species B (dwarfed, smooth, and white) may produce a tall, smooth and blue-hybrid specimen; in the first pair of characteristics (stature), species A will dominate, in the second pair species B, and in the third (color of the corolla), the influences are equal.

So in successive generations we find specimens of highly varied and still more complex form.

The majority of horticultural hybrids have progeny with complex characteristics, which some time ago, led people to imagine that hybrid descendance was capricious, confused, and impossible to follow and classify after several generations. Atavic heredity was only vaguely conceived.

In certain hybridizations, it will happen that some particularly distinctive characteristic in a given organ disappears completely, or is verified only in a part of the descendants. But careful observation will allow us to verify how nothing in hybridization is created and nothing destroyed; what is misleading is that certain characteristics are *transposed,* that is to say, they are no longer localized in the same organ as in the parent.

Here it is necessary to make a distinction, that is, to distinguish between disseminated characteristics and peculiarities circumscribed in one organ.

Usually, there is correlation between the more or less strong tint of leaves, fruit, or flowers of a plant, whether it is a pure species or a hybrid.

This is the case with vines, Aspiran Bouschet, Gamay Fréau, and Tintorino, which have a highly colored juice, and reveal their abundant red pigmentation even in their shoots and leaves which are dark green tinged with a purplish pink.

Blue Stramonio, which has a green-brown foliage, and White Stramonio, which has green foliage produce a wide range of variations between these two tints in their hybrid offspring, which are *attuned* to the analogous range of pigmentation in the flower. In a word, when the faculty of producing anthocyanin, which confers the color in question, exists in any vegetable, this will manifest its presence in many different parts of the specimen. This characteristic is always found even in hybrid descendance, and is proportionately distributed among all organs.

Other anomalous morphological characteristics on the other hand, are restricted to one organ of the plant, and behave differently in respect to heredity. They *are not transmitted in parallel,* that is to say, they do not manifest themselves in the *same* organ in the descendance which, in one of the parents, seemed anomalous.

Always with the intention of limiting myself solely to the results of experiments which I personally carried out and controlled, I will cite two of the most outstanding phenomena of oblique transmission of characteristics.

Upon the crossing of the Chasselas vine *with toothed leaves* (*Vigne ciotat, Petersilientraube*) with strongly dentated, *very toothed leaves,* almost similar to those of the Japanese maples, with the *Ferdinand de Lesseps* variety (a hybrid of V. *vinifera* x V. *labrusca*) with almost round leafage only slightly lobate, I obtained a vine[1] with curled or furrowed *fruit,* similar to a Tropeolo fruit, and with incised tip.

Evidently the *marking pattern* of the foliage constitutes an hereditary alteration, comparable to an ordinary characteristic, and as such subject to insertion into another organ.

In crossing of the *Abutilon Souvenir de Bonn,* having a red-veined, marked flower and *leaves* marginally variegated in white, with an Abutilon having a lacquered rose flower and normal dark-

---

[1] Pirovano Cross No. 6.

green leaves, I obtained two descendants with pure whole *flowers*, others with a pale yellow flower, but none with variegated leaves.

The albinism transmitted to flowers may logically be attributed to that which partially characterized the leaves of the maternal factor.

In hybrid descent, and particularly in that of complex hybrids, such oddities, or sports, can be found so that hasty judgment might lead one to infer that such items are extraneous not only to the laws that have just been enunciated here but to all natural order. Inspection of several hybrid forms, the progenitors of which are known, give the impression that every law has been subverted, and that nothing in Nature is regulated or subject to systematization. However, a closer examination soon leads to a reconsideration of the matter. What is involved is always a matter, latent, but defined, transmitted obliquely to their progeny.

Therefore, by crossing, once more, two precocious black vines having a round acinus, obtained by me many years ago,[1] I obtained a late, or retarded variety, white, bearing enormous clusters with large oval grapes.[2]

Only perfect acquaintance with the varieties that have had favorable conditions to produce the *first* two crosses can account for the introduction of the new characteristics, or properties, of the secondary hybrid. New in appearance these were, nevertheless, present in the ancestors (grandparents): the color white (Greco and Maddalena Angevine), the large cluster (Greco and Bellino), the oval shape (Maddalena), the delayed maturation (Greco), the very tough skin (precocious Ischia). The "pigment" factor then seems to be transferred to the vine-shoot, or vine-twig, which is purple-blue in color.

In summary, it must be repeated that in the hybrid, the properties of the components, represented by the chromosomes of the genital plasma, unite among themselves in a *complex and free association*, for which reason there are no manifest hereditary exponents and proportionality of the properties of each biotype.

[1] This refers to Pirovano Cross No. 17 (white Greek, precocious Malachia). Pirovano Cross No. 14 (Bellino x Maddalena Angevine).
[2] Pirovano Cross No. 60.

87.

Effect of Ionolysis on Chromosomes Considered as the Structure Elements of the Species

It is in place here to recall to the attention of the Reader the reasoning by which, in section 76, an interpretation was sought of the origin of hybrid life.

The origin of the formation of the embryo, growth, the order of functioning, were supposed to be dependent upon the *interlocking and complementary collaboration* of the sex plasma, in conjunction with fertilization. Inasmuch as each species, each variety, is supposed to possess its own special innate arrangement, a specific molecular set-up that characterizes the chromosomes of its genital plasma and which visibly corresponds to the specific physiognomy, it is evident that the abandonment of several elements, or units, infinitesimal, it is true, but of great importance, as initiators of the living structure, should bring about *debilitative modifications* regarding the activity of the species that has undergone the treatment, as against the normal hybrid.

According to the experiments described in the preceding chapter, the Reader will have convinced himself of the effect of ionolysis upon the elementary electric charges determining the ubication and connections of the plasma and of its chromosomes. These, as has been pointed out, cannot possibly be immediately and directly verified, inasmuch as the transpositions of atoms and molecules that have taken place are limited and imperceptible. However, the indirect proofs, based on the exterior exponents of the type varied by ionolization, establish the fact that the latter enfeebles or destroys the life force, or transforms the normal developmental direction of the species that has been so exposed.

The experiments described up to this point refer to modifications induced, by ionolysis, in the species. Very much more interesting are those tried on hybrids, inasmuch as they offer the advantage of permitting a follow-up and, I might almost say, the *regulation* of the effect of the process upon the genital plasma exposed to it.

Armando Gauthier compares the mutual action of the sex plasmas coming together to form the hybrid, to two complementary parts of one element that can enclose one another, re-enter upon each other (*interlock*).[1]

Fertilization can take place between two diverse species every time that the sex elements satisfy the necessary conditions. The possibility of coming out alive is similarly dependent on this requisite of complete *closure*, or better put, of *integrative connection*.

Hybridization—and practice confirms this—succeeds also if the cover is not actually that of the box, ideally conceived, which it is to enclose. It is enough that it close tight, that it be able, in some way, to intertwine with the elements of the different species with which it is being mated, in this way closing the imaginary circuit.

In view of the fact that fertilization and development of the seed is to be effected between different species, the first substantial condition to be satisfied, it is advisable to repeat, is that of strict kinship, corresponding in no uncertain way to the composition and almost identical molecular structure of the plasmas that are to be united to form the hybrid.

In section 76, I have analyzed a new idea tending to justify the compatibility and the mutual pursuit of work by the unispecific elements comprising the hybrid. These elements are comparable to a system of *two coupled gears*. The botanical affinity is coupled with the step, or gap, that is to say, with the distance between any two teeth. The possibility of motion, which would correspond to the pursuit of life, is also subject above all to the gap, but is dependent besides on the ambient heat. Since it is not essential for two gears to have the same diameter to operate once they are coupled, just so does hybridological genetics demonstrate how it is not rigidly required that union take place between sexes of the same species, but that it is enough for the possibility to exist for the specific elements of one sex to be able, at the very beginning, to be engrafted, and after a while, to replace one another without harm to the physiological functions which they are called upon to perform in common.

Heat is the first stimulus of vital movements. In the operation of the virtual mechanism thus conceived, thermic movements have

---

[1] A. Gauthier, *Le mécanisme de l'hibridation.* Review cit., p. 587.

an importance second not even to nutrition (Section 43). Every physiologic phase of the development of a plant has a strict relationship to the total number of calories that it receives from the immediate environment. Above all, fertilization is exacting in this connection.

The chromosomes of the genital plasma might be said to be *the structural units* (aediles) of the species. Each species has its own group, enabled to build in accordance with *a method quite its own and immutable*. In the hybrid, the two groups of structural units, engrafted on the plant axis, build in common the hybrid (bastard) structure, each element of which has the imprint of one or the other contributing groups. Obviously, if one of the groups of structural units, (the chromosomes), is *enfeebled in its union,* or else, attenuated, is arrested in its functioning by any other element, *the hybrid structure will be built with the other group in dominance,* which group remains fully efficient.

Therefore, in the hybrid the charcteristics of the latter, that is to say of the undisturbed species, will prevail.

That is why, when the pollen is exposed to suitable ionolizing treatment, *there is immediately produced in the F^1 an anomalous descent.* The genetic behavior becomes completely individualistic. The laws of heredity no longer operate. From its status as an aggressive or dominant race, species, or variety, the type the pollen of which has undergone ionolization, becomes recessive, sometimes completely so, sometimes only in part so.

The experiments performed so far tend to strengthen the supposition that the species, in line with all else that happens in Creation, reacts to the process or withdraws from its influence after a limited Time. Whenever, however, the acting force were to overcome the *critical point* the resistance would all at once diminish. Then a *series of breakdowns,* of consequent molecular shifts, within a brief moment almost completely obliterate the hereditary faculty of the species. This might explain the morphological dualism of many ionogenetic hybrids.

Both in hybridization and in normal fertilization, the value of ionolysis is measured in terms of the same data, frequency, intensity, and timing. As already explained in Chapter VI, the next chapter will offer confirmation of the fact that reaction to treatment is quite diverse from species to species. Finally, there is a perfect analogy between the structural breakdowns induced by ionolysis in pure species and the degree of specific regression evoked by the same means of hybridization.

And so, ionilization of pollen offers a means of weakening, at will, the genital plasma of the species used as the male. Since there is as yet no owner of this device, it is honestly not possible to announce in advance its range, or scope. However, inasmuch as in many species, even with means as yet rudimentary, it has been possible to exert so much influence on the pollen as to render recessive species that are normally dominant in hybrid matings, it is more than legitimate to hope that, with correct methods, success will attend the *disciplining*, in the broadest sense of the term, genetic heredity, subordinating it completely to the human will.

CHAPTER VIII

Ionolysis in Hybridization

88.

Ionolysis in Somniferous Poppy Crosses

THE READER has already had ample information about the behavior of this species in connection with the action of ionolysis. However, in Chapter VI consideration was given only to the transformations induced in one variety (the double white) fertilized with its own pollen.

It was interesting to learn the behavior of pigmentation of flowers of colored varieties under the same stimuli that have called forth such interesting variations in the white variety.

As need has dictated, I have selected as pollen bearers varieties with dark or scarlet flowers, that are dominant with respect to white, at the same time setting up others of the same variety for comparison, control experiments, comprising fertilization with pollen gathered six days earlier.

The following experiments were carried on simultaneously, with every care taken to insure the correctness of the results.

GROUP A—Somniferous Poppy Double White ♀ x Somniferous
Poppy Double Scarlet ♂

I. Control fertilization with fresh pollen.

II. As above, with 6-day-old pollen, preserved in barely tepid medium (pollen-preservative).

III. Fertilization with pollen obtained from anthers ionolized *in the plant,* with a device analogous to those of experiments *i* (Section 61) and *G* (Section 92), with the identical magnets. 42-cycle exciting current. The uninterrupted action lasted the 5 days preceding flowering. Maximum field intensity 900 gauss. (calculated approximately on the ground of the position of the anthers).

IV. Analogous treatment, with 400-cycle exciting current, 500 gauss, maintained during 6 hours, at 20 minute intervals each, during the week preceding flowering.

GROUP B—Somniferous Poppy Double ♀ x Somniferous Poppy
Violet-Dark ♂ .

V. Control fertilization with fresh pollen.

VI. As above, with 6-day-old pollen, preserved as above.

VII. Fertilization with pollen exposed to pulsating magnetic field produced by 80 v. A.C., 42 cycles, interrupted by Wenhelt. Rest period 1 hour. Maximum intensity, 12,300 gauss.

Results

Group A - I. The standard, or model, flower-bed consists of plants with pale rose flowers and petals with white centers.

II. The use of old pollen in no substantial way changed any of the distinctive properties of the control hybrid.

III. The quite homogeneous lot of erect plants, straight and strong, a little lower than those of the model or control flower-bed. Flowers quite double, pale-rose, opening up a few days later than normal (Fig. 56).

A small percentage have white flowers, with stalks somewhat twisted and more retarded flowering.

IV. In this lot (Fig. 59), there is an absolute breakdown of the red pigment, with the exception of 4 examples. The stature, contrary to what was noted in the analogous experiment (Chap. VI), its mature pollen achieved, is somewhat inferior to the comparable lot I. The plants are prevailingly dwarfed, strong, upright; but there is no lack of individual ones with twisted stalks, as well as peony-flower shapes, ball-shaped, flowers quite full and with lasting power. Regardless of size, the individual specimens of this lot are reflorescent ones; and Fig. 59 reproduces, in this connection, three plants photographed at the time of reflowering (July 4th), having stalks a bit contorted, and a flower that is not greenish as in the experiments with ultra-violet rays (Section 64), but has morphological relationship, or pertinency.

Group B-V. The population of this group is absolutely homogeneous. It consists of tall plants with slate-violet flower, lighter towards the top (Fig. 57).

VI. A homogeneous lot, in every way like the preceding one except in the tint of its petals, which is somewhat lighter, especially at the center of the flower. Plants a little flaccid, with delayed florescence.

VII. Among the experiments on colored poppy crosses, this one has given the most conspicuous results, not so much as regards the retraction of pigment as for the robustness that it has bestowed on its progeny.

The flower-bed consists of plants prevailingly dwarfed, bearing on their rigid and short stalks many extremely big flowers, quite full, opening almost simultaneously (Fig. 58). In all of them the tint and color are a pale lilac except for about 6 percent of them that are white.

Thus as regards the pigment, then, there has been demonstrated the efficacy of the various ionolizing treatments. The effect should hold to a considerable extent also in experiment IV, in view of the scanty magnetic force involved.

89.

Ionolysis in Somniferous Poppy Hybrid x Bracteate Poppy Papavero d' Oriente

At the end of 1900 I had successfully tried the hybridization of these two poppy species, botanically quite different in each of their properties. The somniferous poppy is an annual plant, glabrous (smooth skinned) in all its parts, and having glaucous, or greyish-green-blue leaves, dentated only at their border. It is always quite fertile and has a white latex substance which, when it coagulates, yields opium.

The bracteate poppy is a perennial, has a stalk and coarsely tomentose leaves; the latter are dark green, clear, deeply grooved, covered with thin hair. Their latex substance is yellowish, thick and very limited quantitatively.

At the point of insertion of the sepals, which are also hairy, at the tip of the stalk, there originate from the stalk two grooved bracts in the form of leaves. This species owes its name to this very peculiarity, which distinguishes it from any other species of poppy. It is distinguished besides for its gigantic build and for its beautiful dark-violet pollen. It is barely fertile.

The pollen of the somniferous poppy is a straw-yellow, while inside the petals there is the whole gamut of from white, to red, all the way to dark-violet with petals more or less fringed. The somniferous opium poppy flowers are always simple, but, for our part, we cultivate far more extensively in our gardens the double-flower variety, which maintain themselves as such throughout re-sowings, even without special devices.

The bracteate poppy does not have a varied range of colors. Its petals are always scarlet, clear, tending slightly to orange in some varieties, with a smooth border, crossed with black at the center of the flower. There are no known double varieties in this species.

The first hybridization was effected between a variety of scarlet double somniferous poppy with a white center, taken as the female, and the bracteate poppy type. The seeds of a single capsule have yielded me about 300 plants.

The hybridization was repeated in the same way with the use of the somniferous opium poppy, which is simple, pure, white instead of the red double one.

In both of the hybridizations the product of the first poppy variety is in every respect similar to the parent species. The dominance of the bracteate poppy species is so marked that not a single differentiating characteristic permits the distinguishing of the hybrid from the species employed as the male factor. Only towards the end of the vegetative process is it possible to observe a difference in the foliage, which, in the hybrid plant has a light bluish velvetiness.

The flower, in the case of the double-flowered female as well as in that of the simple flower, red or white, is always scarlet, clear, brilliant; however, it is bare of bracts.

As has already been pointed out, this hybrid is absolutely sterile, since it lacks any suture of the anthers, and since there is atrophic degeneration of the ovarian capsule. It does not flower during the first year of semination, not even if this has taken place the preceding autumn, but it reappears after a brief rest, like the parent species, and lasts two or three years. Only in the matter of longevity is this hybrid intermediate between the parent species, one of which is an annual, and the other a perennial.

In well spaced culture, when the stumps are quite strong, there are some plants that produce banded, that is branched, stalks. Fig. 60 represents, at the left, a stalk of a common hybrid variety of plant and, at the right, the abnormal, branched form, photographed a few days after flowering.

This type of exception arises only in the group descending from the simple somniferous poppy. In the original hybridization, with the double-poppy as the seed-carrier, its approximately 300 plants yielded only a single extremely tenuous variation in one plant, the flower of which had a tonality slightly paler than that of the rest of that group.

It is therefore purely exceptional for a genetic difference to show up in this sterile hybridization of the somniferous poppy with the bracteate poppy.

Among the many hybridizations of these two species, I have not had the good fortune to achieve a series of experiments with the various forms of ionolysis. This has not been due to any deleterious element in the ionolysis process but to some unknown exigency in the fertilization process.

As a whole, the scant results, scant as compared with the vast application attempted, are interesting enough to induce me to consider them at great length.

Simple Somniferous (Opium) Poppy ♀ x Scarlet Bracteate Poppy ♂

1. Comparison: 5-day-old pollen.
2. Fertilization with pollen, as above, exposed to a variable magnetic field for 2 hours, with a closed-field apparatus of Fig. 15, excited by a 500-cycle alternating current. Maximum field intensity: 3250 g.
3. Fertilization as above, one-half hour exposure to 600-cycle exciter current. Maximum field intensity: 4100 g.
4. Fertilization with pollen exposed to pulsating magnetism by means of the apparatus in Fig. 13, with *homonymous polarity*, excited by means of a 42-cycle 80 v. alternating current, interrupted at 1½ hour intervals by a Wenhelt apparatus. Maximum field intensity; about 6000 g.
5. Fertilization with pollen lying under radiations of 1 milligram radium bromide for 8 hours, at a distance of ½ cm. from the radioactive salt.
6. Fertilization as above; duration of exposure: 24 hours.

Results

1. Homogeneous group all characteristic of the parent species with the exception of the absence of bacteates, as per preceding description.

2. From the appearance of the first leaves, the plants of this series, all coming from a single capsule, are quite notably different to the degree that they may be placed without hesitation into two groups with clearly differentiated shapes. The first, the more numerous one, comprises the more developed ones, which resemble, and more than that, seem *identical* with, the somniferous poppy; the other one, covering about one-third of the total number, offers *characteristics intermediate* between the parents.

The somniferous poppy does not stand up to transplanting, or adapts itself to it poorly, whereas the hybrid, of either form, takes to it without difficulty.

By chance, I discovered this peculiarity, which I had not assumed to be the case, at least not in a form like that of the somniferous poppy, as a result of the need to thin out the plantings. The diminished dominance of the bracteate poppy becomes clear from the first leaves on, increasing the interest in the experiment.

The plants of either form or shape maintain their respective properties right down to the time of florescence. It is at that stage that the difference between the plants of the first group and those of the parent species becomes more evident, through the greater spread and thickness of the foliage, its symmetry, and the decreased dentation of the borders.

In some individual instances, the plants are irregularly stained, or spotted, with a darker shade of green, and are less greyish-green-blue, indicating the presence of the elements of the bracteate poppy plasma, which, by some unknown mechanism, but not one new to hybrids, regroup themselves, establishing themselves at given points.

The cause determining the asymmetry, I believe, may be attributed specifically to the imperfect mixing of the plasma of the two parent species, either of which has a quite divergent development and vegetative tendency.

While in the hybrid control group the plants flower only in the second year of sowing (20 months later), in the group under consideration florescence takes place in eight months for plants of type 1 (female), and in about nine months for plants of type 2 (intermediate), this constituting a distinct advantage, brought about by the predominance of the somniferous poppy species, which tends to promote florescence.

The *first type* bears completely white flowers, well formed, in all respects identical with the somniferous poppy; however, the capsules are somewhat smaller and more elongated than in the normal species (Fig. 65).

In contrast with the somniferous poppy, the stalk of which ends in a single large capsule (Fig. 64 represents a group of eleven somniferous poppy plants), the white hybrid type blossoms in *continual succession from the middle of May to July,* the period in which the photographs reproduced here were developed. The secondary branchings become quite blunted at the bottom, very close to the ground, arranged in candelabra or branched fashion, not very unlike those reproduced in Fig. 60.

229

The flowers of this type, like that of the somniferous poppy, are perfect, and the capsules that mature successively parallel to the blooming intervals, are full of well-bodied seeds.

The second type has developed flowers, capsules of the *intermediate characteristics,* and leaves, considerably more slowly than did those of the parent unit.

In connection with the slow development, blossoming of the plants of this type does not set in before the end of June, while at that time individual units of group 1 are beginning to mature their first capsules.

Regarding this peculiarity, too, the group is intermediate between the seed-bearing species, which blooms within the year of the seed-sowing, and the normal hybrid, which bears flowers only within the second year.

The stalks are light-green, erect, hairy. Some of the lateral branches show delayed blooming; a characteristic not to be found in the male species. The sepals, also hairy, are in every detail like those of the parent species, but lacking in bracts. In some flowers, instead of two sepals, there may be counted three and even four, in which case the petals are, in their turn, asymmetrical, supernumerary, curled and inserted abnormally on the thalamus.

The petals, a beautiful satin rose tending to salmon color, are invariably characterized by the black cross, distinctive for the bracteate poppy species. The anthers are dark violet in color, always sterile, as in the control hybrid group. The stigmata, light purple-blue rose in color, are similarly sterile. The ovaric capsule is almost always surrounded by pistilloid truncated-cone segments, more or less numerous, curled, arranged in ring formation, and curved in toward the center (Fig. 66).

The pistilloid units in the poppy variety are not a new variation. De Vries devotes a whole chapter to it in his famous work, "Species and Varieties."

This anomaly crops up quite frequently also in *P. croceum* and in *P. alpinum,* but as far as I have been able to ascertain, it has never been verified in the *P. bracteatum* (bracteate poppy) hybrid.

Like the fringed character of foliage, the pistilloid character of type 2 must be called forth by the *partial* alteration induced in the genital plasma of the bracteate poppy species, the species from which comes the altered pollen which is evidently compelled (in its mating with heterogeneous female organs), in spite of its naturally dominant characteristic, to give up the formation of another organism's accessory organs. This disorientation may give rise to supplementary organs, which are not formed in any of the original species, in which, in the normal course of events, every element has its precise and constant direction.

Another peculiarity worth pointing out is the spontaneous, abundant exudation of the latex-substance which gushes out of the ovaries and along the stalks of the hybrid plant, condensing spontaneously into opium. This phenomenon might have some practical bearing but does not have unusual scientific interest, there being a basis for maintaining the corollary regarding sterility, to which this extremely special hybrid type is susceptible.

It is easy to convince oneself of this by practicing the ablation of the anthers in a somniferous poppy bud, with precautions taken as indicated in section 61 and provision for assuring the flowers freedom from visits from insects for several days.

Fertilizing only a portion of the stigmata so preserved, there is registered an equal and simultaneous enlargement of the capsule. In view of the fact that the latter does not use its lymph or the substance provided for seed-formation except to an extremely limited degree, the excess of lymph or latex that is exuded to the outside at several points of the capsule, becomes coagulated.

Unfortunately, the ionogenetic hybrids of type 2 are totally sterile.

If the genetic dualism of the F^1 of this hybrid is interesting, no less so is the behavior of the F^2 obtained by the seeds from the fertile form, similar to the somniferous poppy, through partial atavistic return towards the dominant species, which electrical compulsion had to all appearance totally excluded from the composition of the hybrid.

In the first days of life, the F^2 buds show they have a deep-rooted kinship with the bracteate poppy; they have long, violet bordered cotyledons, tiny leaves of lengthened ellipsoid shape, only slightly fringed, somewhat fat, covered with fine down.

As vegetation proceeds, the morphology of the plant tends to shift towards the maternal species. Toward April, the leaves decidedly take on the grooving pattern and greyish blue-green appearance of the somniferous poppy. Upon examination, however, one notices a reddening of the median vein, then in the secondary leaves of the majority of the individual plants; and it becomes evident that the form, the development, and the time of the latter is not rigorously identical for all the plants.

The shape of the leaves is somewhat diversified, but the majority are like the somniferous poppy.

As growth continues still further, the indications of kinship with the bracteate poppy disappear entirely. Upon blooming, the plants are no longer distinguishable from the original maternal species.

3. The increase of the frequency from 500 to 600 cycles considerably aids the ionolization of the pollen, so much so that, despite treatment for even half the duration (of time) in this experiment, the proportion of individual plants mutated in the original form (that is to say, similar to the maternal species) is 92 percent, while in the previous experiment it was about one-third. Besides, in this lot there remains the clear dualism of the two forms previously described.

4. The pulsating magnetic field, demonstrating in other genera its energetic response to variations, despite the high intensity and perfect tuning with the interrupter, has not, however, yielded any individual type of the original variety. This lot consists of plants in equal prevalence with those already described in type 2 (Exper. 2, Fig. 66), with which are united various morphologically intermediate gradations between the normal hybrid and the second form.

Their leaves present extensive polymorphism, and the flowers, varying but little in color from those of the comparison hybrid (Exper. 1), sometimes have 3-4 sepals, even 2, and petals splashed or lined with white and delicately bordered in green in the middle section, toward the outside of them. In tiny specimens one sees traces of pistilloid stamens. Anthers normal in appearance, that open up, but yield infecund pollen; stigmata, normal in appearance, but these also are sterile.

5. From this fertilization there has already been a yield of a few perfect seeds. Their germination has been a rare occurrence, a total of only some thirty individuals. These, however, are all of the orig-

inal type, which demonstrates the efficacy of consecutive radioliza-tion.

6. With difficulty, eight specimens of this lot have been salvaged, from which above data have been derived.

The genetic behavior of the F^1 of the descendant units of indi-vidual specimens of the original types of groups 3, 5, 6, and, like them, that of the similar fertile type of experiment 2, is similar.

Many of these experiments have been repeated with the female chosen being the white-double somniferous poppy, also the simple type. Climatic causes account for the destruction of a large portion of the plants. Of the few specimens remaining, however, it has been possible to ascertain that there is perfect agreement with the results obtained with the previous series, both as regards dualism of types and the proportionality of mutated units.

Noteworthy, instead, is the individual difference in pigmentation of the flowers in the mutation of Type 1. In the previous experi-ments these have always shown up as a pure white flower; while with a female of a double-flower type, there are single flowers, semi-double, and double ones; flowers with white petals crossed with canary-colored ones, with yellowish petals, and lastly with greenish petals.

Individual specimens born of the same hybridization, coming from the seed of the same fruit (of a single capsule), never come out strictly identical, but usually differ from one another in some small detail.

In normal hybridization between somniferous poppy and bracte-ate poppy, the individual differences between various plants con-stituting a semination lot, or population, in popular parlance, are extremely rare and almost imperceptible.

It is quite true that variations appear in the form of branched or candelabra-type stalks (Fig. 60); but these, rather than substantial and congenital forms of mutations, must be looked upon as acci-dental products of coupling originating in the stump at the start of vegetative development, as in the case of many species that bear so-called *bound* branches. In fact the branching begins with the plants half bare, *the same plants that the year before had been nor-mal.* Since sprouting of branches is a peculiar characteristic of the somniferous poppy, whether this shows up to a greater or lesser degree, according to available space, it is probable that the hybrids of the somniferous poppy x the bracteated one all have, *in latent form*, the property of sprouting bound branches and manifest it only in exceptional contingencies of space, vigor, and cultivational stimuli.

Outline of Genetic Behavior of Hybridization
Between the Somniferous Poppy and the Bracteate Poppy.

Normal fertilization

Simple somniferous poppy ♀ ✕ Bracteate poppy ♂

↓

F¹ *Entire descent similar to Bracteate poppy*

↓

F² .... Does not yield seeds

Fertilization with ionolized pollen
♀ ✕ ♂ (I)

F¹ Plants similar to maternal   Intermediate plants with pistilloid
    species, but reflorescent.   rose-colored flower.

↓   ↓

F² Plants undergoing various   .... Do not yield seeds.
    metamorphoses until they
    assume the stable appear-
    rance of maternal species.

Normal Fertilization

Double somniferous poppy ♀ ✕ *Bracteate poppy* ♂

↓

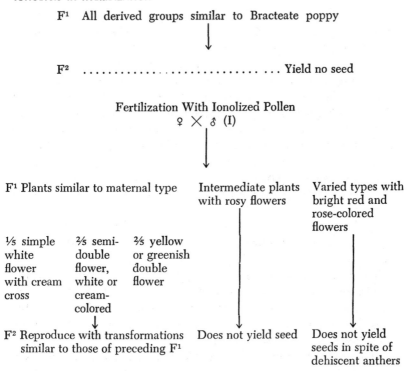

F¹ All derived groups similar to Bracteate poppy

F² .... Yield no seed

Fertilization With Ionolized Pollen
♀ × ♂ (I)

F¹ Plants similar to maternal type			Intermediate plants with rosy flowers	Varied types with bright red and rose-colored flowers
⅕ simple white flower with cream cross	⅖ semi-double flower, white or cream-colored	⅖ yellow or greenish double flower		
F² Reproduce with transformations similar to those of preceding F¹			Does not yield seed	Does not yield seeds in spite of dehiscent anthers

When ionolytic debilitation enters the field, as the Reader will be able to convince himself shortly, it is not only in the poppy class that clear dualism sets in between the plants of the same hybrid lot. Investigation as to the causes of two sole distinct forms, without intermediate morphological stages, is not free of difficulty, because the coefficients that can determine the anomaly are many and sundry.

Among those that seem to me worthy of consideration are the following:

1. Distance from the polar expansion.

2. Position of the pollen in their relation to the lines of force or to the incidence of the rays.

3. Ubication of chromosomes with regard to same.

235

The critical point for the degrading of the constitutive particles determining the mutations is given by the collaboration of these factors and of the aforementioned circumstances.

I deem it *apropos* to repeat an idea already numerously pointed out in this book, in order to present my thought with full clarity.

It is evident that the artificial stimulus directed at the live genital plasma, as happens in any other phenomenon in the physics of physiology, corresponds to, or rather follows immediately upon, a reaction, every phase of a shift is followed by an immediate rearrangement.

In the long run, however, there may ensue a slowdown in the ability to repair, as happens in the case of elastic bodies exposed to too frequent stretching.

Failing to achieve repair, or rearrangement, during the pause between periods of ionolization, there would follow *shortly and all at once* complete breakdown.

The genetic dualism of this poppy hybrid, as of other species, would correspond, then, respectively to *two distinct phases* of ionolization of the plasma, the first (partial) one being limited to the most labile molecular groups of the chromosomes, the other corresponding to a general slowdown.

It is useful to repeat (section 42) that the pollen is never deposited at one same level, but is often heaped up. By way of example, a grain of pollen 0.1 mm. from the polar surface has available an iono-motor force four times greater than that of a similar grain 0.2 mm. distant from the same surface[1], inasmuch as the magnetic flow decreases in the ratio of the square of the distance, for which reason the first granule can reach the critical point of total annihilation of its chromosomes, while the second one has changed only the most labile ones.

As to the position of the pollen with respect to the magnetic or electric force that reacts on it, one must consider that the granules of pollen are hardly ever perfectly round (Sections 16, 17); generally, they are ellipsoid, thick-pointed, lobed, or grooved.

---

[1] This rule is completely correct only in the case where a single magnetic pole is operating. In the case of opposite poles or those close together, as in the electro-magnets in connection with pollen, the situation becomes more complex.

It goes without saying that, in view of their tiny size, it is not possible to arrange the pollen granules in the same direction with respect to the lines of magnetic force or to the source of the rays, as would have to be done for complete exactitude of comparison.

The iono-motor force may be quite diverse according to whether an ellipsoid granule of pollen intersects the lines of magnetic force of the trajectory of the rays in the direction of its major axis or perpendicular to it (Section 42).

The ubication of the chromosome may also be independent of the various possibilities of pollen placement, because it is not posited that the chromosomes themselves are in the genital plasma in a given position with respect to the figure axis of a specific pollen species. And inasmuch as the variation of the characteristics depends solely on the chromosomes, which are precisely the determiners of the characteristics, the question should probably be restricted to the electro-magnetic force in operation.

These are the most salient considerations, those that come to mind as the most probable justifications for the morphological dualism of the descent of many hybrids, among which the above-mentioned poppies are the most sharply differentiated.

The genetic dualism of the hybrid class is a phenomenon of extreme interest, worthy of more profound investigation.

Coordinating the results already obtained, it may be stated from here on that the hybrid of the somniferous poppy x the bracteate poppy, of which the latter species had been exposed to ionolyzing treatment, indicate:

1. That it is possible with the identical treatment to have two quite distinct groups of descendants.

2. That the various means of inducing ionolysis into the genital plasma can be equal in the deformative effects that they induce.

3. That there may be produced fertile hybrids in the selfsame situation where ordinary mating of the same species yields sterile hybrids; a new conformation attesting to the fact that sterility is not due to a somatic cause but to asynchronism of the movements governing the anthesis.

4. That the F^2 of such fertile hybrids follows a course different from the normal; that is to say, it achieves metamorphosis during growth.

237

90.

Ionolysis in Hybrid of Turbaned Gourd with Portmanteau'd Gourd

PORTMANTEAU OR JERUSALEM GOURD (*Cucurbita moschata*) ♀ x GREEN-TURBANED GOURD (*Cucurbita maxima*, var. *turbaniformis*) ♂ (Reproduced in Fig. 68 and 69)

After the first period, I had the fortunate intuition to choose for the original experiments some species with coarse pollen.

Gourds, because of their rapid growth, short life cycle, thin consistency of their tissue, to which corresponds a gracile composition of the pollen, were the subject of the first tests. And it was a stroke of luck, because with the slow period and slow interruption treatments then in use, the experiments would not have succeeded had they been applied to other species. In the long run, I would have been discouraged, and the experiments would not have been carried on further[1].

Hybrid fertilization of gourds is quite capricious and holds delusion. The results here set down are the pitiable compendium of a long series of fruitless attempts!!

In order to stimulate more and more the fruit to be realized, one part of the stigma, corresponding to a definite part of the ovary which it is necessary to mark (with an incision in the wall of the ovulary, Fig. 67), is fertilized with pollen exposed to ionizing treatment, the rest, with fresh and intact pollen.

This device prevents, if not completely at least partially, easy failure, or miscarriage, because at least in one part of the fruit the vital humors are restored by the fertilizing action and assure the realization of the fruit. The pollen, enfeebled by the electromagnetic treatment, frequently fails by and of itself to bring forth the fruit.

Once it reaches maturity, the artificially fertilized gourd is split open, care being taken to divide it into the sectors as marked. The

[1]The electrogenetic experiments on gourds are within the reach of all. Whoever has a small kitchen-garden and alternating current terminal can repeat the experiments on gourds by providing himself with a small, suitable electromagnet costing a few tens of lire. (Model of Fig. 15 or 16.)

238

seeds of the respective slices are to be kept, obviously, quite apart and labelled; only those products with ionized pollen are kept.

But here are the experimental data:

1. Comparison: Fertilization with fresh pollen.

2. Fertilization with pollen exposed to a pulsating magnetic field, produced with continuous current interrupted by spark coil with vibrating break. Maximum field intensity between opposite pole surfaces: about 5,000 gauss.

Results

1. The plants born of the control seeds, also having their foliage spotted in white, like the female of the species, with silvery shading or nuance, have fruit morphologically akin to the male species, except in the skin, which is orange-colored (a maternal characteristic), as well as green and red. The flesh is almost like that of the Jerusalem gourd.

Therefore, in the complex, the characteristics of the maternal species are dominant provided exception is made of the shape of the fruit, where the paternal character *absolutely predominates* (Fig. 69-A).

2. Growth weaker than in model, or control. Foliage a bit more grooved; flowers hardly different; *fruits almost identical with those of the female species* (Fig. 69-B), in form, in the color of the skin, in the pulp (flesh), and lastly in the taste. Only the neck is somewhat shorter.

If one takes into account the exiguity, or scantiness, of the means employed (truly rudimentary), one can get an idea of how responsive this type must be to more ample and refined ionolization.

Both forms, whether the control lot or the one obtained by ionolization, are completely *devoid of seeds,* nor are there any elements of these discernible. The absence of seeds in the fruit actually is not prejudicial to the successful growth of the fruit deprived of them. Strictly speaking there should be advantage in this, inasmuch as that portion of the nutritive substance normally reserved for the formation of seeds is compelled to go back into the mesocarp, or pulp, of the fruit. For that reason, the fructiferous varieties that are extremely precocious always have imperfect or aborted seeds.

Among fructiferous plants, there are very many varieties absolutely devoid of seeds[1], and they multiply agamically. In hybridization among the gourds, this phenomenon was pointed out, as known and recorded, by the learned Ragionieri, already referred to several times.

In these seedless types of plants, the flower, or blossom, including the genital organs, is perfect. Pollen, stigma, and micropyle, all are usually in full operational shape. And, since the onset of the call for lymph to the fruit requires the stimulus that only the consummation of fertilizer can bring about, it is useful to assume that this actually does *begin, but that it is* suddenly followed by abortion of the ovules.

91.

Ionolysis in Hybrids of Pasticina Gourd with Portmanteau Gourd

PASTRY, OR BERET, GOURD (*Cucurbita pepo*, var. *Melopepo*)
♀ x ♂ JERUSALEM OR PORTMANTEAU GOURD (*Cucurbita moschata*)

The ascertained responsiveness to electro-magnetic treatment of the pollen of the genus Cucurbita and the access offered by its component annual species for the rapid observation of results, obtainable the year after sowing, as well as the facility offered by it for artificial insemination, or fertilization, has induced me to prefer it.

Although belonging to the same genus, these two species are somewhat removed from each other. They actually differ in stature, disposition (the one of the climbing type, the other dwarfed, and compact), in the shape of the fruit, the size and structure of the seed, the design and coloration of the leaf.

After having tried out many hybrid fertilizations on the pasticina gourd with the pollen of the Jerusalem gourd with negative results, success was achieved with the adoption of the device for mixed, sectorial fertilization, mentioned in a previous paragraph.

---

[1] In the Vine: Black, red, and white Sultana; the Corinth. But without seed: Medlar-tree, plum-tree, etc.

Into this experiment there intrudes a *phenomenon completely extraneous* to the ionolization effect of the variable magnetic field, since it occurs in equal proportions in the plants born of the control fertilization. Millardet,[1] citing an analogous phenomenon arising in hybridization of *Vitis vinifera with V. vulpina,* calls it false hybridization. My very dear friend, the erudite Ragionieri, confirms for me ᵗhe use of this name, as used by others, and I also am adopting it.

Fortunately, false hybridization is only partially that. That is to say, it is mixed in with the abnormal plants, hybrid plants in the true sense of the word. What is more, the characteristics of the male species are dominant in the group of comparison plants.

These cases count for nothing as against those that cover plants actually hybrid referred to by Mendel as dominant.

It is presumed that in hybrid matings among those species that vary somewhat between or among themselves in the set-up of their characteristics, the pollen has no other function than that of *stimulating* fertilization, determining the increase of growth of the ovule. The plasma of the pollen tube, unable to amalgamate with that of the ovule because of its constitution being so different, has no hold at all; in the constructive mechanism, it does not, in any way, participate. The embryo consequently models itself solely on the shape of the species that functions as the female.[2]

However, abnormal fertilization has sad days in store for plants born of those seeds. These betray at the end of their first period of growth a congenital weakness, grow with difficulty, delay in bearing fruit, and they turn out smaller and more deformed than the type species, as can be easily observed by comparing Fig. 73 with Fig. 70.

In eight experiments carried out with varying excitants, intensity and duration of exposure, in this hybridization, I have been able to obtain fruit solely from the three additional groups reproduced below (Fig. 72).

---

[1] *False hybridization among the ampelideae,* in "Revue de Viticulture" V. XV, p. 676, Paris.

[2] Analogous cases were observed also in the Fragaria genera, and in the "Zygopetalum Makay" orchid; Dr. Ragionieri has observed some in the Ranunculus, Gladiolus, Ornitogalum, and other genera.

These fruits belong to the hybrid plants of each group, easily distinguishable from pseudo-hybridated plants by their leafage, silver-hued at the nervatures, and by the incomparably more rapid growth of the aforementioned ones. This original experiment, therefore, takes in only three tests:

1. Fertilization of comparison specimen with fresh pollen.

2. Fertilization with pollen exposed to a fluctuating magnetic field; excitation for 3 hours with 42-cycle alternating current. Maximum field intensity: 5,900 gauss.

3. Id. for 24 hours.

Results

1. Dominant in this lot, by a large majority, are the pseudo-hybridated zucchettos. On these plants (extremely dwarfed) emerge a few branches with elongated fruit, dark yellow-chrome in color, slightly knotty, which, in composition, are like the portmanteau gourd, which is the paternal factor (Fig. 72-A). The pulp, or flesh, is yellowish; its seeds well developed and somewhat bigger than those of the maternal species.

2. In this lot, too, nearly all the plants are of the pseudo-hybrid type. There was a single fine specimen of hybrid genus, with quite characteristic leafage, splashed with silver color, as in the first lot. The fruit is pear-shaped (Fig. 72-B) through partial recession of the male characteristic, due to a three-hour exposure to an extremely low cycle.

3. In this group, the hybrid specimens are numerous, being characterized only by the white-silver spottiness of their leaves, to a lesser extent, however, than in lots 1 and 2, a sign foretelling noteworthy enfeeblement of the pollen.

In fact, the fruit (Fig. 72-C) by no means recalls the portmanteau gourd; but instead, except for some variations in color and thickness of the pulp, it is almost like the maternal species; the seeds are long grained, smaller than those of the model and of lot 2.

Sown again, the seeds of lot 2 have yielded results that can be seen in Fig. 74, remarkable for the appearance of green pigment in the skin, which is certainly not caused because of proximity since the lot was at quite a distance from any gourd with a green skin.

92.

Ionolysis in Hybrids of Zucca Pasticina (Pumpkin) with Zucchetta (Vegetable Marrow) D'Italia

ZUCCA PASTICINA (Melon, melopepo variety) ♀ x ZUCCHETTA
D'ITALIA (Pumpkin) ♂ (cucurbitella variety)

These two species have quite differentiated leaves and fruit. From the morphological standpoint, they represent type extremes of the Cucurbita (vine) genus.

The *Zucca pasticina* is flat-shaped, has 5 apophyses, in the form of a crown (Fig. 75-A), corresponding to the five sections into which the fruit is divided. Each section ends in a lobe of the stigma. The epidermis of the fruit, is white, clear, waxy; the seeds are quite small.

The *Zucchetta D'Italia* (Fig. 75-B) has cylindrical fruit, quite elongated, is dark-green, furrowed by chrome-yellow streaks until it matures; it is only half-grown structurally. That is how it gets its improper name; improper, because full-grown the fruits measure 70-80 cm. in length and have a considerable weight.

Hybridization between these two species was more successful than the others and, for the present, constitutes the most complete series of experiments that offer a concrete notion of the efficacy of ionolization via various treatments; an efficacy that is inferred from the attenuation of the dominant power peculiar to the male species.

The experiments were performed as follows:

A. Control fertilization, with fresh pollen.

B. Fertilization with pollen exposed to a variable magnetic field by the apparatus shown in Fig. 16, 42-cycle alternating exciter current. Maximum field intensity, 6000 gauss. Duration of treatment 1 hr.

C. Fertilization as above. Duration of treatment 2 hours.

D. Fertilization as above, of similar duration, with iron filings mixed with the pollen in ratio of 1:3.

F. Fertilization with pollen mixed with iron, as in preceding. Duration of exposure 8 hours. (The anthers were exposed from the onset of their dehiscence.) Maximum field intensity about 3000 gauss.

G. Fertilization with pollen extracted from a single anther maintained for a week in a variable magnetic field, that is to say, throughout the entire phase of growth of the male flower (Fig. 12). 42-cycle alternating exciter current. Maximum field intensity at the anther about 700 gauss.

H. Fertilization with pollen exposed in the apparatus of Fig. 13 to a pulsating magnetic field produced with an electrolytic interrupter. Complementary polarity (section 31). Duration of exposure 15 minutes. 40 v. exciter current. Maximum field intensity, 4750 gauss.

I. Fertilization as above, with apparatus of Fig. 13 (not perfectly attuned to the interrupter). Complementary polarity. Duration of exposure 1 hour. 80 v. exciter current. Maximum field intensity, 7500 gauss.

J. Fertilization as above, under conditions identical with those of preceding but with pollen less than one day old.

K. Fertilization with pollen exposed to rapidly variable and alternating magnetic field in the apparatus of Fig. 15. 400-cycle exciter current. Maximum field intensity, 4750 gauss. Duration of exposure, the first 10 minutes.

L. Fertilization with pollen placed under X-ray developed by a large Roentgen-ray tube of medium hardness near which the pollen rests but without touching it. The tube was excited by Rühmkorff 50 cm.-spark inductor, activated by mercury rotative interrupter. Duration of exposure, 15 minutes initially.

M. Fertilization as above and under identical conditions. In order to attenuate the action of the X-rays, the pollen (spread out in a thin layer), was mixed with 1/3 impalpable powder. Same duration of exposure.

NB. Fertilization did not succeed with ionolized pollen, also for short exposure with radium, ultra-violet rays, and with magnetic field produced with high frequency current. In great part, they have yielded seeds, but non-vital ones, although apparently perfect. An analogous phenomenon has been currently observed in the althaea or marsh mallow (section 98).

Results

A. In the comparison cross, the shape of the fruit, without being fully homogeneous, indicates the dominance of the paternal factor. Besides, the leafage, somewhat wrinkled, and the bushy, compact, erect "stance" of the plants attest to the fact that the male species is dominant in every organ of the hybrid plant. Some of the fruits are longer, bulging, and slightly twisted (Fig. 76), others almost cylindrical, straight, slightly ribbed, in line with the internal sector divisions; there are slight variations common to all hybrid plants.

Spread over the surface of some fruits are noted excrescences, or agglomerates in the guise of pimples, probably due to the imperfect tendency to form the apophyses, which characterize the maternal species.

The plants born of this hybridization are of exceptional vigor and fertility, assuredly superior by far to both the female species.

B. Although the electro-magnetic force involved in this experiment has been quite inconsiderable, the results obtained are outstanding, and let us consider the possibility of substituting for the usual means of producing ionization the method of the variable magnetic field, which calls for an expenditure of energy far lower than that needed to obtain an equal effect with X-rays, ultra-violet rays, etc.

Fig. 77 represents a group of fruits, with respective leaves, photographed from plants arising from this lot.

In the leafage, in the draggy posture and in the fruit, this lot of hybrids hardly reveals the co-participation of the male species. In contrast with the other experimental lots, the three matings exposed to a 42-cycle alternating magnetic field present a remarkable morphological homogeneity in all of their organs, which is not to be met with any more in lots derived from pollen energetically ionolized with rapid frequency or with rays.

The fruits are largely similar to the female species; they are distinguishable because of the fuller growth of their calotte. The color of the skin, pulp, shape of the seeds, peduncles, are simply equal to those of the maternal species, which also characterizes the course of growth and period of flowering.

C. Fig. 78 offers a clear idea of the even greater withdrawal, or recession, of every characteristic of the male factor.

In this lot, too, there is no individual difference between the components, whether in the vegetative characteristics or in those of the fruit. These are almost absolutely similar to the maternal species, the only difference being a slight yellowish tint, particularly in the parts exposed to the sun.

D. With considerable protraction of ionolization, the hereditary faculty of the pollen is completely spent; its function is reduced to the pure and simple one of stimulating fertilization, a stimulus that still reacts efficaciously on the ovule, inasmuch as the ionolysis does not alter its physio-chemical properties (section 32), which has no real influence on the conception through the confusion that ionolysis has induced there.

Fig. 79 reproduces some of the fruits of this lot, the growth of which is much poorer than the previous ones. Because of its small fruit and the marked deformation which characterizes it, it may be compared to those products of pseudo-hybridization of the *Zucca pasticina with the Zucca portamantello or the Zucca Gerusalemme* (Fig. 73).

E. The addition of iron filings distributed with the pollen, while it intensifies the field, diminishes, as a result of the induced current which the variation excites in each granule of iron, the useful effect. Unfortunately the negative of the photograph taken of this lot was spoiled; the fruits resemble those of Fig. 77.

F and G. Since electro-magnetic exposures are efficacious on mature pollen, it was to be expected that the results obtained would be all the better when the electro-magnetic influx would have to act on the anthers in the last phase of maturation. In the meantime, however, it is possible to bring to bear on the mature pollen itself, in a thin layer, an intense magnetic field, and in practice almost impossible to do as much with the thick gourd anthers, all the more so as it is planned to initiate the treatment while the flower is not yet open.

Fig. 80 reproduces the results of a couple of experiments of this type with pollen obtained from an anther exposed to electro-magnetic treatment at 42 cycles for eight hours before flowering. Fig. 81 shows a similar treatment initiated one week before florescence, at extremely low field intensity, as a consequence of the marked distance from the polar surface to the anther.

246

As quite clearly demonstrated in Fig. 81, the modification obtained is, by far, inferior to that obtained on mature pollen, by briefer exposures in a much more intense magnetic field.

In quite protracted slight ionolization, there occurs, as quite apparent in Fig. 81, a peculiar phenomenon; that is, the anomalous enlargement of the peduncle of each fruit, a phenomenon that is not new to ionolysis of the genus Cucurbita (Section 66), but which appears in this hybridization at a time when an intense and brief field, one at frequent variation, is in operation. The result obtained in a subdued or weak field makes one think of the variety of results that could be obtained with devices of different frequencies and gradual intensities. Also confirmed is the already outlined hypothesis of the necessity to arrive at a fixed product of intensity x time, so as to effect the detachment of some ions of the more labile of the molecular groups and prove at last that it is, above all, the field intensity that is the principle cause of genetic variation in this plant genus.

H. The pulsating magnet field treatment obtained with the Wenhelt interrupter has yielded quite bizarre results; it is not honestly possible to draw conclusions except after a considerably greater and more precise experimentation.

The wide range of shapes obtained in a score and more of specimens does not permit of their being completely reproduced; however, for the consideration of the reader I have thought it apropos to select only three plants representing the types of the most fully, least fully, and medially developed of the fruits.

Worthy of note is the disproportion between the total weight of the fruits of each plant: 4, 2, 7, and 35 kg (Fig. 82).

The thickest plant at the left is a colossus of the genus. It rivals lot K, which already represents a noteworthy improvement over the results of the controlled fertilization. It has yellowish fruit, streaked with green, and irregularly disseminated pustules or knots along the entire surface of the fruit.

With brief treatments, though at rapid interruptions, there are no debilitative phenomena as regards vigor or fertility of the plant, not even in the specimens of smaller and extremely tardy fruit, like those reproduced in Fig. 82.

In the meantime, the parent species are bushy as to build, com-

247

pact; the plants obtained from ionolized pollen—and especially those of this lot—are stringy and stretch out, carrying their tips at three-quarters of a meter away from the stump.

I and J. In these two similar experiments, bracketed for brevity's sake, the small amperage used did not permit obtaining perfect functioning, which is never obtainable without a carefully studied intonation. Nevertheless, in view of the great susceptibility of the gourd-vine pollen to magnetic ionolysis, the results obtained have been appreciable ones. Worthy of note is the disproportion between the size of fruits obtained, noteworthy even in these two lots.

In Figs. 83 and 84 are represented the products of two lots that have been exposed in the same way to a pulsating field; but the first is the result of fertilization with fresh pollen, while the second was obtained from pollen collected the day before.

As a whole, it cannot be said that there is a substantial difference, because in the group to the left one finds some types tending to the male character; there can also be found small, shrunken forms similar to the female type. However, it is noted that the pollen used the day later comes out largely enfeebled. This observation is altogether consonant with those already mentioned in connection with aging of pollen in a normal medium (Sections 61, 65).

The plants in both lots, as of all the rest of the different experimental groups, with very few exceptions, are quite robust and, although bearing a few thick fruits, produce many of them medium or small. Just looking at the figure could give the impression that some small fruits are such because they were produced by poor plants; that is why I think it advisable to make the Reader aware of the foregoing.

K. Neither have the multiple fertilizations with pollen exposed to rapid alternation of a magnetic field been fortunate as regards certain facts extraneous to the alleged items. Of the series prepared, only some twenty of the plants of this lot have achieved fruition.

This demonstrates how, and to what point, a form of ionolysis *accidentally expedient can also bring about practical and immediately fruitful results in the improvement of the cultivated horto-cultural genus.* Fig. 85 represents three entire plants of this lot, which have quite homogeneous constitutions. Rarely do plants obtained by fertilization of the control (A) contain more than two or three fruits per plant; the nutritive reserves produced by the plants are all absorbed by the fruits themselves. Or else, in the plants of this lot, the fruits, although they are barely smaller than those of comparison lot A, are quite numerous. They contain four to seven of them per plant. On the whole, the weight of the fruits of this lot is more than double (almost triple) the normal weight. As regards the shape, whether of the fruit or of the leaves, this lot is very close to the comparison lot; however, on the skin, or bark, the bullous characteristics are dominant.

The superior yield in weight of the fruits is not an unconnected factor; more than that, it certainly depends on the optimal vigor of the exposed units, which stay in the same conditions of cultivation as all the other lots described herein. Perhaps the stimulating biological mechanism of such great abundance resides in the congenital disposition of plants to ramify abundantly from the start of their existence.

The foliage of this group is identical with that of the ordinary comparison hybrid, and the maturation of the fruits is somewhat more delayed.

L. The well-known penetrative property of X-rays made it possible to forecast a most homogeneous result inasmuch as, even in the case of some agglomerate or superposed pollen mass, the irradiation strikes every granule in almost the same way. Contrary to expectations, this lot, instead, has quite a wide range of forms, among which is noteworthy one individual specimen that is vigorous, has flaccid stalks, abnormally thick, with full and slightly cut leafage, tending to the male species, with flowers perfect in appearance, but asymmetrical, and fruits which, intermediate between the parent species, set badly, so that their growth is arrested at about one-third of normal growth. Consequently, the budding fruits die in the plant.

Fig. 86 reproduces a group of fruits of this lot the plants, of which, with the exception of the individual specimen indicated above, are fertile, yet do not possess the vigor of the parent groups. All the while, this group can balance experiment B; if one thinks of the amount of energy required by the excitation of a large Roentgen tube, like the one used for this experiment, with a 15-minute duration, and compares it with the scant amount of current absorbed by the electro-magnet which has served in the B experiment, with analogous results, if not better, one cannot help being surprised at the superiority of electro-magnetic ionolysis over that obtained via X-rays.

M. The considerable individual differences in plants of this lot can be explained by the mixing of powdered bismuth with the pollen, whereby each grain came to be partially and sometimes totally protected against the action of the rays, according to the position of the particles of bismuth with respect to the position of the latter.

Bismuth was selected in preference to other metals, because, although finely subdivided, it attenuates the penetration of the X-rays, and is almost wholly immune to attack by organic acids, with the result that it does not alter the vitality of the granule-holders even when, perchance during manipulation, a scratch is inflicted. It goes without saying that the layer of bismuth containing pollen was extremely thin.

The Reader can discern in Fig. 87 the effect produced by the various attenuations of some dominant factor or another induced by the action of radiolization, which in some instances have a new and elegant characteristic; the variegation of the fruit with green, even in the forms tending towards the maternal species.

Behavior of the ionogenetically born hybrids described in F² above.

Figs. 88, 89, 90 indicate three groups of hybrid gourds, taken from the comparison group and two ionogenetic groups, treated via electro-magnetic and X-rays, selected for the purpose of testing the reaction[1] in the F².

The figures presented below give an idea of the respective variations in the single descent.

Significant in each of the three cases is the tendency to the return to the male species, which tendency in the F¹ seemed wholly, or in large part, eliminated in the fruits of the ionogeneticized hybrids (Fig. 89, 90).

---

[1] Sritctly speaking, each fruit intended for these experiments should have been fertilized artificially with its own pollen, but since the plants were surrounded with other similar ones from the same lot, the omission does not appreciably prejudice the evaluation that one may make thereof.

Getting down to respective details, there stands out the tendency to green pigmentation of the skin in the robust descent of the normal hybrid (Fig. 91); an extensive variability in group II (Fig. 92), deformed through action of X-rays, can be judged by the more reduced shape, with white skin, and those that are larger, green, elongated, running the gamut of variations of intermediate forms (outstanding among which is one top-shaped in form) with pink skin. Lastly, in group III (Fig. 93), a more homogeneous offshoot, the reversion of which, although still limited, to the male form proves that, even in the ionogenetic hybrid, the specific vitality of the paternal species is not extinct.

93.

Ionolysis of Crosses of Yellow Tomato with Cherry Tomato

SMOOTH ROUND YELLOW TOMATO (*Solanum lycopersicum fr. luteo*) ♀ x CHERRY TOMATO WITH SMALL RED FRUIT (*Solanum lycopersicum racemigerum*) ♂

The main difficulty with the fertilization of the Solanaceae lies in the castration of the flower. The Solanum genus has a thin, extremely delicate style, inclined toward the ground when the bloom is in the fullness of its growth, ringed by a cone-shaped involucre, formed by six anthers (or more, in the giant-sized tomato with ribbed fruit) firmly bound to each other, which therefore enwrap the style tightly so as to make it difficult to remove the style or the stigma without damage.

It is best, therefore, to cut all around the base, that is to say at the insertion of the anthers on the thalamus, the staminal cone. What is needed is an extremely sharp instrument and a light touch, because any pressure, however slight, can dislodge the style, detaching it from the ovary. When the circular incision is completed, the anthers cluster in a mass, because they are joined.

The operation must be carried out early in the morning, while the anthers have not as yet opened up.

Solanum plants are not visited by insects; therefore it is useless to wrap the castrated flowers in small bags for safety. However, it is wise to keep them in the shade, away from the sun, so as not to expose the style, which is diaphanous, and might, otherwise, be in danger of desiccation.

Moreover, the flowers that are to be used in the extraction of pollen should be picked early in the morning and set apart. At once they must be laid down laterally, in the direction parallel to that of the sutures of the anthers (the staminal cones), cutting into them with a pin. It does not take long for the pollen to issue from the cup, if one is forewarned to expose the anthers in the sun for several hours.

The amount of pollen that can be extracted from each flower is very scant. This makes it necessary to sacrifice quite a number of flowers in order to obtain a visible quantity of pollen. To make up for this, since the pollen of the Solanaceae is among the thinnest known, and the surface of the stigma is of the order of a mm², a milligram of pollen may be enough for the fertilization of tens of flowers, even counting in the inevitable waste.

The pollen, whether obtained in a natural condition for the fertilization of the control, or after it is treated, should be collected and carried to the field *over a clear and black paper* so as to reduce to the minimum *dispersion* and to insure, through chromatic contrast, good visibility.

The aforesaid paper should be rolled into an upside-down cone so that the pollen is collected at the bottom of the cone. At the moment it is used, the vortex is cut off and held with a pair of small pincers, or tweezers. In that very tiny cone turned upside-down in this manner (with the pollen inside), the stigmata are submerged, the cone being successively brought below each of them, *with no effort made to bend the styles in any way whatsoever*. Once assured that the stigmata have been thoroughly daubed with pollen, one marks each fertilized flower with a woolen string of a different color, to which correspond respective notations as to the treatment that the pollen has been exposed to.

For this species, with a peduncle that is initially extremely fragile, the ordinary wooden labels with galvanized iron wire are unsuitable.

The pollen of the tomato, like that of the petunia, and of the Solanaceae, retains its functional activity for several days.

The kinds selected for these experiments are both very stable; the male (the cherry tomato) is clearly dominant in the property of pigment and, prevailingly, also in the shape of the fruit and stature of the plant, as well as in the arrangement of the racemes.

I have undertaken these experiments in the conviction that, as regards extremely small pollen, covering the deductions, vide section 42, it could require a considerable ionizing energy to be able to obtain significant results. That is why the brief runs were ignored.

Experimental scrupulousness dictated, both in the comparison as well as the subsequent experiments, the collection of the pollen four days earlier.

The experiments were conducted in this way:

1. Fertilization of the control.

2. Fertilization with pollen exposed for four days via apparatus of Fig. 16 to a variable magnetic field excited with a 42-cycle alternating current. Maximum field intensity: 2800 gauss.

3. As above, with porphyrized iron mixed with the pollen in the ratio of 1:3.

4. Fertilization with pollen exposed to a variable magnetic field in the electro-magnet pictured in Fig. 15. 400-cycle exciter current. Maximum field intensity, 2800 gauss. Duration of exposure, 4 hours.

5. Fertilization with pollen treated in the apparatus pictured in Fig. 13, excited by a 42-cycle alternating current, 80 v., interrupted with a Wenhelt interrupter in perfect intonation. Maximum field intensity, 7,430 gauss. Duration of run, 15 minutes.

6. Conditions identical with those of previous experiment, with pollen irradiated with ultra-violet light produced by synchronous spark at maximum variation of magnetic field. Equal duration of exposure.

7. Fertilization with pollen exposed for one hour, with a device like that in the preceding experiment.

8. Fertilization with pollen ionolized with rectilinear electro-magnet of Fig. 11, excited with the usual 42-cycle, 40 v., alternating current, interrupted with Wenhelt. Maximum field intensity, 2,600 gauss. Duration of treatment, 12 hours.

Results

By means of the fertilizations catalogued above, a considerable quantity of seeds have been obtained; but for lack of space, there have been accepted for examination only a hundred plants for each experiment, which were growing in as many plots.

1. The comparison lot is composed of robust plants, with stalks of medium thickness, bearing numerous clusters of 6-8 pieces of fruit each, the volume of which is about half of that of the parent species. The fruits are dark-red, therefore darker than the "cherry" (pollen bearing) variety, which has fiery red ones. They are round-shaped, regular. The maturation covers the same period as does the paternal type (Fig. 94). No anomaly, however small, is observable in any organ of this hybrid lot, consisting of absolutely "twin" plants.

2. The list devoted to this lot is, in every detail, similar to the comparison one. Only late in Autumn does one note some plant, or fruit, that is a little lighter, irregularly orange-stained.

3. In all respects similar to the preceding item.

4. From the rapidly alternating magnetic field applied for a relatively long time, it was to be expected that some good proof of repression of the dominant species would ensue. As a matter of fact, such proof was not lacking; but if the modifications are numerous, they are also vary rare, three only, which is as much as saying 3% of the total number, which, on the whole, does not differ from the normal.

The three individual anomalies are, on the other hand, *very distinct*. As I already had pointed out in the analogous case of the poppies, there do not exist intermediate forms. Probably the three plants come from grains of pollen which, through their special distribution and pattern with respect to the lines of force of the magnetic field, or because they happened to be where the magnetic field was extremely intense, were able to enjoy the entire ionomotor effect provoked by field variations.

The anomalous plants resemble each other greatly; they all have an enormous trunk, with a diameter twice the size of the normal plant, whereas their stature is medium. From their dense foliage, fleshy, paler than their congeners and tending to curl precociously about themselves, arise various, quite curious, filiations (Fig. 96). They spring from the median nervation of the adult leaves and in the beginning they resemble bulbiferous Asplentium buds. They then develop in small tufts from the quite tiny and irregularly shaped leaf that produces them, which, still re-enforcing itself through the unaccustomed excess of lymph to which it affords a passage, bends back, falling against the stalk.

Fig. 96 shows such a leaf at the start of the auto-filiation; Fig. 97 reproduces two similar leaves at completed growth of secondary vegetation.

Another interesting aspect in this variegated plant is the fructification, both the normal and the subsequent one. The first takes place in a normal period; the second in late autumn and is of no benefit. In both, the fruit is somewhat irregular, yellowish-orange in color, rather than red, bearing rather thick peduncles, which, however, poorly nourish the fruit buds at the end of the cluster.

The fruit is hardly matured when the second line determined by the pre-existing flaw, or crack, splits open, drawing a thin, light suberose network on the epidermis, like some variety of the genus Diospyrus.

In that way, the fruits dry up on the plant in due time, or else rot from the rain. Fig. 95 reproduces some sour, or bitter, ones and some ultra-mature ones that are drying up.

5. The plants of this lot, too, produced from pollen exposed for a short while, and energetically so, to a pulsating magnetic field, have yielded only ephemeral varieties, different from the preceding ones inasmuch as they are limited to the abnormal pigmentation of the leaves, and above all of the borders, which take on a vivid violet tint.

The fruits, scarce in this specimen, resemble those of lot No. 2 above.

6. The combination of two means of ionization acting simultaneously on the pollen is bound to produce two modifications, not really similar to the analogous experiment No. 5, however, alike as regards the deformation produced by the 400-cycle alternating magnetic field.

Thus, the supplementary treatment with ultraviolet rays has caused a deviation in the tendency to form purple-blue pigment, impelling it to the more conspicuous phenomenon of the general curling up of the plant, a phenomenon common also to the following experiment.

7. This does not differ from No. 6 except with respect to the duration of exposure (four times longer but somewhat weaker); however, towards the end of the treatment, because of the excessive heating of the cable tank of the electrolytic interrupter, which must be made to operate four intervals, it was necessary to have two to three hours stoppage between intervals to give the liquid a chance to cool down.

This is the lot that has yielded the largest number of anomalies; that is to say, No. 6 plants with curly fruits similar to those of group No. 4 (Fig. 95), and No. 4 plants with smooth yellow flowers barely streaked with rose.

Fig. 95-B reproduced a group of both forms obtained with this ionization device through rays coupled with magnetic ionolysis.

The plant anomalies, in this lot, as well as in those of No. 4 and No. 6, as a result of the numerous "suckers" from the leaves, assume in the Fall the appearance of colossal ferns, so much does their foliage criss-cross and curl. The useful fruit yield, despite the numerous adventitious shoots sprouted by the ribs of each leaf, is far lower than the normal yield, because of the smaller size as well as the gigantic conformation of the last flowers of the secondary inflorescence, which does not permit of their setting.

The decrease in the dominant power of the ionolized male factor is then difficult to achieve and is lacking in normal homogeneity in this crossing of varieties of tomato. The regression in dominance is accompanied by the appearance of a new characteristic extraneous to the species,[1] extending their layers into every organ, which causes deformation in a more or less evident way.

8. The prolonged treatment should doubtlessly have enfeebled the pollen inmeasurably, all the more so since the ionolytic action

---

[1] In the yellow tomato, there is often observed a degeneration, commonly referred to as curling (limited to the upper organs and to the adjacent leaves), which appears near the end of the vegetative cycle. It comprises mostly the transformation of the apical flowers into foliate, chlorophyllate organs—bizarre hybridisms, one might say, between leaves and petals. The phenomenon is, as regards similar differences, quite unique, but is not lacking in some analogous respects, to deformation induced by ionolysis.

was disturbed in similar time intervals during a total of 6 hours.

From the single, lean fruit obtained, few seeds were obtained, and these yielded individuals hardly different from the comparison types, except for the delayed fruition, and—in one case among twelve—curly leaves.

94.

Ionolysis in Crosses of King Humbert Tomato with Ribbed Tomato

OBLONG "KING HUMBERT" OR SMALL FLASK TOMATO (*Solanum lycopersicum, var. ovaliformis*) ♀ x COMMON RIBBED TOMATO (*Solanum lycopersicum, var. monstruosus*) ♂

A. Fertilization of the control, with pollen collected two days earlier.

B. Fertilization with pollen as above treated with the electromagnet of Fig. II, excited by a 42-cycle electro-magnet. Maximum field intensity, 5,500 gauss. Duration of treatment, 20 hours.

Results

A. The comparison lot comprises plants with normal growth, speeded up to yield flowers and fruit. These grow little during the first inflorescence; they come out thicker than the maternal species, and they are perfectly round. They bear long clusters of which they have 10 to 12 each.

Towards autumn, the inflorescences grow shorter. Consequently, the fruits are less abundant but thicker, frequently marked with furrows which remind one of the male progenitor species (Fig. 99).

B. The plants of this flower-bed (about 200) have normal growth and stature like that of the preceding group. Among the fructifications are noticeable two forms, differentiated *distinctly* from the dominant ones—about ⅚ identical with the comparison lot.

The remaining ones, that is to say, ⅙, resemble the female variety, but on each cluster of fruit there is one part that has a narrowing at midway, so that these look like small Indian clubs.

No individual specimen shows externally any indication of a transitional stage from one form to another.[1]

95.

Ionolysis of Crosses of Cherry Tomato with Ribbed Tomato

CHERRY TOMATO (*Solanum lycopersicum racemigerum*) ♀ x
RIBBED COMMON RED TOMATO (*Solanum lycopersicum monstruosus*) ♂

I. Comparison unit: Fertilization with fresh pollen.

II. Fertilization with pollen exposed to X-rays, against a thick Roentgen tube. Apparatus as per Section 92, experiment L. Duration of exposure, first 15 minutes.

III. Analogous to the preceding one, with pollen mixed with powdered bismuth in the ratio of about 1:3 by volume.

IV. Mixed treatment, with variable magnetic field excited:
   a. by 42-cycle alternating current with closed magnetic field; 4,740 gauss per 10 hours.
   b. with the same at 80v. interrupted by Wenhelt, in open magnetic field with complementary polarity for two hours; 2,400 gauss.

V. Equal treatment, with pollen mixed with bismuth as in III

VI. Equal treatment, with pollen mixed with iron, as above.

VII. Fertilization with ionolyzed pollen with 42-cycle alternating current for seven days.

Results

I. The comparison lot demonstrates the dominance of the female species in form, in structure, and also in size.

II. and III. There is no perceptible difference from the control lot.

---

[1] See sections 30, 31, and 89 for the reasons adduced to justify the clear dualism of the ionolized progeny.

IV. and V. Some specimens showed partial regression of the male character.

VI. Comparable to lots II and III.

VII. Fertilization has produced few berries, and has yielded no vital seeds.

Although not having any great interest in the matter, I have nevertheless cited the foregoing because it is the only study that has included two treatments with X-rays. Although these have not any perceptible efficacy, it cannot be inferred that their action would have been the same if the male species had had clearly dominant characters, capable of revealing the diminution of this dominance by means of the examination of the components of each ionolyzed experimental lot.

96.

Ionolysis in Hybrids of Giant Sunflower with the Perennial (Small) Sunflower

GIANT SUNFLOWER OF RUSSIA (*Helianthus uniflorus*) ♀ x
PERENNIAL STERILE SUNFLOWER (*Helianthus multiflorus*) ♂

For anyone who wishes to repeat this interesting series of experiments, which is within the reach of anyone owning a modest supply of instruments, I believe it worthwhile to recall the inherent arrangements in preparing and isolating the flower castrated for the artificial fertilization.

When it is the giant sunflower that is used as the seed-bearer the little parchment-paper bags no longer suffice for the purpose of preserving the great amount of matter of this species from visits of insects; there are available large gauze cones, held stiff by light interlacings of wicker, well closed at the bottom, against the stalk of the flower.

As has already been pointed out in section 72, the ablation of the anther is relatively easy, if one has been wise enough to operate a few hours before the style has entered the staminal tube, formed by the collateral interwelding of the two anthers, which envelop it completely. In the first hours of the morning, the style becomes rapidly elongated. Compelled to thread into the staminal tube, it expels the pollen, staining itself with it. The elongation of the style, in the flowerets of the disk (3-4 rows per day) intended for flowering on the following day, comes at a speed rarely met with in analogous circumstances.

In little more than an hour, in spite of variance in the case of several units, the style elongates from the base to the apex of the staminal tube; hardly does it reach the outside than it spreads the two stigmal filaments which immediately twist back again.

It is necessary to proceed *before* the styles become elongated but not too soon, because in that case the staminal tubelets are hard to grasp, since they are still hidden among the sepals.

The first flowers to blossom in each flower-bud, or head, in the sun-flower species, are the best; they are sorted out during the fertilization process (prepared in the manner referred to earlier), the flowerets placed at the periphery of each disk, that is to say, those nearest the ligules, being best formed, passing over those nearer the center, which it does no harm to leave there because they do not fertilize and do not yield seed, once the flower is protected against pronubal insects. The style becomes smeared with pollen, as has been said, by passing through the staminal tubelets; however, for the time being, fertilization does not occur, the stigmal papillae being in the internal part of the corresponding "bores." Strictly speaking, the ablation of the anthers would therefore be superfluous, but for the sake of experimental scrupulousness, it is better to include it.

The pollen of the composites is resistant for a long time with ordinary preservation and may be brought into parental relations within one and the same genus. The giant sunflower is an enormous annual plant, has a single and thick trunk, is gigantic in its every organ, is quite fertile, and has white seeds streaked with gray, its flowers having sepals and yellow styles. The perennial sunflower is of modest stature, has small foliage, small stellated flowers; it yields pollen in reasonable amount, with quite irregular granules, and is absolutely sterile. The sepals of the flowerets are yellow, the stalks a mottled brown-purple-blue. Figs. 101 and 102 represent these two species.

Here are the experiments.

P. Fertilization of the control, with two-day-old pollen.

I. Fertilization with pollen exposed for three days to 42-cycle fluctuating magnetic field. Maximum field intensity, 4,750 gauss.

II. As above for 5 days.

III. Fertilization with pollen placed for one hour in a 500-cycle fluctuating magnetic field. Maximum field intensity, 3,250 gauss.

IV. As above, for 2 hours.

V. As above, for 3 hours.

VI. Fertilization with pollen placed first into a 500-cycle fluctuating magnetic field for 40 minutes first, then in a 42-cycle one for 28 hours. Maximum field intensities, respectively, 3,250 and 4,750 gauss.

VII. Fertilization with pollen exposed to a pulsating magnetic field with electrolytic interrupter; 40 v. exciter current, for 7 hours. Maximum field intensity, 5,580 gauss.

VIII. Same as above, with homonymous polarity, 80 v. exciter current, for 2 hours. Maximum field intensity, 4,500 gauss.

IX. Fertilization with thinly spread pollen, irradiated by ultraviolet light at 3 cm. from the spark supplied by the apparatus of Fig. 13. Duration of exposure, 2 hours.

N.B. As will be more clearly seen in section 97, the sunflower gives way to extensive polymorphy in its hybrid descent. It is logical that also the ionogenetic hybrids are not immune to it.

Despite this, one survey of the various lots produced with ionolyzed pollen gives one the feeling of homogeneity and indicates the approximate equivalence of the various means of ionolization adopted.

In the description of the individual results, in order not to incur frequent repetitions, I place in evidence only the forms obtained *which differ from the normal ionogeneticized hybrid.* Each lot consists of thirty plants.

Results

P. The comparison lot consists of very tall plants, ramified in shape, pyramidal. Each plant is a cyclopic bunch, always covered with a goodly quantity of flowers and buds, the florescence of which, delayed with respect to all the original species, is protracted until the autumn. The strong specimens produce 120-150 and more flowers in succession. The first leaves, like those that garnish the trunk, are somewhat big, morphologically akin to the female species; later on, and especially on the secondary stalks, there grow small leaves lanceolate in form, similar to the male species. The primary tuft and the numerous stalks that keep pullulating are green, streaked or shaded in violet in the parts most exposed to the sun.

The flowers in shape and size are intermediate among the parent species. They have yellow-colored ligules, contrasting with the disk, which is a velvety black, like the seeds. These are thick, a bit less so than the common variety of sunflower, but have a much more elongated shape. The interstitial bractea that separate the different rows of seeds extend outward from many of these, are pointed, while both the parent species have short and yellowing ones.

Fig. 103 represents a plant of this lot.

I. In this lot as in subsequent ionogenetic ones, while the pyramidal shape remains in most of the plants, the disks are yellow, not black (Fig. 103), and some plants are single-flowered. The tops, in this lot, are convex, often folded back on themselves in a queer way. But the most salient characteristic consists of a light-colored ligule (represented by two specimens), differing throughout completely from the common variety of hybrid type in having its leaves more tightly held together, more grooved, more hairy, paler in coloring. The ligules are thick, slim, cream-yellow, tending to salmon color (Figs. 107-111). The flowerets of the disk have the same straw-like tint, and the seeds, very hooked and small, are of different colors but always quite pale in comparison with the normal type.

II. Similar to the preceding as a whole, this lot contains five plants (out of thirty) with cream-white flowers, with characteristics all of the type described above. Of these plants, two are uniflorous and three reflorescent. Their heads (Figs. 107-111) are all convex and asymmetrically controlled.

The seeds are numerous but little nourished toward the center of the disk.

III. The rapidly fluctuating magnetic field has not induced into this progeny any marked peculiarity, except for the thinning of the ligule, in a few specimens.

IV. As above; there stands out a giant plant, the only one in the lot, with dark-purple flowers at the disk. Many uniflorous plants.

V. The lot is analogous to the preceding one, including about one-half of the plants which are uniflorous, as well as one specimen of reflorescent plant with twisted branch, many-sheathed, or banded, inserted on the primary stalk across a gnarled, or knotty or a bulging juncture.

VI. The ionolysis composed of the genital plasma gives rise, in this group, to a phenomenon opposite to the one that is the usual case in plant species and hybrids; that is to say, it impels a *speed-up of florescence,* which cannot be attributed to the factor, a common one, of a breakdown of male dominance, delayed in its florescence, but to some mysterious cause, which is the subject of new research on which I am working.

The precocity of this ionolyzed hybrid is not so only with respect to the normal hybrid, but *surpasses even that of the seed-bearing one,* which, also in the case of absolute dominance, would be the limited case realizable in a hybrid.

Fig. 105 represents two specimens of this hybrid, obtained simultaneously with the others of the preceding figure. Their disks are already matured while those of lot P., and I, II, III, still have flowers and buds. Their leaves, in every respect similar to the maternal species, are enormous, a good deal bigger than the latter, about 60 cm. long by 50 cm. wide. They are borne by robust peduncles, subject to splitting (actually a new characteristic) in the upper part, at the points of maximum convexity of the peduncles themselves.

The trunk, thick, short, extremely robust, somewhat stocky both in the maternal species and in the normal hybrid, has nodes close to one another, and reveals several wide-open cracks like those of the peduncles. In the parts most exposed to the sun it is suffused with violet. The insertion of the leaves on the stalk is by means of thick and knotty nodes. The flowers are as large as those of the maternal species, but the disk is somewhat reduced; on maturing it assumes a flat shape, or a convex one, as in uniflorous species H, and in the comparison hybrid. The flowerets of the crest (head) have dark red sepals and also yellow ones, with black stalks.

The seeds of the mauve-rose specimen (mauve-rose is actually a color new to the genus) shade into purple-blue, assuming at maturity a light hazelnut shade. In some specimens there are lighter shades, with more or less extensive zebra-stripes of black and yellowish shadings upon maturity.

All the seeds are very well set, these seeds being more than twice as thick as the hybrid comparison plants.

Until full florescence, the stalk bears no trace of pollen. Once pollen is produced, there appear, in most of the individual plants, various suckers which emerge *almost at ground level* and vegetate rapidly, within a few days displaying their beautiful radiating flowers, with characteristics intermediate between their parent species; these characteristics, in fact, being common to the leaves of the secondary gestation.

In this lot, then, there has been produced, thanks to ionolysis at two frequencies, a multiple rise of new, important, and useful characteristics, some of which reveal the competition of the male species *to a greater extent than in the normal hybrid.*

The Reader will then see better in section 103 how ionolysis, in the case of hybridism *between very distant species, strengthens* the ionolyzed species, rather than weakening it, permitting partial dominance. The male units, rendered in ordinary life absolutely unable to collaborate with the complementary units of the ovule, too diverse in structure, can usefully mate when they are to a certain extent unbound by sudden ionolysis. The phenomenon of pseudo-hybridization (section 91) in such a case no longer takes place.

The complex of the new characteristic induced in this lot encourages the attempt to test its reaction in the F^2.

This important mutation—and it actually should be considered as such, since it reproduces itself, except for stature, with excellent fidelity—has no counterpart in treatments of similar experiments. That confirms the usefulness of testing extensively the experiments worked out here, from which it is likely that one definite frequency brings out a loosening or decomposition in some chromosomes, while the other frequency does so on other chromosomes, irreducible by the first frequency.

In the F^2 there are two principal new forms: dark-gold flowers (Figs. 107-111), and those having long ligules (Fig. id.) with giant trunks, and extremely long peduncles. But the great majority of the plants, (although this is a matter of hybrid reproduction) preserve the characteristics that they had in the F^1.

VII. This lot, obtained with pulsating field, has no salient characteristics except greater nanism compared with the comparison lot, and with a concave rather than convex form of the fruit-bearing disk. Florescence occurs a little later than in the normal hybrid. Several individual plants were observed that produced greenish speckled seeds, and these have been reproduced in the F^2.

Re-sowing has offered a means of determining how fully a third of the individual specimens gave rise to forms which, either with the black disk or else the type of growth, favored the comparison type, (P).

A small part has a rosy-gold flower; some plants resemble lot VI either because of the color of their tiny calices or because of the flat shape of the disks and the lily color of the seeds, which turns a hazelnut color upon maturing. In individual plants that preserve better the characteristic of the parent species, there is a considerable abortion, or failure to develop, in the seeds, which are irregularly arranged in small, quite convex disks with large green scales in the center.

VIII. The lot is somewhat different from the preceding one, as a whole, it resembles the previously described III. IV, and V, but includes 2 specimens with canary-yellow flowers similar to those of lot II and several plants and flowers with narrow, or tight, ligule, but not actually cactiform like those in Fig. 107-IV.

IX. Ultraviolet light has marked this lot with a characteristic altogether special, which, however, finds a perfect analogy with the similar experiment (Section 64) on the poppies: giantism, twisted stalks from the very start of vegetation, and delayed florescence characterised in the extreme cases by a mossy efflorescence at the center of the disk. The plant reproduced in Fig. 106 was photographed after three weeks of the comparison hybrid.

This group includes also two specimens of the cactiflorescent type, the secondary inflorescences of which are reproduced on the fourth row of Fig. 107.

97.

Ionolysis in Crosses of Giant Sunflower with Red Gold Sunflower

GIANT SUNFLOWER OF RUSSIA (*Helianthus uniflorus*) ♀ x
YELLOW-BROWN SUNFLOWER (*Helianthus annus, var. rubrum*) ♂.

In the preceding experimental group a description has already been given of the seed-carrier. The variety that has furnished the pollen is, by nature, quite variable, and tends, even if perfectly isolated, to produce varieties with bigger and paler flowers, approximating the similar common species (*Helianthus annus*).

The reason for this instability is attributed to atavistic return toward the species from which, in all probability, it originated. The individual diversity which is met with most extensively in this lot, finds a counterpart and justification in the perceptible difference in the size of the pollen granules, quite apparently also modestly larger. Inductively, one is led to think that to volumetric differences correspond anisotropic systematizations or deficiencies in the units constituting the plasma. For these reasons the variety is among those less well adapted to demonstrational experiments. The *H. annus rubrum* is dwarfed, bushy, compact, with wrinkled, dark green leaves, with purple-blue stalks, peduncles, and nervatures. The flowers are simple, well laid out, have a plate or a bright yellow background more or less with a dark red halo in the middle portion of the ligule. The disk consists of flowerets orange-tinted from the orange-black stigma.

The experimental results, in view of the intrinsic individual variability, overwhelming that produced by ionolization, are described in summary with respect to the *universal* mutation induced in the respective lots:

1. Fertilization with pollen kept in a pollen-pouch, kept dry for eight days.

2. Fertilization with pollen exposed for 24 hours to a 42-cycle variable magnetic field. Maximum field intensity, 4,500 gauss.

3. Fertilization with pollen exposed to pulsating magnetic field, in the apparatus of Fig. 13 (open magnet field type). Exciter current 42-cycle 80 v. Wenhelt interrupter. Maximum field intensity, 5,270 gauss. Duration of exposure, one hour.

4. As above, duration of exposure, two hours.

5. As above, id. with pollen mixed with ½ iron.

Results

The groups of comparison hybrid plants consist of a vast series of intermediate forms among the species, among which it is difficult, except as an opinion, to give a well-grounded appraisal of the prevalence or the number of such forms. The polymorphism of this "population" does not permit it; also because the florescence is not simultaneous, which will necessitate the establishment of a true *civil status* all its own, a diligent statistical study would becomes a desperate, or hopeless, undertaking.

2. There are no noticeable relevant differences between the comparison flower-bed and the one in question; but what has been noted is a *delayed florescence* of the yellow forms, which, in both the first and the second lots, are the first to flower, or blossom, first by a dozen or more days. They follow forms more or less variegated, suffused, ablaze with red, these still with analogous delay, on the basis of the comparison lot.

3-4-5. These three lots differ from the comparison plant in the same sense as the preceding No. 2, but with less delayed florescence.

98.

Ionolysis in Crosses Between Different Varieties of Althaea (Marsh Mallows)

WHITE ROSE MALLOW (*Althaea rosea, var. alba*) ♀ x BLACK MALLOW (*Althaea rosea, var. atropurpurea*) ♂

The process of castration and of preservation appropriate to these species has already been diffusely treated in Chapter VI, section 69.

The very clear contrast between the two pigments characterizing these two varieties seemed the best way to differentiate the action induced by ionolization in the genital plasma. Vice versa, I have had to determine how, in this hybridization, either natural or forced, there can be such a gamut of individual variations in the coloring of the flowers that it is difficult to base oneself on them for the comparison.

The experiments attempted are the following:

1. Fertilization with fresh pollen, collected 24 hours earlier.

2. Fertilization with fresh pollen exposed to a magnetic field with fixed polarity, in the rectilinear electromagnet of Fig. 11, with maximum field of 4,500 gauss, for one-half hour.

3. Fertilization with pollen placed between the polar surfaces of the electromagnet Fig. 15, with 42-cycle alternating current for 11 hours.

4. Fertilization as above, with polarized iron mixed with pollen.

5. Identical conditions of preceding No. 3. Duration, 28 hours.

6. As above, pulverized iron mixed with pollen.

7. Fertilization with pollen treated directly in the plant, on the flower bud, beginning with the fourth day anteceding florescence by means of the rectilinear electromagnet of Fig. 11. 42-cycle exciter current; maximum field intensity about 900 gauss. Duration of the exposure, 4 days. (Device of Fig. 12).

8. Fertilization with pollen treated with variable magnetic field depending on 400-cycle exciter current. Maximum intensity of magnetic field, 3,250 gauss. Duration of treatment, one-half hour.

9. Fertilization with pollen exposed to pulsating magnetic field. Interruption with Wenhelt apparatus. 42-cycle, 80 v., alternating exciter current. Maximum field intensity, 9,430 gauss, for one-half hour.

10. As above, with an hour and a half duration.

N.B. The treatment of the pollen with ultraviolet light and with radium has demonstrated itself to be lethal for this species. The formation of the seeds does not materialize, or does so imperfectly.

Results

1. The comparison lot consists of tall, slender plants, with well opened flowers, including the whole gamut of the colors inter-

mediate between those of the parent varieties, including dark violet.

2. It differs from the comparison variety only in greater robustness of the plants.

3. Stature and morphological characteristics of the comparison type. Florescence in normal time. Coloring of pure white to bright rose. Two plants have flowers united by threes at each foliar axil, whereas in the normal course of events they are united in pairs.

4. Similar to the preceding, without supernumerary flowers.

5. This lot includes some plants with lilac-colored flowers, more closed than those of the preceding lots. Light shades predominate.

6. Comparable to preceding items, with some plants having purple-blue flowers.

7. Quite outstanding is the behavior of this lot for the strange result that it occasions. While the somewhat prolonged ionolysis, on mature pollen, evokes delay in florescence (Section 69) in this species, while the pollen is ionolyzing during maturation, still enclosed in the unripe anther, there takes place a *homogeneous speed-up* of florescence, accompanied by dwarfism which, as I look upon the matter, is nothing else than the result of the precocious flowering arrangement (Section 61). Ionolysis, however, has not affected color, which, in this lot, is predominantly dark.

8. The use of ionolyzed pollen with rapid alternation of magnetic field has yielded a good capsule, normal and with perfect seeds. However, its germination, although the seed was created under the best conditions and simultaneously with that of the other lots, has been quite poor, only two plants from a total of forty seeds. These two specimens are tall of stature, with a normal floral opening, and normal florescence period. Both are white (which demonstrates that the ionolysis has reacted strongly even on the pigmental characteristic, which in the other lots has resulted in only exiguous attenuation).

9. The pulsating magnetic field has produced only one original, individual specimen distinctly different, in various aspects, from the normal species: a plant with extremely slender branches, with numerous lateral branchings, long internodes, anomalous and a-symmetrical arrangement of the leaves. This lot includes also ¼ of the plants with groups of three at every foliar axil. All the

specimens of this lot have light coloring, stature hardly lower than that of the comparison lot, and normal florescence period.

10. Despite an exposure period three times that of the preceding analogous experiment, fertilization has created a fruit most normal in appearance, with perfect seeds. However, in spite of every care taken in the semination process, not even a single plant was yielded from the given seeds.

As a whole, this group of experiences confirms:

a) The necessity of attempting with a rational, coordinated system, and on a vast scale, the magnetic ionolizatioon on unripe anthers, while the pollen is completing the last phase of its growth, since experiment No. 7, as well as the one designated as i) in section 61, demonstrate how, in the period preceding florescence, there exists a greater facility for the deformation, or breakdown, of the intimate structure of the chromosomes, despite the sparse intensity of magnetic field, and consequently of the iono-motor effect from which the anther can profit in comparison with the pollen loosened or free.

b) Among the various electro-biological phenomena which ionolysis can occasion in the hybrid, there have been considered, so far, 4 cases:

1. Inefficacy.
2. Partial influence, or efficacy.
3. Apparent disappearance of every characteristic of the ion-olized species.
4. Loss of vitality of the ionolized plasma, and consequently unsuccessful fertilization.

Experiment No. 10, which compares with the analogous one in section 69 and is closely related to many other unpublished ones which I have made no note of, since I had undertaken not to needlessly stuff this brief work with sterile descriptions of manv failures, demonstrates how ionolysis can give rise to another phenomenon intermediate between the 3rd and the 4th, a phenomenon that may be considered, or called, limitation of vitality, a limitation that permits the completion of the seed but takes away from it every germinative power.

99.

Ionolysis of Varieties of Cabbages

BRUSSELS SPROUTS (*Brassica oleracea, var. gemnifera*) ♀ x
EARLY VIOLET CAULIFLOWER (*Brassica oleracea. var. botrytis cauliflora*) ♂ .

The process of castration and isolation suited to this species is fully analogous to that adopted for the wallflower, previously described in Chap. VI.

The hybrid appears interesting not for any value it may have in culture but for the number of characteristics of a quite diverse kind that the two species possess.

The successful experimental tests are:

1. Fertilization of the control with two-day-old pollen.

2. Fertilization with ionolized pollen with a magnetic field produced by a 42-cycle alternating current with the apparatus in Fig. 11, for 3 days. Maximum field intensity, 5,580 gauss.

3. Fertilization with same apparatus. Duration of treatment, 5 days.

4. Fertilization with pollen treated with current of more than 50 volts, interrupted by Wenhelt switch for about 10 hours, at intervals. Maximum field intensity, from 4,000 to 6,000 gauss.

Results

1. The plants of this lot are of a lower stature than the parent species, similar in the general structure of their organs to that of the garden variety of cabbage, with very elongated and grayish-green leaves, as in broccoli. Scattered lateral offshoots denote the kinship with Brussels sprouts. Compact, globose inflorescence, with flowers similar to those of the pollen-bearer species. Florescence at the beginning of May. All plants bear flowers, and in their general appearance resemble the male species.

2. The numerous plants born of this lot, however, turn out some-what more vigorous than the model or comparison plant. Their

inflorescence in general is more slender and more well endowed than those of No. 1, which have their florescence at the same time. Some plants were observed to be slightly grooved and studded.

3. The specimens of this lot are in no wise different from the preceding experimental test. The height of the plants is perceptibly less, and their florescence a little more delayed.

4. Nothing noteworthy has been observed in this lot in comparison with the three preceding ones. The removal of the seeds takes place simultaneously, as also the first phases of growth, until the time of the transplanting. From then on, with the progress of the vegetation, the plants of this group remain far behind in their development. In the spring, when lots 1, 2, and 3 are already in seed, the plants of this variety have not as yet reached the halfway point of their growth. Their leaves, thick and a much darker green than that of the aforementioned lots, denote the diminishing virulence (sic!) of the male species, characterized by leaves that are quite glaucous and elongated.

In this hybrid, the ionolysis of the genital plasma has produced an effort substantially contrary to that of the ionolyzed crossing between the somniferous and the bracteate poppies, inasmuch as the device, instead of favoring growth and self-fertilization has removed from the plants their power of florescence.

In fact, this lot has not reached florescence. It would have been interesting to preserve the plants all summer and observe their behavior at the autumnal revival of vegetation, but a field-hand ignorant of the importance which those plants, so obstinately stunted, might have, pulled them out. Of this experiment carried out during the war, I was unable to get a photograph. Nevertheless, the regularity of the results were all that could be desired. It was repeated, with different ionolyzing means, but unfortunately the young plants that were born of the experiment were destroyed.

At any rate, it has been established that in the two cruciferous species exposed to the action of ionolysis, there is no reaction to the slow cycle but only to changing vibrations of the magnetic field value.

Another altogether special peculiarity up to now limited to this hybrid, is the predominance of the debilitative effect of growth on morphological withdrawal, which is usually the first indication of the ionolization undergone by the fertilizing plasma.

100.

Ionolysis In Crosses Between Indian Corn Varieties

WHITE INDIAN CORN, HORSE'S TOOTH VARIETY (*Zea mais*, var. *Caragua*) ♀ x YELLOW PIGNOLETTE INDIAN CORN (*Zea mais*, var. *pignoletto*) ♂ .

During the period of normal hybridization of this monoecious genus, it is extremely advantageous to have its male flowers separate from its female ones, so that it suffices to plant side by side, and in alternate rows, the varieties selected for hybridization, and to eliminate the male flowers of the variety designated to be the seed-bearer; fertilization turns out particularly difficult whenever the pollen has to be collected, removed for exposure to various treatments and brought back to the field for fertilization. At the start, by using scrupulous care to eliminate the danger, if only partially, of fertilization by the pollen of a neighboring culture, I have successfully carried out similar fertilizations including the different systems of magnetic ionolization, protecting the female flowers with small, transparent parchment-paper bags, kept adhering successfully to the embryonal cob by means of a suitable device. I had many failures. I attributed to the lack of rain, that can help to expel the pollen "pouch," the very small yield of grain obtained by that means. I changed the system, completely isolating the seed-bearer plants, removing from them their male flowers even before they appeared, and I obtained better results omitting the protective little bags.

The genus Zea (maize) is susceptible to xenia (Section 75). Every hybrid cob is a bizarre mosaic of grains of one color or the other of the two parent varieties and of their shadings.

The appraisal, which in other species is ordinarily based on the characteristics of the upper organs (flowers and fruits), should be

based, in the case of the genus Zea, on the morphological characteristics of the plant, and, insofar as the cob is concerned, only on
its growth and on the shape of its seeds, passing over the color
of the latter items, since a hybrid lot may be altered by the pollen
of neighboring plants or by those of the same group having different
characteristics.

Ionolysis, however, succeeds in completely removing the pigment
character, so that it becomes advisable to separate from the rest
of the hybrid lot the individual units *decisively varied by ionolysis,*
the number of such units being quite different from one lot to
another.

Since the "Horse's tooth" variety of Indian maize is slightly
retarded, I took care to retard the "Pignoletto" seed to ensure
simultaneous florescence.

I transcribe here the experiments in which I succeeded in obtaining seeds:

1. Fertilization of the control, with fresh pollen.

2. Fertilization with pollen exposed for 5 hours to a variable
magnetic field in the apparatus of Fig. 16, excited with a 42-cycle
alternating current. Maximum field intensity, 4,750 gauss.

3. As above, for 24 hours.

4. As above, for 48 hours.

5. Fertilization with pollen exposed for 2 hours to a rapidly
variable (500-cycle) magnetic field. Maximum field intensity,
3,250 gauss.

6. Fertilization with pollen placed under a pulsating field (electrolytic interrupter), 42-cycle, 48 v., alternating current inciter,
homonymous polarity yielding about 4,500 gauss.

7. Fertilization with pollen exposed for an hour and a half to a
variable magnetic field supplied by a 500-cycle alternating current,
then to the action of ionolysis at 42-cycles of the apparatus referred to in No. 2, above. Maximum field intensity, 3,250 gauss.

8. Fertilization with pollen radiolized for 2 hours with ultra-
violet light, produced by a series of short high-frequency sparks
(1,000 per sec.)

9. Fertilization with pollen exposed for two days to rays emitted
by 1 milligram of radium bromide in the apparatus of Fig. 6 (1.15
cm.).

Results

1. In stature and in behavior the female factor predominates while florescence is somewhat advanced.

It yields ears clearly similar to those of the Caragua species; however, the seeds are arranged quite more spaciously than in the aforesaid variety, and have a roundish instead of a flat shape.

Fig. 109 reproduces in *1* three cobs from this lot.

2. From this lot, I obtained few seeds. The young plants, then, were in large part lost. The plants of this plant-bed, as a whole, are not far removed from the model, or comparison plant. In the meager lot, however, there stands out one plant, outstanding for its greater vigor, robustness, and delayed florescence, completely white seeds, more roundish, however, than those of the Caragua maize. Another plant of this group has a characteristic purple-blue shade, which is not found in the parent species.

3. Dose not differ much from the preceding one.

4. In this lot, too, the hybrid form is dominant, but in a few specimens the seeds, rather than long and flat, are somewhat acuminate (tapering to a point). One plant bears a curious ear with rather infrequent rows, and another plant, quite robust, bears a fruit with large white seeds.

Generally, then, the slow cycle turns out to be almost ineffectual for this genus.

5. In this lot there is a marked tendency toward the maternal species. Numerous are the plants with pale seeds, and in a full third of them, there are *completely white* ears. The shape of the seeds, *however, is marked by the male species,* which would go to prove that with this treatment only the "pigment" characteristic is debilitated.

In the matter of dominance, the stature of the plant does not differ from the comparison plant.

6. About one-half of this lot consists of plants with white ears; but in vigor they are somewhat lower. Shorter also are the husks stripped at the top.

7. The coupling of two treatments with different cycle was of no use in this experiment, the results of which may be compared to those of lot 4.

8. The ultraviolet rays have yielded, in nearly half the specimens of this lot, whitish cobs, generally having few kernels.

9. Almost equal in this lot, too, is the percentage of white cobs. However, there are manifest signs of organic deficiency, a grave failure in nearly all the white cobs, pointed seeds or seeds located in the queerest places, and greatly delayed maturation.

As a whole, therefore, the experiments on Indian corn allow one to glimpse the possibility of a useful undertaking. From the standpoint of usefulness, experiment No. 5 seems the best of the series insofar as a clear mutation of a characteristic without damaging or diminishing vegetative vigor (vitality) is concerned.

At the same time as the above stressed experiments, I instituted similar tests with the same hybridization carried out in reverse, and here it is:

YELLOW INDIAN CORN (*Zea mais, var. lutea*) ♀ x HORSE'S TOOTH INDIAN CORN (*Zea mais, var. Caragua*) ♂

The results agree sufficiently well with the tests analyzed. Worthy of special mention is Experiment No. 3, which demonstrates one possibility of improving this hybrid "race" by means of ionolysis. However, there is no cause for self-praise unless one can obtain improvements with certainty of success. It will be only after long investigations that it will become possible to map a good way that will lead to useful deformations.

101.

Ionolysis in the Bigeneric Hybrid Marsh Mallow

ROSY MALLOW (*Althaea rosea, var. atropurpurea*) ♀ x
COMMON MALLOW (*Malva officinalis*) ♂

This bigeneric hybrid has the possibility of success only when the mallow (Althaea) is used for the female mate. Unfortunately, it is just this which acts aggressively with respect to the mallow; that is why experimental findings can be based only on the difference in the shadings of flowers. In its remaining characteristics, the mallow species is thus dominant enough to make one think of false hybridization, were it not that in some specimens there is also the pattern of the leaf, the property of reflorescence until the frosts set in, and the longevity of the plants beyond the normal two-year period, to prove that what is involved is a genuine hybrid.

Since I was already aware that tolerance for magnetic ionolysis is very low in this genus, I have limited the experiments to short tests with moderate intensity (density of magnetic flux).

The following are the experiments:

1. Comparison fertilization.

2. Fertilization with pollen exposed to 42-cycle fluctuating magnetic field, for 12 hours. Maximum density of magnetic flux, 4,750 gauss.

3. Fertilization as above, pulverized iron mixed with the pollen.

4. Fertilization with pollen exposed to rapidly variable (500-cycle) field for half-hour. Maximum density of magnetic flow, 3,250 gauss.

5. Fertilization under conditions identical with those of 4. Duration of treatment, one hour.

Results

1. The color of the flowers in all groups varied widely, the greatest similarity to the mallow occurring in the comparison lot. Fig. 110 actually represents, in A, one extreme of this group which, in addition to the color, somewhat resembles the paternal species also in the pattern and in the reduced size of the leaves, the stature and the fruits.

2. The lot is homogeneous as to stature but differing in the color of the flowers, among which dark red is a very dominant color almost black in the maternal species (Fig. 110B).

3. Similar to preceding.

4. Different from the preceding, especially in two cases which tend, in the form of leaves, toward the paternal type.

5. Fertilization has yielded a good capsule with apparently normal seeds, but from these only a single plant has been born and reached florescence.

102.

Ionolysis in Crosses of Peas

EXTREMELY UNDERSIZED GREEN PEAS (*Pisum sativum nanum*) ♀ x THE PURPLE POD VARIETY (*Pisum sativum, var. atroviolacem*) ♂

Preceded by several fruitless experiments on the pure species, the following experiments confirm the difficulty of mutating in this useful papilionaceous plant. Castration of the anthers contained in the keel together with the pistil should be performed with the flowers quite immature and with great care. The operation is an easy one, if the petals are removed from the standard, if an edge of the bottom is grasped with a pair of pincers and then it is plucked backward with a slow diagonal movement. Stripped bare in this way, the stamens are easily removed with the pincers themselves, after which comes the sheathing of the style. Fertilization should be undertaken then when the flower hardly suggests readiness to open naturally. The pollen of the pea is to be preserved *al fresco* and in a *humid* atmosphere; otherwise it dries up, losing its germinative power.

The two species differ in many characteristics. The green dwarfed pea is 25-30 cm. high, has white flowers, green, glabrous pods, round seeds, smooth and yellow; its leaves are small and close together. The purple pod variety is a climbing plant, has large leaves striped in white, robust and long stalks which in a short while reach a man's height; it has lilac-rose flowers with violet upper petal, dark-violet pods with wrinkled surface, very wrinkled seeds, pale-green or ashen-grey in color. Here are the experimental data:

1. Fertilization of the control plants.
2. Fertilization with pollen exposed to fluctuating 42-cycle magnetic field for three hours. Maximum density of magnetic flux, 5,000 gauss.
3. As above, for 6 hours.
4. As above, for 12 hours.
5. As above, for 12 hours, with pulverized iron mixed in with the pollen.

6. Fertilization with ionolyzed pollen in an unripe anther with a 42-cycle fluctuating field beginning two days before florescence. Density of magnetic flow, about 2,000 gauss.

7. Fertilization with pollen exposed for one hour to a 500-cycle fluctuating magnetic field. Maximum density of magnetic flux, about 3,200 gauss.

8. As above, with pulverized iron mixed in with the pollen.

9. Fertilization with pollen exposed to pulsating current, produced by 42-cycle, 50 v., alternating current, interrupted by Wenhelt, for one hour. Maximum density of magnetic flow, 4,000 gauss.

10. As above, for 2 hours.

11. As above, for 3 hours.

12. As above, with pulverized iron.

13. Fertilization with pollen exposed to strongly shifting field by alternating current, 80 volts, 42-cycles, interrupted with Wenhelt, with complementary polarity. Maximum density of magnetic flow, 9,400 gauss.

14. As above, with opposite polarity. Maximum density of magnetic flow, 5,500 gauss.

15. Fertilization with pollen radiolized for 1, 2, and 3 days.

Results

1. The comparison lot, both in its characteristic development, and in the form of the rosy color of the flowers and the purple-blue of the fruits, is the same as the paternal species, dominant in each of its characteristics. Only towards the time of maturation of the pods does it become possible to differentiate between the hybrid and the paternal species, because the shells and the seeds are somewhat more greenish and glabrous in the hybrid.

2. It is not differentiated from the comparison lot; rose-colored flowers.

3. As above.

4. As above, with some more retarded specimens.

5. This lot flowers about a fortnight after the normal hybrid.

6. Identical with comparison lot, although a bit more retarded.

7. There are noted some more precocious plants, with a pod shorter than the comparison one, with an almost green shell.

8. A little taller, stronger and more retarded.

9. Barely dissimilar to the comparison type.

10. As above.

11. As above, a bit more dwarfed.

12. As above.

13. This lot shows how only with violent and irregular shifts of magnetic field, an effective reaction is possible on the pollen of the pea. Only in this lot and the following one are there any plants which, being still almost as tall as the paternal species, have pure white flowers and a smooth green shell. While, however, the stature of the mutated plant is proportional (from 70 to 100 cm.), the corolla is absolutely white, without any rose-colored shading; there is also in this instance a clear chromatic dualism. This lot contains a small number of dwarfed individual plants with a rose-colored flower, which could be assumed to be also products of the same ionolysis which must act on the characteristic of "stature" rather than on that of color.

The proportion of the plants mutated by ionolysis is, in this lot, about 16%.

14. In this lot, too, there are specimens mutated to white, in the remarkable proportion of 25%, while the field density of magnetic flow in action is almost half. Let this result serve to confirm, for the last time, the fact that ionolysis does not depend on density, but profits rather from the speed at which the field varies, at the time that the homonymous poles are present.

15. This fertilization was an enormous failure. Of the seeds that were obtained, only some fifteen plants materialized, absolutely like the maternal genus, which only a single specimen exceeded in height. It is strange, then, that almost the same number of aborted seeds were obtained after 1 as after 3 days of continued radiolization.

In the F2, the comparison variety, as well as the ionogenetic ones up to No. 12, separate, regrouping the various characteristics in a vast number of variations, outstanding among which is the tall type with rose-colored flower and the tall type with white-colored flower. The proportional percentages of the various types are not very different among the various lots, nor with that of the comparison lot.

The progeny of the individual speciments mutated of lots 13 and 14 also occasion some atavistic return to the violet species, but the proportion, *instead of giving the usual ¾ dominant and ¼ recessive, gives about 80% of the plants with a white flower (recessive characteristic) and 20% with a violet-lilac (dominant).* One notes, then, that the dominant characteristic, while it is clearly distinguishable in the flower, is not so in the pod, which offers only a few light purple-blue streaks.

Among the ionogenetic descendants, therefore, there are a great number of dwarfed and semi-dwarfed plants, which are very rare in the reseeding either of the comparison hybrid or of the other lots on which ionolysis has not acted efficaciously.

103.

Argument Regarding a Phenomenon Countering the Theory and the General Result

"GINGERBREAD" GOURD (*Cucurbita pepo, var. melopepo*) ♀
x POOR MAN'S BREAD GOURD (*Cucurbita maxima, var. autantiaca*) ♂

Of the two species in question, the "Gingerbread" gourd is already well known to the reader (Sections 91, 92); the Poor Man's Bread gourd is a variety of the *Cucurbita maxima* (large gourd) with thick, globose fruit, with a smooth, orange-colored peel, soft, farinose pulp and white seeds.

Figs. 111 and 112 represent the two parent species.

The experiments were registered as follows:

a. Fertilization of control with fresh pollen.

b. Fertilization with pollen exposed for 3 hours to a 42-cycle fluctuating magnetic current. Maximum density of magnetic density of magnetic flow, 6,000 gauss.

c. As above, with pulverized iron.

d. Fertilization with pollen exposed to pulsating magnetic field (electrolytic interrupter). 42-cycle, 83 v., exciter current, for a half hour. Maximum density of magnetic flow, 5,270 gauss.

e. As above, for one hour.

Results

a. The comparison lot, very little fertile, yields creeping plants, having little vigor, with foliage similar to that of the maternal species, which the fruits also resemble, these fruits, however, being far smaller, stunted, at times oddly deformed.

As can easily be marked by comparisons with Fig. 73 (Section 91), it is a question of a new case of pseudo-hybridization, analogous to the one that is produced in the Portmanteau gourd, a common characteristic being the flat shape of the fruits, marked reduction of ovaric capacity and size of seeds, very scanty fertility.

The difference between the two false hybridizations of the comparison units lies in the following: one of them (Section 91) is false only in part, that is to say, it yields a percentage of actual individual hybrids, while the other one, with which I have been working, is constantly false in all the individual specimens of the lot.

b, c, d and e. I am grouping these lots because their density is so slight and the individual differences within each parcel are so small that it is not worth the while to differentiate them.

Fig. 114 shows a fine group of all these ionogenitized hybrids the characteristics of which, through their growth, proneness to drag, amplitude of their foliage, the shape (and a little, also, the color) of the fruit, are closer *to the paternal species than is the normal hybrid produced with natural pollen.*

Ionolysis of the pollen in the various experiments so far described here has always yielded results that agree; it is always the male species that loses its virulence because of the treatment. In experiments b, c, d and e, the contrary phenomenon is observed; precisely because in double contrast, fertilization with normal pollen yields a false hybrid, while ionolized pollen yields them in equal or nearly equal numbers.

Incidentally, while the matter of false hybridization was being considered in section 91, it was already mentioned that this was caused by the incompatibility of the hybrid make-up, through the evident incongruity of form among the units destined to unite in the hybrid structure (Section 87).

To ionolyze pollen of such a hybridization may seem like a vain task, inasmuch as the recessivity of the male species *is already at its peak*. So it would be, but that means confirming a new fact, contradicting the theory of the enfeeblement of the genital plasma by ionolysis.

Is hybridization then given the right to be able, with the same means that normally is used as a breakdown device (in hybrids with male dominance, or something of the same nature), to offer to guarantee hybridization in mates which yield a false hybridization? The phenomenon cannot fail to leave one perplexed. I have sought even this past year to repeat the seed-sowing of this experiment done in 1919, and I have had a new and vaster confirmation. Awaiting new facts, it may now be anticipated that in order to explain it, it is not necessary to attribute to ionolysis the property of evoking a *different* action on the molecules of the chromosomes.

Ionolysis acts always in the same way on them: it splits them, disrupts them, and displaces a part of them. And just as it can happen with two rigid pieces of any material whatsoever, intended to penetrate one another,[1] when one of them is softened, the solidity of juncture is impaired (an ordinary case), so it is that the same softening of one piece can *under exceptional conditions* be turned to good use if two pieces are to be joined that cannot penetrate one another because of a difference of entrance, or opening (extraordinary case) as in the present instance.

CONCLUSION

This is not the time to predict as to the range of usefulness of a science like electro-genetics, which is still in its infancy. The innovator in love with his subject cannot be a dispassionate prophet.

A kind of positive concept, with a predetermined criterion, was tried out by me with empirical trials, or tests. However, these could not be diversified inasmuch as the problem contains the eternal unknown: life. And it will be only by tests that the continuance of the explorative investigation will be made possible whereby to

---

[1] I have adopted the felicitous concept of A. Gauthier, whose comparison I offered in section 76.

establish the most suitable field value, frequency, and time at which to activate mutation in each individual species.

Research into the maximum limit of exposure presupposes a gradual investigation procedure also among the combined various ionolizing media; a terrible task, which perhaps will even grow while it is being carried on, through concomitant phenomena the existence of which, at this time, is not even suspected.

The exact knowledge of the different relationships between stimulus and effect and of the best moment for the application of ionolysis (to the pollen or to the anthers) is a necessary pre-condition for a useful undertaking. Established on a systematic experimental base, ionolysis of plasma will open up a new, vast, alluring horizon.

From the experiments carried out up to now, at the very worst, there is already an idea of what profound variations, or changes, are in prospect. Among the outstanding ones worthy of note are the multiform series of the poppies, the hibiscoid marsh mallow, the dioecious and hermaphroditic gourds. And it is not claimed that the results obtained offer the best exponent of what can be obtained.

There is no doubt but that ionolysis, applied at the propitious time, should induce mutation in every kind of plant, given the random application of extensive sowings, year after year, where, with Fortune smiling, one may look for a mutated plant or a meager group of mutated plants.

It will be no longer the "test of the species" as it is called by the botanists, who, having the urge to find something new, carry on extensive sowings to ascertain whether or not a given species is susceptible of spontaneous variation. It will suffice to ionolize a few milligrams of pollen in order to find out, on the basis of the supply already tested and of that about to be tested, the most suitable treatment without impairment of its robustness.

The obtaining of new forms will then be possible even in the modest garden of the individual. However, far more important is the phenomenon of work in hybridization.

The possibility of regulating dominance has now been verified in several ways. Thanks to ionolysis, the laws of heredity are now subverted in a considerable number of species.

In the gourds, it has been possible to obtain regression of dominance even with very slow variations of magnetic field and their F^2 is a tangible revelation of the anomalous architecture artificially induced in the ionogenetic gametes.

In the somniferous poppy x the bracteate poppy hybrid, there has been obtained the proof of the possibility of revolutionizing the immutable natural genetic rule. The normal hybrid with scarlet flowers, always sterile, mutates, according to the degree of ionolization of which the pollen has availed itself, into a rose-colored, pistilloid, multicephalic one, or else into a white, glabrous, fertile reflorescent one.

The astonishing result has scant practical interest; however, no one can fail to glimpse what interest this process may have in bigeneric hybridization, especially in fruit culture, in bestowing fertility on some hybrids, of the fruit-bearing Rosaceae. Acting on perennial species, multipliable agamically (through scions, grafts, etc.), will make it possible to perpetuate integrally individual types which, in the gamut of hybrid descent, will offer the best requisites. And it is in this species specifically that the device will yield advantages.

In these past years, and particularly with the objective of obtaining fructiferous species resistant to cryptogamic diseases that threaten the most excellent essences (the peach-tree in particular), several hybrid-breeders, among them my very dear Hon. Attilio Ragionieri, have worked on bigeneric hybridization among Rosaceae.

Most interesting is the plum-peach, which I have admired in Castello (Florence) at the house of the famous hybridization expert. The main defect of this hybrid among such diverse genera is sterility. Flowers in abundance; but results—nil.

Also the plum-cocoatree, also brimming with vigor and floriferous to excess, yields very scant fruit and not constantly.

Ionolysis on the pollen of the species that through experience knows how to remain dominant, is able to give in the F^1 forms that are well-balanced and fertile, if, as is justifiable to expect, the behavior of the ionogenetic descents is similar to that met with in the hybrids of the poppy, the gourd, etc.

The sight of the vast number of filiations issuing from the nervature of leaves which are just bearing fruit is perhaps the maximum that can be granted. Indubitably it is a great leap outside of the laws of Nature, of whose obstinate straightforwardness every cultivator is fully cognizant. This important mutational phenomenon has some affinity with reflorescence, which is a common factor in many lots of different ionolized species, especially in the poppies.

Magnificent, too, is the series of results obtained in hybrid peas, and interesting for the unexpected induction of precocity in the ionogenitized family. If the result operative in fructiferous plants were of the same type, it would be of supreme usefulness. Then, as a whole, without a build-up of excessively optimistic preconceived notions, something good may be reasonably expected.

To forecast, even approximately, is not possible. Instead, in this new science, there is a great place for the still unthought-of.

Isn't the unthought-of, quite often the origin of discoveries?

Ionolysis, too, at the beginning, was a wrongly appraised undertaking. Recognized later and within true limits, after a comparison with other means of ionoization, it has not in any way set limits to action in the field.

Perhaps the aforegoing, precise knowledge of the physical phenomena activating ionization—and therefore ionolysis—have led to the adoption of the methods already indicated, impeding the carrying out of the experiments with magnetic ionolysis, while, for the possibility of intonation that it renders possible, offering the best for genetic purposes.

In the meantime, magnetic ionolysis has offered a new means of verification of the molecular breakdown of live matter, organized, in a variant magnetic field, which is not without interest as a new acquisition in the purely physical field.

The process of ionolysis could have an application to plants also in an agamic way, and it can happen that, in this sense, the process should yield results a good deal more important and speedy than by way of sex.

The gemma is sometimes also merely a stalk; a fraction of a leaf of a plant (Cyperus, Begonia, Peperomia, etc.) may be considered as a reproduction unit. In fact, detached and put into the ground, with timely foresight, a gemma, or segment, of a leaf can give rise to an identical new plant.

To act on a gemma in this way in order to modify, or change, it, is equivalent to having varied the species.

Many are the horticultural varieties that have originated in mutations by way of gemmae via stimuli not as yet controlled.

Mutation by way of sports is quite more frequent and conspicuous than those obtained by sexual means; since ionolysis stimulates the latter, all the more reason for its giving rise to the former, being able to operate for a long time during the entire time between the formation and the complete growth of the gemma, or sport. The process would be the same; identical, too, the outcome: to derange the normal environmental balance of the elements characterizing the species. However, in the meantime, it is not possible to impose artificial stimulus on the pollen beyond narrow limits in the gemma, where cellular increase is already in process and where there is no obstacle to fertilization, which is essential.

As I briefly hinted in the preface to this book, for the purposes of a well-organized systematization, for a profitable yield, it is essential that each cultivator, applying ionolization, concentrate his activity on the one single genus of the plant in which he is specializing.

Above all, there is needed an affiliated cooperation. Botany, Electro-technique, Genetics, all are to participate, without mentioning the fact that cultivation, skillful seed-planting, in and by themselves constitute considerable difficulties.

The task presents quite a vast prospect; it is meticulous, engaging, and takes up a great deal of time; however, it brings great satisfaction. The patience with which one must arm himself is repaid by the results obtained, results that are always interesting, like those that conceal an unforeseen strange phenomenon. However, it must be admitted that it offers something better than the *chaos* bristling with unknown phenomena which I had originally to begin working with.

Index

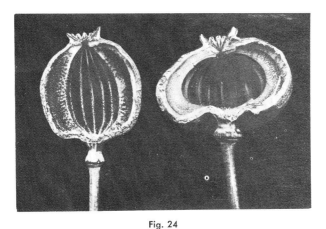

Fig. 24

Left: Interior of a Somniferous Poppy capsule.

Right. Similar capsule from seeds completely aborted by protracted radiolization of the pollen.

Fig. 25

Left: *Magdalena reale* (Regal Magdalen) grape cluster, artificially fertilized with normal pollen.

Right: Identical and contemporaneous fertilization with pollen exposed to ultra-violet rays.

Fig. 26
Cob of Indian Corn
Above: Seeds yielded by normal pollen.
Below: Pollen, after long ionilization, has produced aborted seeds.

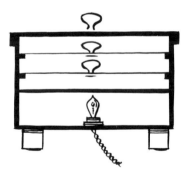

Fig. 27
Pollen-Container Box

Fig. 28
Double Somniferous Poppy
(Plant with mature capsule.)

Fig. 29
Experiment C
Deformation induced by slow magnetic ionolysis — Duration: 4 days

Fig. 30
Experiment h
The interposition of powdered iron, at low fre-
quency, increases ionolysis of the pollen.

Fig. 31
Experiment i
Persistence of petals resulting from ionolysis via
magnetism at the anthers.

Fig. 31a
(Rep.)
The curvature is a latent and inconstant characteristic.

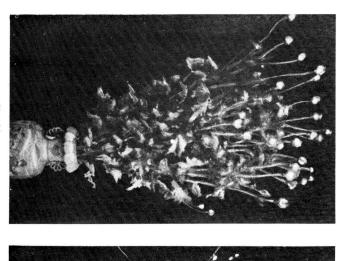

Fig. 32

Dwarfism induced by rapid variability of the magnetic field on pollen.

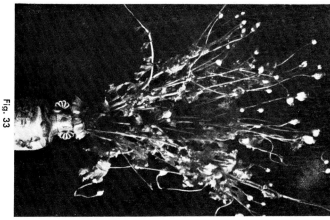

Fig. 33

Experiment C

Deformations that were obtained by a longer duration of similar treatment.

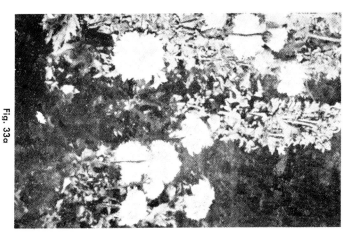

Fig. 33a

Rep. — Experiment C

An extreme specimen of the group, compared with adjacent normal lot.

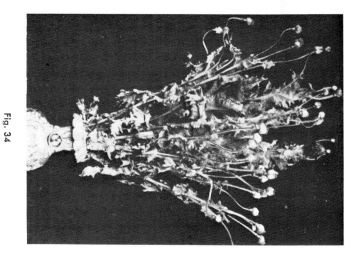

Fig. 34
Experiment III
Decrease in height produced by weak pulsating field.

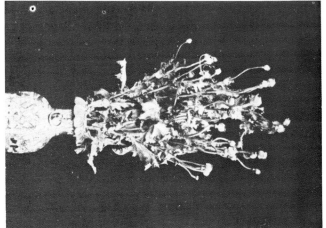

Fig. 35
Experiment IV
Dwarfism induced by greater density of magnetic flow of pulsating field.

Fig. 36

Detail of the oddest forms of Experiment Lot 5, resulting from frequent shifts of magnetic field (insurgence of petalody at completion of florescence).

Fig. 37

Morphological anomaly induced in capsule by irregular rapid switching obtained via electrolytic switch in Experiment Lot V.

Fig. 38

A curious phenomenon of carpellary petalody: From the vertex of the ovaric capsule, after florescence, there opens up, blooms, a new strange corulla. (From Lot V — life size.)

Fig. 39

Experiment VI

On first level: two flowers decidedly greenish, of one specimen of precocious florescence.

Fig. 40

Experiment a

The action of ultra-violet rays. — A single plant fills the lamp
portion of the vase with its enormous branched, twisted stalk.

Fig. 41
Experiment b
Dwarfism and verdancy induced by mixed ionolysis.
In E: an extreme specimen of the group.

Fig. 42
Experiment C
Extreme dwarfism induced by radiolization of the
pollen.

Fig. 43
Gray Gourd (Marucca pumpkin)

Fig. 44
Deformations and red-and-bronze-tinted pigmentation produced by ionolysis at slow-cycle.

Fig. 45
Pie-shaped Gourd

Fig. 46
Modification induced in same by ionolysis of pulsating type.

Fig. 46a
Zuccetta Gourd of Italy

Fig. 47
Experiment 3
Same, shortened, rendered more fertile and yellow by slow-cycle ionolysis.

Fig. 48
Experiment 7

Dioecious and acauline (stemless) Gourdplant, via effect of rapidly fluctuating magnetic field.
(Photographed from above.)

Fig. 47a
Experiment 6

Shortening of fruit in hermaphrodite plants, their "twinning" and elongation of peduncle stimulated through pulsating magnetic field.

Fig. 49
Rose-colored natural, uncultivated Althea
(Marsh Mallow)

Fig. 50
Hibiscus-type Althea: form, or type, produced by slow-cycle ionolysis, reproducing itself faithfully via seed. (Experiment B). (Photograph taken with plant raised collaterally.)

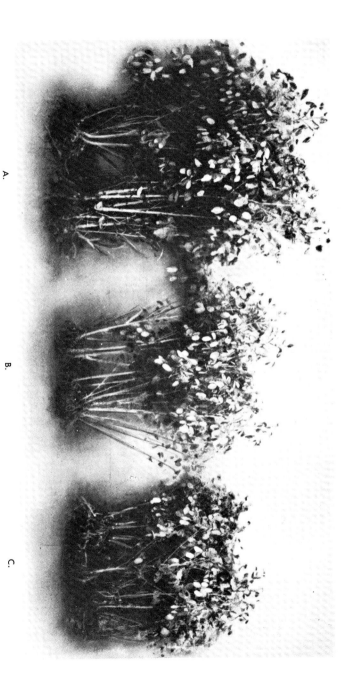

A.

B.

C.

Fig. 51

A. *Lunaria biennis* (**B**iennial Lunaria). (Comparison)

B. Experiment 8. Stature reduced by slow-cycle ionolysis.

C. Experiment 122. Nanism induced by ionolysis at 500-cycles.

B.   Fig. 52 Giant Russian Sunflower   A.

B. Experiment 11.
    With ultraviolet as well as with radio ray, causes a long delay in flowering and the growth
    of leaves along the peduncle and on the reverse of the flower heads.

C. Experiment 8.

Fig. 53
Leaves of young hybrid vines.

Fig. 55
Experiment A I
Comparison flower-bed with live rose-colored flowers.

Fig. 56
Experiment A IV
Same hybrid, with ionolized pollen, having become almost white.

Fig. 57
Experiment B V
Hybrid of White Poppy with Violet Poppy. Comparison flower-bed with violet flowers.

Fig. 58
Experiment B VII
Besides bestowing robust nanism, ionolysis has attenuated the violet shade,
converting it to pale-lilac.

Fig. 59
Experiment A III
Three extreme cases of retardation, rendered completely white by
ionolization at the anther.
(Photograph of reflorescence: July 4, 1921.)

Fig. 60

Left: Normal sterile capsule of Somniferous Poppy Hybrid. Bracteal Poppy.

Right: Plant of same hybrid, with sheathed branches, arranged naturally in candle-stick pattern.

Fig. 61
Somniferous Poppy

Fig. 62
Bracteal Poppy

Fig. 63
Their normal Hybrid.

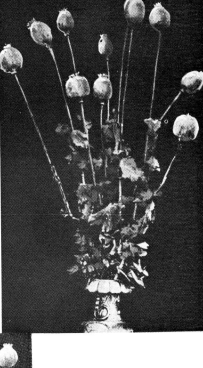

Fig. 64
Opium-yielding Somniferous Poppy, with thick capsule. (11 plants)

Fig. 65
Ionolization of male species, yields two principal forms: one, a simple flower: white, tufted, reflorescent, here shown pulled back, . . .

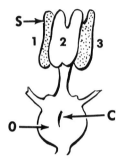

Fig. 67
Incision in wall of gourd ovulary

Fig. 66
The other: (ibid.) with soft, rose-tinted flowers,
provided profusely with pistils ridged about the
ovaric capsule, which is sterile.

Fig. 68
Portmanteau Gourd

Fig. 69
Turbaned Gourd

Fig. 69-A
Normal hybrid

Fig. 69-B
Hybrid produced by slow
pulsating ionolysis.

Fig. 70
Pie-shaped Gourd

Fig. 71
Portmanteau Gourd

Fig. 72

A. Normal Hybrid   B. With 3 hours   C. with 12 hours, slow-cycle
magnetic ionolization.

Fig. 72a

Reproduction of F^2 from ionolized fruit

Fig. 73
Degenerate fruits, from stunted plants, resulting from false
hybridization (pseudo-hybridization)

Fig. 74
The Pie-shaped Gourd

Fig. 75
Long green Zuccetta Gourd — "The Italian Zuccetta"

Fig. 76
Normal hybrid

Gradual retractive deformations of male dominance induced by slow magnetic ionolysis.

Fig. 77 — 1 hour treatment. (Experiment B)

Fig. 78 — 2 hours treatment (Experiment C)

Fig. 79 — 3 hours treatment. (Experiment D)

Fig. 80
Experiment F
With 8 hours weak-field electro-magnetic teratment.

Fig. 81
Experiment G
Effect of extremely weak ionolysis at the anthers, protracted
for one week.

Fig. 82
Experiment K
Brief and rapid alterations of magnetic field results in a useful ionolysis;
it contributes to the species incomparable growth and fertility.

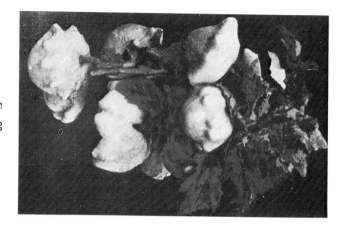

Fig. 83
Experiment I
Equal treatment. With weak field: ionolysis
continued for one hour.

Fig. 84
Experimental conditions identical with those
of 1, with pollen of the day before.

Fig. 85
Experiment H
Multiform progeny produced by energetic pulsating magnetic field.

Fig. 86
Experiment L

The X-rays ionolize the pollen in a short while and produce a genetic effect equal to that of the slow-cycle magnetic ionolysis.

Fig. 87
Experiment M

Still with attenuated X-rays. There appear elongated forms, probably produced by pollen partially protected by the action of the rays.

— Smooth yellow tomato

— Cherry tomato

Fig. 94

— Their normal hybrid

Fig. 95
Experiment 4
Group of orange-colored fruits, with iono-
lized pollen.

Fig. 95a
Experiment 6
Yellow and orange fruits ob-
tained by mixed ionolization.

Fig. 96
Incipient stage of formation of secondary pollen.

Fig. 97
Monstrous effect induced by efficacious ionolization.
From the medium vein of every leaf issue new stems with orange leaflets, often sterile.

Fig. 99
Experiment A
The normal hybrid

Fig. 100
Experiment B
Total disappearance of distinctive male character obtained by magnetic ionolysis.

Modifications induced in hybridization of Flask-shaped with Ribbed Tomato.

Fig. 101
Perennial Small Sunflower

Fig. 102
Giant Sunflower of Russia

Fig. 103
Their normal hybrid

Fig. 104
Average type of isogenetic hybrid, prevalent in the various
experimental lots.

Fig. 105
Experiment VI
Conspicuous effect of ionolysis with two different cycle-frequencies.

Fig. 106
Experiment IX
Twisting of stems by ultra-violet light.

Fig. 107
I-IV

I. Flowers from normal hybrid (from secondary stems).
II. Flowers with long, orange-tinted, stems with mature discs, taken from Lot V.
III. Straw-colored flowers, and relatively gibbous.
IV. Flowers with rolled-up ligules (cactus-shaped), common to Lot VII and Lot IX.

Fig. 109

Indian Corn—Pine-seed variety   Normal hybrid   Ionolized hybrid   Indian Corn ("Horse's Tooth" variety)

Fig. 110

Above: Althea (Marsh Mallow) with black flowers.
Below: The common Mallow
A. Normal hybrid — small, with rose-tinted flower.
B. Ionolized hybrid — (average type).

A.

B.

Fig. 111
Pie-shaped Gourd (Pumpkin). Female

Fig. 112
"Poor man's bread" Gourd.
Male

Fig. 113

Comparison Hybrid (pseudo-hybridization reproducing the maternal species with considerable decrease and atrophy).

Fig. 114

Ionolized hybrid, contrary to the rule, tends toward the male species.